This book had to be written to c
reporting by many media out
suppression of facts which are indi
and open discussion. A thesis withou
leads to synthesis, but to dictatorship
unworthy of a free society. If the media ─ger fulfil their
mandate of diversity of opinion, then others must take on
this task. For only those who have heard the pleas of both
sides may form a judgement.

Dedicated to my father, from whom I was able to learn a lot.

Hermann von Bering

The Corona Lie

- unmasked -

Evidence, facts, backgrounds

© *2021 Hermann von Bering*
1st edition March 2021
The German original was published by "tredition" on January 2021:
"Die Coronalüge - demaskiert"
Cover design: Hermann von Bering
Publisher and printer: tredition GmbH,
Halenreie 40-44,
22359 Hamburg, Germany
ISBN Paperback: 978-3-347-28084-7
ISBN Hardcover: 978-3-347-28085-4
ISBN e-book: 978-3-347-28086-1

Bibliographic information of the German National Library:
The German National Library lists this publication in the German National Bibliography; detailed bibliographic data are available on the Internet at http://dnb.d-nb.de.

The author has permission from the copyright holder for all quotations and the graphic.

Table of contents

J' accuse!

"J' accuse!" - "I accuse!" was the beginning of an open letter by the French writer Émile Zola to the President of the French Republic in 1898. It was about the so-called "Dreyfus Affair", a political espionage scandal of enormous scope. Zola's accusation was hotly debated and eventually led to the uncovering of the scandal, the conviction of the guilty and legal reforms of the French Constitution regarding human rights.

Why do I begin my book with this old story? Because today it is once again time to openly take a stand on a tragedy that is bringing great suffering to humanity worldwide and that urgently needs to be clarified before the world is led into a dictatorship on the pretext of a pandemic that never actually existed. I know that these are serious accusations that must be substantiated. Therefore, the evidence must be as meticulous and conclusive as in a tribunal. The jury is you, my readers. You decide, after I have presented my arguments, whether the charges are valid.

I denounce the fact that many people's livelihoods are being ruined without a public and democratic discussion on the pros and cons of a lockdown having taken place beforehand. There would have been time for this and it should have been taken in view of the drastic consequences.

I am making accusation that the detection methods for Covid19 infection are uncertain and error-prone. The PCR tests can be manipulated, and so they are.

I am making accusation that it has never been proven conclusively that SARS-CoV2 causes all the cases of illness attributed to it.

I am making accusation that the statistics on infection and deaths are deliberately manipulated upwards to give the impression of a dangerous pandemic.

I am making accusation that critics, including scientists, doctors and lawyers, are ignored, vilified and muzzled to the point of losing their livelihoods.

I am making accusation that the constitutional fundamental rights and freedoms are permanently restricted. The emergency powers are not democratically legitimate.

I am claiming that people's fear of illness has been heightened to a collective fear psychosis by months of media suggestion to stifle any resistance to the coercive measures.

The mass psychosis has become so widespread – especially through the media – that critics are now forced to refute the Corona construct with facts. Actually, the onus is on governments to prove that the scientific basis for their measures is sound. But instead of facts, there are only assertions, which are repeated hundreds of times. However, the alleged "evidence" for the dangerousness of the Corona virus is easy to refute with a little expertise and good research. That is exactly what I will do in this book. I will also address the questions that keep coming up:

- Where do the numbers of allegedly infected people come from?
- What did the dead really die of?
- What about images of horror, such as the coffins in Italy?
- Why should politicians ruin their country's economy if there is no pandemic?
- How can it be that (almost) all countries in the world play along?

These are all legitimate questions. To answer them, one must examine many areas closely, not only in medicine. I maintain that the Corona crisis is a very complex undertaking, prepared over many years, and difficult to see through. But it is possible. The motives are, as so often, money, greed and power. If you follow the threads of the spider's web, you will eventually come across the spider.

I am aware that such research is defamed as *"conspiracy theory"*. To believe that there are no conspiracies where there is a lot of power at stake would be naive. There have been at all times and there always will be. It has always been part of the strategy to ridicule those who want to shed light on them. So, who is to be condemned? The conspiracy practitioner or the theorist who uncovers his tracks? So, when, as in the Corona case, there is clear evidence of an actual plot, it is not only the right but even the duty of every investigative writer to pursue the leads.

You can already tell, dear reader, that I am angry about all this. However, I will remain objective and let the facts speak. We are all currently living in a psychologically very cleverly constructed trap, and that trap is fear. Fear is the key to the Corona plot. Many are afraid of the virus and of contagion. Others are afraid of punishment, of social ostracism or of a police state. We are all afraid of the economic disaster caused by the coercive measures and the lock-down. And we are afraid for our children. But fear has always been a bad advisor. So, what can we do?

Our primal instincts, which we have in common with animals, allow for three reactions when faced with danger, for example from a predator: 1. attack, 2. flee, or 3. play dead. So, if they want to force us to stay at home, wear masks, stop visiting our family, accept travel bans, take tests or be vaccinated with barely tested substances, they want to counter that. But you can't because of the penalties. The state has the upper hand. So, escape? Where to? This time it is a pandemic, there is no "where to" anymore. So, play dead in the knowledge that it is basically of no use either. Not even repression is left to us, because we are confronted with the misery every day. We live in permanent stress, and its psychosomatic consequences are well known. Then there is a mask on top of it, so that you can't even breathe through it.

I felt the same way until I realised that a large part of my fear is actually anger. Repressed anger. I decided to be angry rather than afraid, that was the first step towards liberation. The second was deciding to get to the bottom of the corona story. I researched for months. I had time because of the lock-down, and I used it. The knowledge about the whole hoax brought me another piece of liberation. And then I decided to become active with what I'm good at, namely writing.

This book is the result of my search and should also bring you liberation from fear. If we succeed in transforming it into a "holy anger", then we can also change something. The most important weapon in this struggle, however, is a solid knowledge of all that is going on. So, I invite you to follow with me the invitation of the philosopher Immanuel Kant:

"Sapere aude! Have courage to use your own mind!"

PS.: A word about the structure of the book. It has two parts:

The first part deals with the virus, the disease, the tests and the real infection figures. I looked very closely at the PCR test, because all the coercive measures are based on its results. If the test falls, then the justification for lock-down, masks and everything else falls.

I will prove that Covid19 is not a dangerous pandemic and show what is really happening. I will also discuss vaccinations in general and the Corona vaccination in particular. Here I will explain exactly why you should not get vaccinated with it under any circumstances.

The second part explores the question: What is the point? What is behind it? Who benefits from it? What are the goals?

This dichotomy is important because it reflects the two most important aspects of the crisis itself: the medical and the political. You can understand the medical aspect by looking at it systematically, but the question always remains in the back of your mind: *why would someone stage something like this?* You only really understand it when you see the complete picture, without the political background it remains a mystery. Only when the political goals become known does the whole thing make sense.

The third hurdle to understanding is that most people can imagine racketeering, fraud and corruption, but not on a global scale. This is something people shy away from, and yet it is so, because madness becomes invisible when it reaches very large proportions.[1] But this should not deter us. Only when we see through things can we draw the right con-clusions.

As I am German, the original edition was written in German. Even if the focus of the book is on the situation in Germany, Austria and Switzerland the system is the same all over the world, and thus the fraud is the same, and so are the conclusions. I am sure you will find a lot of similar proves in your country when you take a closer look on the facts.

Some readers may be surprised that I go into so much detail and bring so many footnotes. Remember: this book is an indictment, and such an indictment must be well supported with facts and sources. All my statements are substantiated, because only with clear evidence can the jury, that is you, my readers, reach a verdict. You don't have to follow every detail exactly, but if you want to, you have the opportunity to do so. Many of the footnotes are highly interesting and provide additional clues. It is worthwhile to follow up on some of them.

At university we used to have a saying that the student had to know everything, the assistant had to know where it was written, and the professor had to know someone who knew where it was written. At least you will know where to look.

Enjoy reading!

---

1   Modified from a quote by Bertold Brecht. In the original he spoke of stupidity.

How the numbers are manipulated
- the most important tricks

An epidemic always affects many people in an area. In the past, if we had to miss school because of measles or mumps, our friends were usually also affected. Or if a wave of flu spread during cold and wet weather, then we knew quite a few other colleagues and friends with sniffles and coughs. These were epidemics, albeit small ones.

With Corona, everything is different. Few know anyone who knows someone who would have been seriously ill or even died from Corona. Perhaps one knows someone who has tested "positive" and who has flu or nothing at all. Yes, people have died who tested "positive" too. But was the SARS-CoV-2 coronavirus the trigger? Or were there other causes of death? That needs to be clarified first.

At any rate, it doesn't feel like an epidemic, if it weren't for the high numbers of statistics that are announced daily in all media like water level reports at "below the ground". Apparently, the epidemic is taking place elsewhere, but not in our village or district. Yes, it is taking place, but in virtual space, because the "infection figures" are the only "proof" of a pandemic.

To keep it that way, these figures have to be maintained. Not directly falsified, that would be too conspicuous, but manipulated upwards with a few tricks. Especially when there is an urgent need for a "second wave" that just won't come. These tricks are not new, but they work. At least until you take a closer look.

Trick no. 1: The numbers are simply added up

When we look at the data on Corona, we usually get reports that say how many people in our country or around the world have been "newly infected" with Corona or have died.

That says nothing at all at first. Let me give you an example: the number of road deaths in Germany in 2019 was just over 3,000 (and has fortunately fallen compared to previous years). It would not occur to anyone to simply add them up over the years. Then we would have 6,000 road deaths next year and 9,000 the year after. Everyone can see that this is nonsense, but this is exactly how it is done with the Corona cases. The time period is missing: per day, month, year? But here they just add them up, so the number can only grow.

How many have allegedly been "infected" is relatively uninteresting. The question must be: How many of them became ill in the first place? How many of those infected have recovered in the meantime? And how many have died in the last week compared to the weeks before? These are the relevant questions about the course of an epidemic.

The mere piling up of case numbers is not honest statistics. It only serves the purpose of suggesting a steady increase (there are always more, never less) and presenting the highest possible numbers in order to spread fear and terror.

Another trick that is used is the following: If a person tests positive several times, then each test will be counted separately in the statistics, even though it is the same person, because the data for statistics are usually anonymized.

Trick no. 2: The reference data are missing, they are simply concealed

Even if a time period is given like: *"Again over 2,000 new infections per day"* or: *"We have twice as many infected people as 5 weeks ago,"* that still says nothing without the frame of reference. How many tests were done 5 weeks ago? And how many now? Only when you find out after a long search that twice as many tests were done, it is logical that twice as many hits also turned up. This does not mean that the infection rate has doubled, but that it has remained constant.

An example: You send someone into the forest to collect berries. In the forest there are lots of blackberries and also rare forest raspberries. The blackberries represent the vast majority of the non-infected, the raspberries represent the infected. Our friend now collects all the berries he finds. At noon he comes back with 1,000 blackberries and one raspberry. The next day you send two people to collect and they now bring back 2,000 blackberries and two raspberries. If someone were to conclude from this that the number of raspberries in the forest has doubled since yesterday, then they have a problem with logic. But that is exactly what they want us to believe about the Corona case numbers.[2]

It is not as if the experts have forgotten their little basics of statistics. They know very well what they are doing. In an interview on television, Health Minister Jens Spahn blurted out that excessive testing leads to many more false positives than actual positives, even though the incidence of infection is declining. This is due to the fact that the test is not one hundred percent accurate.[3]

---

2   In my example, that would be 0.1%. According to the RKI (the German Centre for Disease Control), however, there are only 16,442 "active corona cases" in Germany with 83.7 million inhabitants, that is only 0.01%. (as of 3.9.2020)

3   https://www.youtube.com/watch?v=ZfWEYeokZiA

Here, for once, the gentleman is right. But the policy did not stick to it, because from the time of his interview (14.6.2020) until the end of August, the number of tests was tripled.[4] So logically, the number of positive test results also tripled, which is then sold to us as a "second wave", although the proportion of people tested positive per 1,000 tests remained constant.[5]

The Chancellor had already used the same trick in March to justify the planned lock-down: In just one week, the "case numbers" reported by the RKI had tripled from 8,000 to 24,000. Chancellor Merkel spoke of an "exponential increase" and that the numbers would "explode". All right, the people said to themselves, where there's a lot of smoke, there must be fire, and dutifully got themselves locked up. But there was no smoke, only stage fog of the show. The RKI had in fact "forgotten" to announce that the number of tests had also almost tripled during the week: from 130,000 to 350,000.

In reality, the proportion of positive test results had barely increased, from six to seven percent. The virologist Hendrik Streeck later confirmed in an interview that there had never been an exponential increase before.[6]

Such tricks are also popular around the world. US Senator Ron Paul writes that in the USA the number of tests has almost quintupled, free coronation tests are offered everywhere, for example, in Houston, which creates a propagandistic "2nd wave".[7]

Although (or because?) it is quite clear that more tests bring more false-positive numbers, there are repeated calls to

---

4   from weekly 326,645 to 987,423
5   https://www.rki.de/DE/Content/InfAZ/N/Neuartiges_Coronavirus/
     Situationsberichte/
6   https://www.rubikon.news/artikel/die-angekundigte-krise
7   http://www.antikrieg.eu/aktuell/2020_07_07_istdieCovidspitze.htm

"test, test, test", for example by the head of the WHO[8] or on German TV-news.[9] Right from the start, people were anxious to present the highest possible numbers.

Trick no. 3:

False positives are simply included in the count

All tests have a certain margin of error, this cannot be avoided. As a result, people are tested as "positive" who are not. This is then called "false positive". Conversely, there are also "false negative" test results, but these would only be mathematically significant if the vast majority were infected. But since the vast majority of people are not infected at all, they can be ignored. Mathematically, this is because, for example, 2% of a large majority are more than 2% of a small minority.

According to the manufacturers' own praise, the error rate is around 1-2%. That sounds good at first, but the fewer real infected people there are, the more noticeable the error becomes.

We can calculate this using the blackberry example: We collect 1,000 blackberries and one raspberry. Let's assume that our collector has forgotten his glasses and has an error rate of 2% when sorting them out, just like the Covid19 test. So, he will mistakenly sort out 20 blackberries, 2% of the 1,000, as "raspberries" because they might look a little reddish. So, 21 berries end up in the pot for the raspberries, that is, 20 false positives and one real one.

Now the quiz question: What is the probability that if you have tested "positive" (therefore, ended up in the raspberry basket), you are really a raspberry? Quite simply: 1:20.

---

8   In: WHO Director-General's opening remarks at the media briefing on COVID-19, 16.3.2020
9   https://www.zdf.de/nachrichten/heute-journal/heute-journal-vom-3-05-2020-100.html

In other words, there are 20 false positives for every one true positive! Because 2% of 1,000 is much more than the one in a thousand. Staggering, but such are the laws of mathematics. So, the test accuracy drops to less than 5% under these circumstances.[10]

If one knows this, and the "experts" should know, one would have to test all those tested positive a second time in order to sort out the false results, if it is possible with a new swab and the test of another company, and in any case in another laboratory. But this is hardly ever done, and so the vast majority of false positives are stigmatised, frightened and sent into quarantine - just to inflate the statistics!

But not even the alleged accuracy of 98% is maintained in practice. The "Indian Council of Medical Research", for example, examined Roche's PCR test "LightMix Modular"[11] more closely and found that the specificities of two of the gene fragments tested with it were only 67% and 60% respectively![12] This would mean that instead of 20, at least 330 blackberries were incorrectly sorted. Now we know why such fantasy figures are always reported from all over the world. They are not necessarily falsified, they are only based on faulty tests with a simultaneously low "prevalence", i.e. real distribution of the virus.

The same faulty tests are of course also applied to deceased persons, who then ensure as many "coronavirus deaths" as possible in the statistics, even if they died of something completely different. There are now hundreds of reports on

---

10 With the low prevalence (infestation) that we have. This is also called the "prevalence error".

11 produced in cooperation with TIB MOLBIOL Syntheselabor GmbH in Berlin, which also marketed Prof. Drosten's first PCR test worldwide in 2003.

12 Express Healthcare; Usha Sharma; ICMr. approves 3 #Covid19 test kits commercial use https://www.expresshealthcare.in/Covid19-updates/icmr-approves-three-Covid19-test-kits-for-commercial-use/417799/
Also at: https://peds-ansichten.de/2020/07/pcr-test-correctiv-deutung/

the net about terminal cancer patients, serious cardiovascular diseases, even accidental deaths registered as "coronavirus deaths". A "positive" PCR test is enough. So, if someone was "positive" once, even false-positive, but never sick, and months later gets run over or commits suicide, that's official - a coronavirus death!

This is how statistics are faked all over the world.

The internist and lung specialist Dr. Wolfgang Wodarg[13] says in the magazine "Rubikon":

"What exists are test orgies that create a false dynamic. Given the low prevalence (frequency) of SARS-CoV-2 infections, a positive test says nothing at all. The number of cases now "found" is equal to the number of healthy people who would be expected to test false positive. The more tests are done, the more incorrectly "positive" healthy people are found. This has nothing to do with disease, but only with the expensive testing that is abused for fear-mongering." [14]

In plain language, this means that the false-positive rates are always at least 1-2%, even without a virus, because the test generates them artificially!

Where is there a real virus when the case numbers have been in the error range of less than 1% since May 2020?

The real total number of tests is mostly concealed so that no one can calculate the positive rate. A woman from Würzburg wrote in a letter to the editor, ‚journalist Boris Reitschuster:

"Dear Mr. Reitschuster, as you have certainly heard, Würzburg is a Corona hotspot. What you may not know is the extent to which testing has taken place here. Even after intensive attempts to find out how high the daily or weekly

---

13 Former medical officer, one of the most competent critics of the Corona policy, see also: http://www.wodarg.com/

14 https://www.rubikon.news/artikel/die-fiktive-pandemie

number of tests actually is and was for the city of Würzburg, neither I nor a journalist managed to find out in writing.

We would have liked to see the course of the positive quota, as the suspicion suggests that the positive cases merely represent the noise of the error tolerance. After all, we now have a verbal statement that as many as 2,900 tests took place on one day last week. On a single day!

However, the number of test positives is in no way related to the number of tests. It is also not clear whether this number was also added to the test results in the case of multiple testing. So, we sometimes had a 7-day incidence of more than 70. And from this, unreasonable measures followed. Würzburg became a risk area and hotspot with additional restrictions on personal rights. I am writing to you because we are bouncing off all those responsible in Würzburg, we are being fobbed off with non-transparent figures and would not like to remain sitting and accept this powerlessness." [15]

Dr. Wodarg is absolutely right when he says:

"Stating "cases", "infected" or "positives" without concurrent information on the population studied and the total number of tests performed in the process should be punishable by a heavy fine for misleading public opinion." [16]

To explain the tactics of the health authorities in another way:

If you test one million men with a pregnancy test with 98% specificity (as with PCR), you will find 20,000 pregnant men.

They are then *"scientifically confirmed"*.

---

15 https://www.reitschuster.de/post/wie-erschaffe-ich-einen-corona-hotspot/
16 https://www.rubikon.news/artikel/die-fiktive-pandemie

Revision is not welcome

Another problem is that the test should actually consist of two parts: A "search test", with high sensitivity but lower accuracy, first looks for the so-called *"E gene"*, which also occurs in other viruses. If this is positive, then a more precise "confirmation test" looks for the *"RdRP gene"*, the *"S gene"* or the *"ORF1 gene"*, which supposedly only occur in SARS-CoV-2 (Covid19). Only the second test achieves the high specificity of >98%. The first test is far below this, thus producing many more false-positive results. The test person is only "positive" if both tests are successful.

So much for the theory. In practice, however, a positive "screening test" is enough, because the regulations and recommendations of the WHO and the RKI allow "two-part" tests with only one positive partial test.[17] Only a "high prevalence" (frequency) of the virus is required for this, but not prescribed.[18]

That is why the laboratories make it easy for themselves, as the website of an Augsburg laboratory shows, where it was pointed out that, following the recommendation of the WHO, the findings would be shown as "positive" if only the E gene was found.[19] And that's the end of the alleged *"high specificity"*, because a "positive" in the non-specific search test is already sufficient. The same was explained in a technical information of the test manufacturer "Biovis Diagnostik".[20]

---

17 https://www.fda.gov/medical-devices/coronavirus-Covid-19-and-medical-devices/faqs-testing-sars-cov-2#validation
18 https://peds-ansichten.de/2020/07/pcr-test-correctiv-deutung/
19 This message has been deleted from the lab's website, but can be found using the Wayback Machine: https://web.archive.org/web/20200504014525/http://www.labor-augsburg-mvz.de/de/aktuelles/coronavirus
20 https://www.heise.de/tp/features/Corona-Lockdown-Droht-tatsaechlich-eine-akute-nationale-Gesundheitsnotlage-4942433.html

The RKI confirmed briefly and succinctly on request that no test repetition is usual for standard tests.[21] The RKI obviously doesn't care what this means for those affected, who then have to spend two weeks in quarantine, and in the case of schoolchildren, the whole class at the same time.

In order to keep the numbers nice and high, they are of course not interested in second tests. If this does happen, the PCR usually looks bad. On 23 June 2020, the German Radio reported that 14 positive tests from the Vogelsberg district had been negative after being checked by another laboratory, because the first laboratory had only tested for one gene. The responsible head of the health department criticised that those affected had to be tested twice and that this should not be a permanent state of affairs.[22]

The deprivation of liberty of hundreds of people in two blocks of flats in Göttingen can also be traced back to faulty tests, because in 600 second tests only four were positive, whereupon the cordoning off of the blocks of flats was lifted.[23]

In a hospital in Upper Bavaria, 60 people had tested positive, but this was not verified by second tests. Only two were confirmed. Allegedly, the laboratory had used the wrong reagents.[24]

Author and publisher Peter Haisenko writes: *"Review tests only exist when the first test result has uncomfortable consequences. Let's remember Thuringia, when a member of parliament was positive and thus the vote in the state*

21 Source: Paul Schreyer: https://multipolar-magazin.de/artikel/das-schweigen-der-viren

22 https://www.hessenschau.de/panorama/coronavirus--vogelsberg-reihenweise-falsche-test-ergebnisse--aus-fuer-deutsche-sunexpress--35-neuinfektionen-,corona-hessen-ticker-314.html

23 Source: https://www.n-tv.de/panorama/Hochhausbewohner-aus-Isolation-entlassen-article21873253.html

24 Source: Bayern 2 Nachrichten, 28.10.2020 05:00 Uhr

parliament could not have taken place. Quickly there was a second test, which of course turned out negative.

This pattern is evident in a large number of cases. In most cases, the second, control test was negative. This is probably the reason why it is generally strongly discouraged to do a control test, because it clearly proves the unreliability of the tests. That would be conclusive evidence!

After the debacle with the large demonstrations, which could not provide any increasing infection figures, they continue to ban large events such as football or concerts because there is also the "danger" that there will be no mass infections. This is precisely what would provide the evidence that the whole Corona racket is a pure pilot issue that only serves political goals."[25]

It is also logical that secondary tests are often negative, because these are the tests with the higher specificity. That's why they are undesirable, because the people in the government know that, of course.

So if you ever test positive, insist on a second test! And be sure to get the test's package insert or remember the name, because it usually says that the test is not approved for diagnostic purposes. (More on this later).

"Normal" people are often refused a second test. Maybe it helps if you play football, because recently we have heard of several footballers who were suddenly negative after second tests and were then allowed to play after all.[26]

Journalist Boris Reitschuster asks: *"Is there a two-tier society when it comes to testing, for example, when football clubs let those affected be tested several times, which would probably be difficult at least for normal positive test persons? Do the*

25 https://www.anderweltonline.com/klartext/klartext-20202/corona-die-erlogene-evidenz/

26 https://www.reitschuster.de/post/zwei-klassen-gesellschaft-bei-corona-tests/

clubs have so little confidence in the tests that they have them retested so often? Or, as in the case of FC Bayern, despite a positive test, do not send the other players into quarantine, or even let them continue to play?"[27] Politicians are also retested so that they are quickly "negative" again.

Trick no. 4: Never tested but counted as "positive"

The dubious practices of the RKI automatically include the "contact persons" of those tested positive (whether genuine or false-positive is completely irrelevant). On the RKI website, a "case" is defined in such a way that no clinical picture (symptoms) has to be present, but only a "contact".[28] This means that contacts to a "case" are themselves counted as a "case". This additionally drives the case numbers up.

By the way, it is actually "forbidden" to criticise the rules established by the RKI because they are said to be standard and should never be questioned.[29]

Who has the cheek to claim something like that? It is the veterinarian Dr. Lothar Wieler, currently head of the RKI. No questions allowed – it could be embarrassing for the RKI.

This is the same Mr. Wieler who on 18 March 2020 predicted an exponential growth of the "epidemic" and forecast ten million infected people in Germany in the following 100 days. One wonders how much idea of epidemiology he can demonstrate. If someone in charge in the business world were to make such a fool of himself, he would have flown the coop long ago. But this is not about science, it's about fear-mongering, and every false prognosis comes in handy.

---

27 ibid
28 https://www.rki.de/DE/Content/InfAZ/N/Neuartiges_Coronavirus/
    Falldefinition.pdf   from 29.5.2020
29 https://www.deutschlandfunk.de/mehr-Covid-19-faelle-in-deutschland-
    rki-praesident-die.676.de.html?dram:article_id=481382

In the USA, they are even more brazen: in some districts, they have started to count as "positive" cases that are *"probable cases"*. The threshold for *"probable"* is ridiculously low. Texas Judge Hill said that a fever and headache would be enough to be considered a Covid-19 patient, as was determined in Collin County. Moreover, up to 15 people would also be classified as *"probable cases"* if they were only close to a *"probable case"*.[30]

The newspaper "Die Welt" wrote on 15.4.2020 that the city of New York also counts "suspected cases" among the Corona deaths who were never tested for the virus. These were 3,700 deaths that were included in the statistics for the 10,000 Covid-19 deaths since 11 March. This is one of the reasons for the exorbitant "case numbers" in New York.

In New York, Elmhurst Hospital in the borough of Queens was such a "corona hotspot". Nurse Erin Marie Olszewski, who worked in the Covid department there in April and May, said in an interview that in the USA there was a bonus of $11,000 for the hospitals for each patient who tested positive. If he was artificially ventilated, the hospital received another $30,000. This put many patients on the Corona wards who did not have Corona at all, or even tested positive. [31]

In the USA, almost all family doctors have been ordered by the health authorities to write "Covid-19" on the death certificate if the cause of death is unclear. There are such reports from all over the world. In Argentina, hospital staff have been unofficially instructed to declare all new patients as "Covid-19 patients", no matter what they are suffering from. Apparently, they get more money from the state, too.

In Spain, the government distributed six billion euros as initial aid, most of it according to the following key: 30% to the districts according to the number of test positives, 10%

---

30 http://www.antikrieg.eu/aktuell/2020_07_07_istdieCovidspitze.htm
31 https://www.compact-online.de/das-war-grob-fahrlaessig-panik-und-pfusch-in-new-york-2/

according to the total number of PCR tests done and 25% according to the number of hospitalised.[32] This is virtually an invitation to report as many cases as possible to Madrid.

Trick No. 5: Positive tested are passed off as "sick"

For the Corona panic, virologists have quickly rewritten medicine. Ever since infectious diseases have been known, a distinction has been made between *"infected"* and *"sick"*. A "sick" person is one who shows symptoms of a disease. One can be "infected" without necessarily being "sick", as in the case of herpes viruses, which can be latent without causing symptoms. This has been thrown out the window with Corona, because the supposedly "infected", i.e. those with a "positive" test result, are simply called *"ill"* and counted, even if they are symptom-free. This way of counting leads to all those who were symptomless positive and later tested negative being called *"recovered" in the* reports, although they were not ill at all.

The RKI has experts who should know the difference between an infection and a disease. If they don't, they only need to take a look at Wikipedia, where it clearly states that infection and infectious disease are two different things, because infections do not automatically trigger a disease.[33] Learning should not end with the acquisition of a doctorate.

In the meantime, we know that over 85% of the *"positives"* do not get sick at all. They have no symptoms and the test eventually becomes negative. Another 10% have only mild symptoms or a normal flu. People cheekily speak of 100% *"sick" people,* but 85% of them are healthy!

Imagine there is a virus that is so dangerous that you have to get tested to see if you even have it.

---

32   https://www.boe.es/boe/dias/2020/06/17/
33   https://de.wikipedia.org/wiki/Infektionskrankheit (if it has not been changed for Corona in the meantime)

27

What is this virus that is sometimes "dangerous" but mostly not? Or does the test have nothing to do with the virus at all? Or does the virus have nothing to do with the disease at all? We will take a closer look at this. But first, let's take a look at what science thinks it knows about viruses.

The wonderful world of viruses

As we have all learned, humans, animals and plants are made up of cells. In bacteria it is just one, in humans it is hundreds of billions. Cells have a shell, which is filled with plasma, and a nucleus. In the cell nucleus, in turn, we find the genetic information for the structure of the entire organism. This is stored in long double chains that are wound up in a spiral: the so-called DNA.[34] Millions of molecules are strung together in a certain order along the double chains, also called "helix". The genetic information is stored here in the sequence of four so-called nucleic acids.[35]

When cells divide, they begin by separating the DNA double chain into two individual chains called RNA[36]. The counterpart then forms anew on each chain, forming exactly the same sequence of the four nucleic acids as before. If there are copying errors ("mutations"), then the faulty cells are destroyed by the immune system (usually, but not always). In this way, two new identical cells arise from one nucleus, which then separate and each forms a new cell around itself.

A virus, on the other hand, is not even a cell like a bacterium. It is much smaller and consists only of a piece of DNA (sometimes RNA) with a shell around it. It is not a living being because it has no metabolism and cannot reproduce except in foreign cells. To do this, it "sneaks" into a cell and waits until it divides. The mechanism that normally ensures the duplication of the cell's RNA now duplicates the virus RNA, causing the cell to die. This alerts the immune system and it responds with inflammation. It either attacks the viruses themselves or the infected cell and then eliminates it. So much for the theory.

---

34   DNA = Deoxyribonucleic acid
35   Adenine, guanine, cytosine and thymine, also called "nucleotides"
36   RNA = Ribonucleic acid

Only in the case that the immune system does not get the infection under control, for whatever reason, is there danger for the infected person. Normally, however, the immune system emerges strengthened from every infection. The organism then remains immune to the attackers. That is why travellers in the Third World often fall ill from germs to which the locals, who have grown up with them, are immune. Incidentally, paediatricians have known for a long time that many children make a developmental leap after overcoming childhood illnesses. Why this is so is not known.

Viruses have been around for millions of years. Most of them exist peacefully in and around us. They are only dangerous in exceptional cases, such as when the immune system is already weakened by other diseases, drugs, medication, stress, etc. The editor of "Peds Ansichten", Peter Frey, says:

"There is something absurd about thinking of viruses as enemies. How many viruses we carry around in our bodies is still unknown, but there must be trillions. And we cannot and do not need to escape them. It has been discovered that there are several million viruses in a teaspoon of seawater alone. Will you, dear readers, no longer go to the sea for a swim in the future?"[37]

In any case, there is no reason to be afraid of viruses as long as humans are healthy and strong. All living beings on this earth have grown up with viruses for millions of years, from childhood onwards. In fact, encountering as many species of microbes as possible is important as training for the immune system. This is just as true for bacteria: About 40 trillion bacteria live in our bodies, ten times as many as body cells, and many of them are essential for survival, such as the intestinal flora.[38] But let's go back to the viruses.

---

37 https://peds-ansichten.de/2020/05/viren-angst-faszination-nutzen/
38 https://www.science.lu/de/die-bewohner-des-koerpers/wie-viele-mikroben-leben-deinem-koerper

Since viruses are very small (in the range of 100 nanometres), they could only be studied from the 1940s onwards, when electron microscopes became available. So far, about 3,000 virus species are known. Virologists assume that there are about 1.6 million virus species, of which we know just 2%.[39]

Coronaviruses

Coronaviruses have been studied since the mid-1960s. Their name comes from the crown-like "spikes" that sit on the surface and are reminiscent of the sun's corona. We all know the typical pictures.[40] Coronaviruses live in many animal species, are said to mutate frequently and are blamed for a wide variety of diseases. In humans, they can trigger influenza, in contrast to influenza usually without fever. The upper respiratory tract, sense of smell and taste, and sometimes the stomach and intestines are affected. As with influenza, pneumonia can be a complication in older or previously injured patients. Except in the case of complications, the disease heals on its own and requires at most palliative (alleviating) treatment. Covid19 does not differ in its symptoms from other corona infections that have been known for a long time.

Not only influenza viruses are found in the annual flu waves, but also coronaviruses in about 10 - 20% of cases. Four of these are known to date, but no vaccine has yet been developed against any of the human coronaviruses, including SARS-CoV-1.[41] Why should SARS-CoV-2 be any different?

39 https://scilogs.spektrum.de/enkapsis/wieviele-viren-koennten-den-menschen-befallen/

40 ... which, however, are all graphics, not photos. The images from the electron microscope are black and white or artificially coloured and relatively unspectacular. Whether viruses can really be seen remains controversial, see also: https://telegra.ph/Wie-erkennt-man-unzureichende-Publikationen-und-behauptete-Virenbilder-08-18

41 The virus of the 2003 SARS epidemic

Moreover, coronaviruses are usually only active in humans during the flu season.

Viruses are distinguished by their "gene sequence", i.e. the sequence of the four nucleic acids on the chain (RNA) or double chain (DNA). Coronaviruses consist of a single chain (RNA) of about 30,000 such nucleic acids, it is the longest chain among the known RNA viruses. Virology is basically nothing else genetic engineering.

Exosome

By the way, viruses are not the only corpuscles that enter or leave cells. There are also the "exosomes"[42] which have only been studied in detail for 20 years. They transport various substances (including peptides or RNA fragments) out of or into the cell and are about the same size as viruses. Some exosomes can degrade or modify RNA, just like viruses. Viruses and exosomes are so similar that some biochemists suspect they may be identical.[43]

"Corona" has reignited a discussion that has been going on for a long time, namely the question of whether viruses really exist as contemporary virology claims. There are many indications that viruses are in fact exosomes that the body itself produces in certain diseases. The German molecular biologist Dr. Stefan Lanka, in particular, repeatedly calls on his colleagues to provide clear evidence for the existence of

---

42 vesicle
43 e.g.: William A. Wells: *"When is a virus an exosome?"* Journal of Cell Biology, 162(6): 960 vom 15.9.2003, oder: **Ken Witwer+Jan Lötvall: *"Is COVID-19 virus or an Exosome?"* Exosome RNA research and industries, www.exosome-rna.com/is-Covid-19-virus-an-exosome/ oder: Esther Nolte-'t Hoen, Tom Cremer, Robert C. Gallo, and Leonid B. Margolis: "*Extracellular vesicles and viruses. Are they close relatives?"* PNAS August 16, 2016 113 (33) 9155-9161; first published July 18, 2016. An interesting Video about: https://www.youtube.com/watch?v=uDDE3PH5SA0

viruses and is prepared to bear the costs of the necessary experiments.[44] Anyone who wants to know more can find detailed material on the Telegram channel "Corona_Fakten".[45]

An interesting topic, especially with the question: What do the virus tests actually hit on? Virus RNA? Fragments of it? Or RNA from exosomes from body cells? There are still many open questions in genetic engineering.

I myself find the topic highly exciting, but I do not want to go into it here. One does not have to doubt the existence of viruses to prove that SARS-CoV-2 (if it exists) is not a particularly dangerous virus and that the "Covid19 pandemic" has entirely different causes. My argument assumes that viruses exist.

---

44 For this he is being attacked in the strongest terms, presumably because of the consequences for virology if it should turn out that he is right.

45 https://t.me/Corona_Fakten

The PCR test is completely unsuitable for virus detection and is not approved at all.

Who says so? First of all, the inventor of the PCR test himself, the American biochemist Kary Mullis. He developed the test in 1983 and was awarded the Nobel Prize in Chemistry for it in 1993.[46] He himself warned that his method was completely unsuitable for proving a virus as the cause of a disease.[47] The PCR was not designed for this purpose at all, but for reproducing nucleic acids millions of times over. At that time, the aim was to detect foreign particles in the air of high-purity laboratories for the production of computer chips.

The second warning against the tests comes from the manufacturers. The package inserts usually say something like: *"Not suitable for diagnosing a corona infection"* or: *"For research purposes only"*.

The US manufacturer with the original name "Creative Diagnostics" not only makes such statements,[48] but one can read there a whole series of restrictions that make the test result appear very questionable. The test also reacts to influenza viruses and a number of other microorganisms.[49]

Even the official US disease agency CDC[50] admits that the so-called "SARS-CoV-2 RT-PCR tests" are not suitable for

---

46 His employer, the company Cetus, paid him $10,000 for his method in 1989. In 1994, Cetus sold the patent to Hoffmann-LaRoche for $300 million, the highest sum paid for a patent up to that time.

47 https://youtu.be/xZGT1AEZjwE and: Celia Farber. "The Corona Simulation Machine": https://uncoverdc.com/2020/04/07/was-the-Covid-19-test-meant-to-detect-a-virus/

48 https://www.creative-diagnostics.com/sars-cov-2-coronavirus-multiplex-rt-qpcr-kit-277854-457.htm

49 Influenza A Virus (H1N1), Influenza B Virus (Yamagata), Respiratory Syncytial Virus (type B), Respiratory Adenovirus (type 3, type 7), Parainfluenza Virus (type 2), Mycoplasma Pneumoniae, Chlamydia Pneumoniae, etc.

50 Centre for Disease Control, US Department of Health and Human Services in Atlanta, Georgia

the Covid19 diagnosis, namely that a virus does not necessarily have to be present if viral RNA is found,[51] and that SARS-CoV2 does not have to have triggered the symptoms or other bacteria or viruses can be responsible for them.[52] And the FDA[53] admits that a positive PCR test is not proof that the virus fragment found caused the disease.[54]

The Institute for Medical Microbiology at the University of Mainz also confirms on its website that the PCR is not able to distinguish between viruses that are able to multiply and other organisms and is therefore not proof of infection.[55]

The German science editorial of the "Science Media Centre" writes that with the PCR test one finds the genetic material of the virus, i.e. also remnants of the virus, and not necessarily the virus itself.[56]The manufacturer of the cobas® SARS-CoV-2 PCR test, Roche, also says the same in its product description. [57]

Marcel Luthe, a non-party member of parliament in Berlin, criticises the test chaos and points out that 550 different tests are used in Germany and that there is no institution for approval. This means that everyone is allowed to market their test, no one knows what exactly is being tested and there is also no data collection.[58]

---

51 The former name of the coronavirus SARS-CoV-2
52 CDC 2019-Novel Coronavirus (2019-nCoV) Real-Time RT-PCR Diagnostic Panel, March 30, 2020
53 Food and Drug Administration, US regulatory authority for medicinal products.
54 https://www.fda.gov/media/136151/download
55 https://www.unimedizin-mainz.de/fileadmin/kliniken/medmikrohyg/Dokumente/Dokumente_Diagnostik/Diagn_Know_how/Mibi_PCR-Grundlagen.pdf
56 https://www.sciencemediacenter.de/alle-angebote/fact-sheet/details/news/verlauf-von-Covid-19-und-kritische-abschnitte-der-infektion/
57 https://pim-eservices.roche.com/eLD/api/downloads/008d5c8b-8ab5-ea11-fa90-005056a772fd?countryIsoCode=ch
58 Source: https://www.reitschuster.de/post/corona-abgeordneter-beklagt-test-chaos/

But what is being done? They continue to diagnose with the unapproved and unsafe tests and justify criminal actions such as coercion (wearing masks, forced tests), deprivation of liberty (quarantine lock-down), bodily harm (oxygen deprivation through masks, soon vaccinations with danger-ous vaccines) and mental injuries with the false figures thus obtained. The health authorities and ministries don't give a damn about their own regulations, but demand unconditional obedience from the citizen, who is slowly but surely being led to the slaughter. How much longer can this go on?

The bogus epidemic

An unpalatable example of how fatal it can be to blindly rely on PCR tests is the false whooping cough epidemic declared in New Hampshire, USA, in 2007. At the large *"Dartmouth-Hitchcock Medical Centre"*, Dr. Brooke Herndon had a cough for weeks that would not go away. When other staff also began coughing, they suspected a whooping cough epidemic and had everyone who showed cold symptoms, about 1,000 of the hospital's more than 4,000 employees, tested with PCR. 142 tested "positive", and so they began to fight the supposed epidemic: 72% of the staff were vaccinated and 1,445 were treated with antibiotics.

But without success, the "epidemic" went on for months until, after eight months, the idea came up to send samples of sick people to the CDC. There they tried to cultivate and detect the pathogen, a bacterium, using the classical method. Without success. The PCR tests were then repeated on 116 of those who had previously tested positive. This time, only one was still "positive". There was no epidemic, the test had given false results. The doctors were surprised, but they said they would not blindly trust any test in the future.[59] In times of Corona, however, they apparently quickly forgot the lesson.

---

59 https://www.nytimes.com/2007/01/22/health/22whoop.html

At least in Sweden, they seem to be willing to learn: At the end of August 2020, the Stockholm Health Authority announced that it had to correct the Corona statistics because 3,700 Swedes had been falsely tested "positive" with PCR tests. The laboratories could not distinguish between low virus concentrations and negative samples. The performance of the tests was simply too poor, it said at the press conference.[60]

How does the PCR test actually work?

In order to avoid confusion, I must point out that there are essentially three procedures for coronary detection: One either looks for virus components by PCR, "virus-typical proteins" (so-called "rapid tests")[61] or the antibodies that the immune system has formed against them (immunoglobulins). I will discuss the antibody tests in more detail later. So let's start with the PCR test.

Attention: The text is now becoming a bit more scientific, unfortunately this cannot be avoided. So please skip the following or read it twice – It's worth the effort!

The classic method for pathogen detection – whether bacteria or viruses – Is to take material (blood, tissue, body fluids) in which the pathogen is suspected. The material is prepared and put on nutrient medium where the pathogen feels comfortable and multiplies. Then it must be "isolated", i.e. separated from the rest, for example by centrifugation. In the process, different materials settle in different layers. Separation by means of electrical fields, so-called *"electrophoresis"*, is also popular.[62] As you can imagine, this is a

---

60 https://www.oe24.at/coronavirus/schock-tausende-schweden-bekamen-falsches-testergebnis/443581008

61 I will not go into detail about the rapid tests, because they are based on the results of the PCR tests and are therefore at least as uncertain.

62 Today, gel electrophoresis has become state of the art

lengthy process, and with viruses it is even more complicated than with bacteria.

The PCR specialises in the multiplication of nucleic acids millions of times over, because that is the stuff genes are made of. PCR means *"polymerase chain reaction"*. Sounds complicated and it is. I will only briefly explain the most important points here so that it is clear what it is all about. More information can be found on the internet.

When the PCR test came onto the market in the 1980s, genetic researchers and virologists rejoiced because it was now easy to multiply viruses at will until enough had been collected to make a diagnosis. They thought they could make diagnoses very easily. But this proved to be a fallacy, which the inventor, Kary Mullis, had already predicted. There are a lot of problems that virologists like to sweep under the carpet:

Polymerases are responsible, among other things, for the duplication of DNA in the cell nucleus, so that it can divide and thus a living being can grow. They are found in every living being. In PCR, gene fragments, whether from the body or from a virus, are first split in a machine and then duplicated by the polymerase. This is called a *"cycle"*. The whole thing is repeated 20-50 times in a chain *reaction.* So, with each cycle we get two, then four, then eight, then 16, etc. times as many new gene fragments (gene sequences) as at the beginning of the process. How often this cycle is repeated depends on the manufacturer's recommendation and can be set on the machine. This setting, the so-called "ct value"[63] decides the sensitivity of the test, as we will see.

---

63 "cycle threshold", more details here:
    https://www.deutschlandfunk.de/Covid-19-pandemie-nicht-jeder-positiv-getestete-ist-noch.676.de.html

The number of cycles is decisive

Correctly adjusted, the test works quite well as long as it is not misused for diagnostic purposes; and if is used, for example, for genetic analyses and parentage reports. However, if you set too many cycles, as happened in the case of the whooping cough "epidemic" described above, you get positive results for almost every gene sequence you are looking for, even if there was little or no starting material. The higher sensitivity comes at the price of a higher false positive rate. How the Covid tests are adjusted in each case is left up to the laboratories and is not disclosed.

In the meantime, it is also known that the "viral load", i.e. the amount of viruses present in a sample, is decisive for whether someone will be labelled "infected". If the test already shows "positive" at a ct value of 15 or 20 cycles, then the proband can be infectious, from 30 and higher, the viral load is low to non-existent. Therefore, one should not exceed 25, values above 30 are considered unreliable. Two studies also showed that the infectivity decreased by 33% with each cycle. [64]

Test manufacturer Olfert Landt, head of TIB-Molbiol, also admits that those who test positive are not necessarily infectious. In an interview, he said that about half of them are not contagious because of too low a viral load. *"To be dangerous to third parties, you would have to have 100 times more viral load in you than the detection limit of the tests."*[65] They are locked up anyway.

The ct values of the laboratories are not shown anywhere, neither in the case of a positive result, nor in the statistics of the RKI. The ct value is therefore an ideal, unverifiable means of manipulating test results on a grand scale.

---

64 https://de.rt.com/gesellschaft/110320-studie-zeigt-pcr-tests-liefern/
65 https://reitschuster.de/post/haelfte-der-positiv-getesteten-nicht-infektioes/

This consequently affects the false positive rate: Dream values of "only" 1-2%, as the test manufacturers claim, can easily be achieved with 15-20 cycles. If one tests in the laboratories with 40 cycles, then the proportion of false results can rise to 96%. That is why over 85% of the people tested have no symptoms and are neither sick nor contagious for the same reason, namely because they have few or no viruses.

On the website of Deutschlandfunk one can read that, according to the "New York Times", too high ct-values are responsible for a large part of the positive numbers in the USA. Tests with more than 30 cycles as a ct value should always be reported as "negative". [66]Most tests work with 40 cycles, the Drosten test even with a ct value of up to 45, as Drosten himself stated. So, it is no wonder that one finds so many "infected" people worldwide without any symptom.

On 14.12.2020, the WHO finally warned against too high ct values in the tests and called on the laboratories and authorities to include the ct value in every test.[67] It remains to be seen whether this will be implemented, because the WHO is not a public institution, even if it appears so, but only a private association without authority to issue directives.

But even with fewer cycles, the PCR can show positive for sequences or fragments of other viruses or even the body's own cells, i.e. exosomes. Wikipedia writes that the test recognises all life forms with the same gene fragment by chance.[68]

"PCR is ultra-sensitive, which means that absurdly low concentrations of DNA can be detected. On the other hand, the method is only moderately specific because PCR ampli-

66 https://www.deutschlandfunk.de/Covid-19-pandemie-nicht-jeder-positiv-getestete-ist-noch.676.de.html?dram:article_id=483722
67 https://www.who.int/news/item/14-12-2020-who-information-notice-for-ivd-users#.X9pjhnAOs2Y.twitter
68 https://de.wikipedia.org/wiki/SARS-CoV-2#cite_ref-RT-PCR-1-Fig2-Desc_154-0   more sources also there

fies everything the primers can dock to. That is the curse of the PCR method." [69]

Author Peter Haisenko writes: *"How do the Corona numbers come about? To state it clearly: They are produced at will. The laboratories only need to be instructed to increase the test cycles until the desired result is obtained.*

For this reason, the government of Florida/USA determined last week that all test results of PCR tests are invalid if more than 30 test cycles have been applied. The fact is that all, repeat all, PCR tests show a positive result as soon as the cycles exceed 45. Florida has thus reduced its Corona numbers by more than 90 percent. This is also the reason why we never use the Corona numbers to indicate the number of cycles applied. So, the 'Corona pandemic' is a test pandemic." [70]

This is now well known in medical circles. In many clinics, medical staff are allowed to continue working even with a positive test if the ct value was above 30, as confirmed by virologist Dittmer from Essen. Doctors with such a test and an antibody test are considered "healthy" and are allowed to continue practising.[71] Why doesn't the same apply to all of us? Nursing staff should actually be held to higher standards than ordinary citizens.

69 Source: https://www.rubikon.news/artikel/der-fluch-der-pcr-methode
70 https://www.anderweltonline.com/klartext/klartext-20202/warum-gibt-es-akzeptable-und-inakzeptable-sterbefaelle/
71 Source: https://kopp-report.de/wie-politik-und-medien-die-ganze-wahrheit-ueber-corona-tests-verschweigen/

Other problems of the test

But the test has even more problems: it cannot search for new, unknown gene sequences, but can only detect what is given to it beforehand. This is done by means of two so-called *"primers", which* are markers that determine which gene segments are duplicated from where to where. To search for a new virus, you first have to take gene sequences of known viruses. If you find matches, then you put them together in the computer in a way that you think "fits". This is how a "new virus" is defined – but not really "found".

The test cannot detect a complete virus because the genetic code of viruses is much too long for PCR. The Covid19 virus, like all coronaviruses, has a length of about 30,000 base pairs (bp)[72]. A base pair is the smallest unit of the genetic code and corresponds to one bit in a computer. For comparison: human DNA has about three billion bp. [73]

The PCR test generally only works up to 3,000 bp. For the SARS-CoV2 search, one chooses two small fragments of the virus[74] that are considered typical for it. The gene snippets are only 76 and 100 bp small, respectively, which is 0.6% of the virus. The remaining 99.4% of the virus are not checked and fall under the table. If the small gene sequences are found, the test is considered "positive". It is basically scandalous to claim that one "finds" a certain virus when one has only detected 0.6% of it!

---

72 Sometimes also: "nt"=nucleotides

73 In order to decode them, millions of individual sequences were analysed in many laboratories around the world from 1990 to 2001 and used to compile the human genome in the computer: "Human Genome Project" https://en.wikipedia.org/wiki/Human_Genome_Project

74 E gene and RdRp, S or ORF1 gene

Because the whole thing is a bit complicated, I'll summarise again:

- The PCR only finds what it is given as a reference beforehand. You cannot simply go looking for viruses, but must "tell" the test beforehand what it should look for. This has consequences for the "discovery of new viruses".

- It can normally only detect parts of a coronavirus, never the complete RNA/DNA. This is later assembled in the computer from various parts.

- The partial sequences are selected beforehand and defined by so-called "primers".

- The recognisable sections are extremely short.

With coronaviruses, there is another possible source of error: the PCR can only reproduce DNA, but coronaviruses are RNA viruses. The RNA must therefore first be converted into DNA before the PCR by a process called "reverse transcription" (RT). [75]

That may be enough to get you started. Before we get to the "discovery" of the Covid19 virus, let's take a quick look at the first Corona "pandemic", which was 18 years ago.

---

75 https://de.wikipedia.org/wiki/Reverse_Transkription
    All Corona tests are therefore called "real-time RT-PCR".

The precursor to Covid19:
The SARS epidemic of 2002/03

There is a back story to "Corona 2020" that you should know:

In November 2002, there were several cases of *"atypical pneumonia"* in southern China. *"Atypical"* means that doctors cannot find any pathogens and the disease hardly responds to the usual treatment with antibiotics, etc. Normally, pneumonia is mostly caused by bacteria such as pneumococci, especially in older, weakened patients, but also by antibiotic-resistant germs in hospitals (hospitalism). According to the RKI, 600,000 patients fall ill from this in Germany alone every year, and up to 20,000 of them die.[76] In 2018, the figure was as high as 40,000, ten times as many as died in road accidents.[77]

The Chinese were initially baffled and in February 2003, after believing they had found a virus, reported 305 cases and five deaths to the WHO. The WHO christened the disease "SARS" (Severe Acute Respiratory Syndrome) and declared it a *"global threat"* on 12 March, which was ridiculous given the low numbers.

At that time, a coronavirus was suspected as the cause. Even then, bats were suspected of being the source of the virus because coronaviruses are common among them. Only two days after Chinese virologists published a suspected gene sequence on the internet, Mr. Christian Heinrich Maria Drosten in Germany had developed a test for the virus in no time at all. It was called SARS-CoV.[78] By mid-2003, only 8,096 people worldwide had tested "positive" with this test, of whom 774 died in the course of the "pandemic" (until July

---

76 According to the RKI, https://www.tagesschau.de/inland/infektionen-101.html

77 https://www.politaia.org/waehrend-corona-vergessen-krankenhauskeime/?source=ENL

78 2020 renamed SARS-CoV-1 to avoid confusion with the "new" SARS-CoV-2, i.e. Covid19

2003).[79] As of 2004, there were no more SARS cases and the pandemic was declared over.

Despite only a few infected and deceased people worldwide, SARS was the second viral disease (after HIV-AIDS) to be accompanied by a fierce media hype. Western media accused China of not having reacted in time and appropriately. The relatively late notification to the WHO was portrayed by the press of the "free West" as a "cover-up attempt".

The most affected countries China, Hong Kong and Malaysia lost 70% of their tourists due to travel warnings. Hong Kong and Singapore went into recession, Singapore Airlines had to be propped up with government money and Singapore had to devalue its currency. Major sporting events were cancelled or moved to the USA. Hong Kong had to support its tourism industry with an aid package of 1.5 billion US dollars. The damage to the image of these countries caused by the press campaign was enormous.

The Chinese government still had all this in mind when the SARS-CoV apparently reappeared in a mutated form in 2019/20 and allegedly threatened another pandemic. This time, they preferred to react quickly and harshly.

Over time, the panic of 2003 was forgotten, but two scientific publications in 2013[80] and 2017[81] (editor: Prof. Drosten again) brought the SARS virus back into play and predicted new outbreaks of mutated SARS viruses because they had discovered similar gene sequences in bats as in SARS-CoV. This is not surprising, since the gene sequence of the SARS virus was also derived from bat viruses.[82]

---

79 https://en.wikipedia.org/wiki/2002%E2%80%932004_SARS_outbreak

80 Xing-Yi Ge et al., Isolation and characterization of a bat SARS-like Coronavirus that uses the ACE2-receptor. Nature. Band 503, 2013, S. 535-538

81 Ben Hu et al.; Christian Drosten (Hrsg.): Discovery of a rich gene pool of bat SARS-related coronaviruses provides new insights into the origin of SARS coronavirus, in: PLOS Pathogens vom 30. November 2017

82 https://de.wikipedia.org/wiki/SARS-CoV

The comeback of the SARS coronavirus

After the experience with the SARS epidemic, the Chinese authorities set up an early warning system to be able to react more quickly in the future. In December 2019, several cases of atypical pneumonia were reported in Wuhan, an industrial city on the Yangtze River. This is not initially noticeable in a city of 8 million people, especially since the climate there is humid and air pollution is very high, as the city is the industrial centre of Central China. With average temperatures of 3°- 10°C (in December), there are also regular waves of flu in Wuhan in winter.

The alarm was raised on 30 December by ophthalmologist Li Wenliang. He had reported in a chat group about allegedly seven confirmed cases of SARS in his hospital. The report went "viral" on the internet and created panic in China, where people still remembered the 2003 epidemic. Beijing sent in a response team, which initially found 44 patients with atypical pneumonia by 3 January. Swabs were taken from four patients. Li Wenliang had to sign a confidentiality agreement because he had *"disturbed public order"*.

On 10 January, Li thought he had been infected and voluntarily went into quarantine. Doctors tested him several times but found nothing at first. It was not until 30 January that a SARS test came back positive. Li commented on the net that he had now tested positive. *"The dust has settled. Finally diagnosed!"* he posted. His condition deteriorated despite (or because of?) the massive use of various antibiotic drugs. He died on 7 February, reportedly from Covid19, but the exact cause of death is not known (overmedication?). It is not possible to research more details because the Chinese do not give any.

This all went viral on the internet and made Li Wenliang a folk hero in China, but also increased panic in Wuhan and the surrounding area as rumours of a large-scale govern-ment cover-up did the rounds. The epidemic, which was not yet an epidemic at the time, inspired frightening speculation among many Chinese. Videos circulated on the web of people dropping in the street, allegedly struck down by the new "killer virus". The government in Beijing was forced to intervene and had Wuhan and five other cities sealed off by the military, especially as a wave of travel was imminent with the Chinese New Year.

After the official end of the epidemic in China on 28 March 2020, the official statistics counted 83,000 infected people and fewer than 5,000 deaths.[83] In a country with 1.4 billion people, this is a vanishingly small number.[84] The reason for this is that in China only those cases that are clinical, i.e. with symptoms *and* a positive test (presumably with a low ct value), are now counted as "corona cases". However, the Chinese lockdown has become a model for the whole world.

How did they find the Corona virus in the first place?

As with SARS in 2003, Prof. Christian Drosten, now chief virologist at Berlin's Charité hospital, was incredibly quick to put together a suitable PCR test. Note the data:

- Li Wenliang sounded the alarm in China on 30 Dec 2019.

- An outreach team from Beijing was ordered to Hunan on 31 Dec 2019.

---

83 https://de.wikipedia.org/wiki/COVID-19-
    Pandemie_in_der_Volksrepublik_China#cite_ref-40
84 That is 0.006% infected and 0.00036% dead in the total population.

- On 1.1.2020, Prof. Drosten developed a PCR test kit for the "new" virus. He followed a hunch from *"social media reports"* that it might be related to SARS-CoV and made a download of data from hundreds of SARS virus fragments from the internet. Of these, three were randomly selected and supplemented with others, also from a database,[85] to test patients with. The whole thing happened without him having had any virus material.[86]

- On 21.1.2020, the WHO recommended that all nations use the "safe" test procedure developed by Prof. Drosten.

- On 23.1.2020, Drosten and his colleagues published their results[87] in "Eurosurveillance", a journal that does not require *peer* review of its articles, as is usually the case in renowned scientific journals.

- On 24.1.2020, the Chinese disease authority CCDC[88] published their first results of short gene sequences that could mentally or in the computer be strung together to form a virus. They explicitly pointed out that the prescribed control experiments had not yet been done that would prove that these gene sequences could trigger the pneumonias in Wuhan (this has not been done to date). The constructed genetic strand had up to 90% similarity with harmless coronaviruses in bats that have been known for decades.[89]

---

85 http://www.gisaid.org/
86 You can find everything in: https://www.eurosurveillance.org/content/10.2807/1560-7917.ES.2020.25.3.2000045
87 *"Detection of 2019 novel coronavirus (2019-nCoV) by real-time RT-PCR"*, same link as above
88 Chinese Centre for Disease Control
89 The China Novel Coronavirus Investigating and Research Team: A Novel Coronavirus from Patients with Pneumonia in China, 2019. In: The New

Anyone who reads the original sources will notice:

- Prof. Drosten developed his test *before* virus sequences were available from China. They were not available until three weeks later (on 24 January).

- The test was later used to test tissue samples and patients with atypical pneumonia. In some, the exact number is not given, the test was successful, but that does not mean more than that some of the suspected gene fragments were found. Whether these come from a virus or from the body itself, for example in the course of the disease, was not investigated.

- Prof. Drosten never had a virus or tissue sample in the lab when he put the test together in January. The hypothetical virus was put together in the computer on the basis of assumptions from various databases with gene fragments from the SARS-CoV-1 and bat viruses from the internet, as he himself wrote.

- The WHO recommended Drosten's test worldwide *before* his work was published and *before* the first Chinese study appeared. Validation of the test (detection, verification) has never taken place. SARS-CoV-2 has never been detected as a whole.

- Since the PCR only ever detects what it is given with the primers, the "discovery of Covid19" is a circular reasoning, a self-fulfilling prophecy, because all tests to date only find the gene sequences that Drosten had selected at the time, and even of these only two tiny sections.

- It is by no means proven that the SARS-CoV-2 virus 1.) exists as claimed and 2.) if it exists, is "new", because the fragments used were all already known.

England Journal of Medicine. 24. Januar 2020 siehe auch:
https://telegra.ph/Wie-die-Fehlannahme-des-behaupteten-SARS-CoV-2-begann-10-08

This makes it clear where SARS-CoV-2 comes from, namely from the computer of Prof. Drosten, who compiled it. However, not in the laboratory, i.e. real, but only as a hypothetical sequence of 30,000 nucleotides, of which only 176[90] are searched for and found worldwide with the PCR. These snippets exist, they are found in many diseases, especially in influenza, in people who have been through certain diseases, and in healthy people.

This also makes it unnecessary to discuss whether the SARS-CoV-2 was created in some laboratory as a bioweapon: What good is a bioweapon that is no more dangerous than a flu virus? A bioweapon would have to be at least as "effective" as the Ebola virus. No, the virus as a whole is a theoretical construct. What the PCR measures are gene parts of real viruses or exosomes that can be active in flu.

Nobody is interested in whether the SARS-CoV2 really looks like what is claimed, because the PCR pandemic works wonderfully with the 176 bp snippets. With such mumbo-jumbo, the world is panicked and ruined. The "being scientific" is only feigned, which is easy in a highly specialised field like virology, which cannot be verified by everyone. In any case, Drosten's brazen approach has nothing to do with clean science, as this fact has been proven by a group of top-class scientists:

---

90 E gene with 76 bp and RdRp gene with 100 bp

The Drosten study is useless

The above-mentioned Drosten study,[91] on which the PCR test is based, was examined at the end of 2020 by 22 scientists from Europe, the USA and Japan, all high-ranking molecular geneticists, biochemists, immunologists and microbiologists. They came to the damning conclusion that the SARS-CoV-2 PCR test was unusable due to errors and mistakes found during the revision.[92]

The experts found ten serious deficiencies. They criticised, among other things, the faulty and non-specific design of the primers, the inability to distinguish between a virus and its fragments, the lack of control experiments and the absence of standardised working instructions. They conclude that the Drosten test is unsuitable for diagnosing SARS-CoV2.

In addition, there was apparently no peer review, as is customary for scientific papers. The paper was published on the second day after submission – too short for peer review.

There were also serious conflicts of interest: two of the authors, including Drosten, sit on the editorial board of "Eurosurveillance", where the study appeared, and three are on the payroll of the first companies that produced the tests. Olfert Landt is head of the test manufacturer TIB Molbiol and earns millions from the test. The scientists called on Eurosurveillance to withdraw the Corman-Drosten paper. Two reports on the botched Drosten study can be found here.[93]

---

91 V. M. Corman, T. Bleicker, S. Brünink, **Christian Drosten, Olfert Landt**, M. P. G. Koopmans, M Zambon, M. Peiris: Diagnostic detection of 2019-nCoV by real-time RT-PCR (protocol-v2-1). Hrsg.: Charité Virologie, 17.1.20

92 https://cormandrostenreview.com/report/

93 https://reitschuster.de/post/wissenschaftler-pcr-test-unbrauchbar/
    https://de.rt.com/meinung/109980-experten-finden-zehn-schwerwiegende-fehler-Covid-19/

Successful despite all contradictions

Prof. Drosten obviously wanted to build on his success with the SARS-CoV-1 test of 2003, because whoever submits a test first not only reaps the laurels, but also gets a head start in the international business with the millions of tests. In the beginning, these were only produced by the Berlin laboratory "TIB Molbiol"[94] , with which Prof. Drosten has already worked together many times. Olfert Landt, the managing director, and Drosten have known each other for many years. Landt was also the first to market Drosten's SARS test in 2003.

It is strange that Drosten and the Charité simply hand over the millions in profits from the tests to private companies,[95] when the research was financed, at least in part, by taxpayers' money. Whether there are also business connections with Olfert Landt is not known and could be worth a closer investigation. In any case, the test is being sold all over the world, scaring humanity, and incidentally bringing in huge amounts of money.[96]

It is still unclear exactly which viruses the test finds and with what precision.[97] Calling it the *"gold standard"* for Covid19 diagnostics is as presumptuous as declaring "the emperor's new clothes" to be the *"top fashion" for the* new fashion season.

Actually, the test should finally be "validated": In several studies, other possible factors, including other virus fragments,

---

94 TIB MOLBIOL Syntheselabor GmbH Berlin Tempelhof has been a partner and initial user of various PCR test methods from Christian Drosten's environment for decades.

95 https://corona-transition.org/die-roche-connection-wie-prof-christian-drosten-mit-steuergeldern-forscht-und

96 According to Wikipedia, Drostens Test has already sold 40,000 test kits, for testing 4 million samples, in over 60 countries in the first two months.

97 https://off-guardian.org/2020/06/27/Covid19-pcr-tests-are-scientifically-meaningless/

would have to be excluded. The effort is considerable and takes years. Those responsible are well aware of this: all Covid 19 tests that are used worldwide (there are currently more than 500) are *not validated and may not even be used for diagnosis,* as I have already explained above.

The official website of the Paul Ehrlich Institute[98] states that PCR tests[99] are regulated by the EU Directive on In Vitro Diagnostics (IVD), and this does not stipulate that anyone has to check the tests before they are put on the market. Therefore, there is no validation, and that is why there is evidence of fakes on the way.[100]

In plain language, this means that the manufacturers certify themselves and do not need independent inspections. A land of milk and honey for pharmaceutical capitalism! This is justified by the "hurry" in view of the "pandemic", which in turn is justified by the false tests. A vicious circle, diligently pushed up by the media.

Even the EU Commission criticises that the tests are not validated and "recommends" a voluntary validation by the manufacturers, which confirms that the tests measure what they claim to measure.[101] A nice recommendation, but one that no one adheres to, because a real check or validation would bring down all test results and statistics like a house of cards.

In the USA, the FDA[102] was officially responsible for the validation and approval of such tests. In August 2020, by order from Washington, they were stripped of their competence to do so.[103] Billion-dollar business with the tests was apparently not to be hindered by lengthy approval proced-

---

98 The German Federal Institute for Vaccines and Biomedical Drugs

99 "in vitro" = in the laboratory, not on the patient

100 https://www.pei.de/DE/newsroom/hp-meldungen/2020/200323-Covid-19-nat-tests.html

101 https://eur-lex.europa.eu/legal-content/DE/TXT/?uri=uriserv:OJ.CI.2020.122.01.0001.01.DEU

102 Food and Drug Administration

ures, or it was a matter of driving the "case numbers" up further through uncontrolled tests. Probably both.

In the meantime, the unreliability of the PCR tests has been confirmed by a British meta-study, which examined the results of 25 other studies.[104] Among other things, it turned out that the test also reacts positively to virus residues from infections long ago, although the test person has not been infectious for a long time.

The "New York Times" reported on worthless PCR tests on 3.9.2020. The website "Journalistenwatch" commented on the article: *"Looking at three sets of tests from Massachusetts, New York and Nevada, due to flawed procedures... "up to 90% of those who tested positive barely showed a viral load". So 90% of those who tested positive were not positive at all - even experts interviewed were "astonished" that these people had been identified as Corona carriers....*

(There) were over 85 million PCR tests performed in the US alone. In total, if the new NYT figures were taken as a basis, almost 13 billion dollars had been wasted on a test that was essentially worthless.... It was a "massive fraud" on the American population, who were sold the PCR test as the "gold standard", and the "biggest fraud" in history." [105]

The lawyer Dr. Reiner Fuellmich is currently preparing a class action lawsuit in the USA, with which mainly companies that had suffered losses due to the lockdown can sue for damages from Prof. Drosten and the RKI. The reason given is that the measures are based on a test that is neither suitable nor approved for diagnosis. I hope he is successful.

---

103 https://www.thailandmedical.news/news/must-read-u-s-medical-news-white-house-removes-us-fda-s-power-to-regulate-and-standardize-all-medical-laboratory-tests-including-for-Covid-19

104 At the Centre for Evidence-Based Medicine at Oxford University and the University of the West of England http://alles-schallundrauch.blogspot.com/2020/09/die-falschen-resultate-der-Covid-tests.html#ixzz6XL6JITCP

105 https://www.journalistenwatch.com/2020/09/08/prozent-positiv-tests/

Because with such suspect tests, innocent people are scared to death, imprisoned and entire economies ruined.

Sensitivity and cross-reactions

But that is by no means all. If the PCR test is over-sensitised by increasing the number of doubling cycles, the "ct value", too far, one is more likely to get a "positive" result. So-called "cross-reactions" become more likely, too. This means that the test detects something other than what it is supposed to look for. This is known, for example, from drug tests that detect an increased concentration of morphine in the urine up to two days after eating poppy-seed cake. [106]

The test is therefore unable to distinguish whether the virus residues found originate from active viruses or are cell components, i.e. residues after an infection that has already occurred. This is because it is always only fragments of the viral genome that are amplified by PCR. In addition, the tests that are used worldwide today are quite different. They test two gene fragments of Covid-19, defined by the primers, but different manufacturers use different primers, so that the test results cannot be compared with each other. [107]

We also never learn from the worldwide statistics which tests were used in each case, which laboratories evaluated them, how many cycles were run in the laboratory, i.e. at which viral load the test indicates "positive". This is dubious, because it makes a reasonable comparison of different countries or of time courses impossible.

Since January 2020, several cross-reactions have become known. The tests also react positively to SARS-CoV-1 and

---

106 https://www.drugcom.de/news/positiver-drogenbefund-nach-mohnbroetchen/
107 https://taz.de/Produzent-von-Corona-Tests/!5671485/

probably to sarbecoviruses[108] Only five coronaviruses are known *not to* react to the test. It is not known about all other viruses. Drosten himself admitted that his test reacts to various coronaviruses, especially from bats.[109]

As early as 2014, on the occasion of the MERS[110] epidemic in the Arab region, Drosten explained in an interview how misleading the highly sensitive PCR can be, because it can find individual molecules of viruses, even in nurses who neither notice anything about it nor are ill, but are classified as MERS cases. This way, even healthy people would get into the statistics, which would explain the increase in numbers in Saudi Arabia at that time. In addition, the media would have played up the numbers.

He called on the Saudi authorities to return to the definitions of the disease because only genuine cases count. He also doubted that symptomless or mildly ill people are contagious. He said that only cases in which antibodies had been detected should be counted. (If we did this with Covid19, the "infection figures" would only be a fraction of the current PCR figures).

Drosten went on to explain that only if antibodies are found has an infection taken place. Most viruses, although present and detectable, are intercepted by the body's own defences on the skin or mucous membranes.[111]

Well spotted, Mr. Drosten, and very sensible! But why have you all forgotten these insights at Corona?

---

108 "Diagnostic detection of 2019-nCoV by real-time RT-PCR (protocol-v2-1)", ed: Charité Virology, Berlin. 17 Jan. 2020, p. 6, title 1, paragraph 3

109 V. M. Corman, T. Bleicker, S. Brünink, **Christian Drosten, Olfert Landt**, M. P. G. Koopmans, M Zambon, M. Peiris: Diagnostic detection of 2019-nCoV by real-time RT-PCR (protocol-v2-1). Hrsg.: Charité Virologie, 17.1.20

110 MERS: Middle East Respiratory Syndrome, a lung disease caused by the MERS-CoV coronavirus.

111 https://www.reitschuster.de/post/wie-drosten-die-corona-tests-zerlegte/

The Covid19 PCR even finds a human gene sequence

But the hammer is yet to come: At the end of August 2020, it became known that one of the primers of the SARS-CoV-2 PCR test is identical to a gene sequence of the human genome![112] It's about a primer[113] with the same gene sequence[114] This sequence is exactly the same in human chromosome No. 8 [115]

This cannot be a coincidence, because the probability of a coincidence would be approximately one in 68 billion.[116] It means: If there is a human cell in the sample whose "chromosome 8" is damaged or the gene sequence in question was excreted via an exosome, the PCR will multiply this and show positive, even without a virus fragment. So, in principle, anyone can test positive under special circumstances! Is this intentional?

Chromosome 8 is responsible for intelligence and fertility. Will it possibly be attacked by the new mRNA vaccination?

The gene databases from which Prof. Drosten had assembled his virus apparently confused a human exosome with a viral component. This at least shows how little the virologists know about their source material.

---

112 https://pieceofmindful.com/2020/04/06/bombshell-who-coronavirus-pcr-test-primer-sequence-is-found-in-all-human-dna/

113 "RdRp/nCoV_IP2-12759Rv"

114 *CTCCCTTTGTTGTTGT* Here C stands for cytosine, T for thymine and G for guanine.

115 https://www.ncbi.nlm.nih.gov/nucleotide/NC_000008.11

116 4^{18} because of 4 possible nucleic acids to the power of 18 digits

Further inconsistencies

The uncertainty of the Drosten test has also been confirmed by clinical studies from China.[117] Numerous cases have been reported where several tests on the same person were alternately positive, then negative and then positive again.

In the Swabian town of Trossingen, all residents and employees of the home for senior citizens "Bethel" were tested for Covid-19 at the end of April. Out of 145 people, 56 were positive. But since none of them showed any symptoms, the director had a second test carried out. This time, only two samples were positive. At first, it was suspected that the laboratory had made a mistake, but it could not find anything wrong with the way the test was carried out. It remains a mystery how this large deviation came about. However, the health department insists on using the first test for its statistics.

In Tanzania in Africa, people apparently distrusted the Covid tests and sent samples of various plants and animals to a testing laboratory. Samples from a goat, a bird and a PawPaw fruit[118] reacted positively to the PCR.[119] The WHO African Regional Office said the test kits had not been previously contaminated with SARS-CoV-2,[120] and the supplier, the *Africa Centres for Disease Control,* also denied that the samples could have been faulty.[121] The President of

117 https://www.wodarg.com/2020/04/01/was-misst-der-test-eigentlich/

118 Indian banana. In some reports, the fruit was confused with the papaya

119 http://www.msn.com/en-xl/news/other/tanzanian-paw-paw-tests-positive-for-Covid-19-president-magufuli/ar-BB13xpD0

120 http://www.n-tv.de/der_tag/Papaya-positiv-auf-Corona-getestet-Tansania-kritisiert-WHO-article21766364.html

121 http://www.reuters.com/article/us-health-coronavirus-tanzania-tests/africa-disease-centre-rejects-tanzanias-allegation-that-its-coronavirus-tests-faulty-idUSKBN22J1FO

Tanzania himself presented the scandal on television and had the WHO expelled from the country.

The University of Barcelona tested wastewater from two of the city's sewage treatment plants for SARS-CoV-2 from April 2020 *"to observe the course of infection"* – and found the virus. Then they examined samples they had conserved in the past and found the strange virus in a sample from 12 March 2019, long before it turned up in Wuhan. The same thing happened in Milan, where water samples from November 2019 also tested positive.[122][123] This leaves only two conclusions: either the virus is older than claimed, or the PCR test is useless. Probably both are true.

Corona Hotspot at the Slaughterhouse

By mid-June 2020, the numbers of people testing positive across Europe had dropped so much that several vaccine manufacturers were already complaining that they couldn't test their vaccines because there were hardly any infected people left on the streets.[124] They were seriously looking for volunteers so that they could infect them as test subjects.

At that time, there were only 4,808 Covid19 "cases" left in Germany, or 0.0058% of the population. Too few to justify further reprisals. A new "hotspot" was needed. It was found in Germany's largest meat company in Gütersloh: Tönnies. 6,650 employees were tested, 1,553 were "positive" - a result

---

122 http://alles-schallundrauch.blogspot.com/2020/06/corona-nicht-zuerst-in-china-aufgetaucht.html#ixzz6R7G6KOV6

123 https://www.compact-online.de/was-hat-die-elite-zu-verbergen-experten-packen-aus/

124 https://www.theguardian.com/society/2020/may/24/uk-scientists-want-to-infect-volunteers-with-Covid-19-in-race-to-find-vaccine and https://www.thetimes.co.uk/edition/news/coronavirus-researchers-may-have-to-chase-infections-to-do-vaccine-tests-h9kcc0wr0

far above the national average. But almost all of the "positives" worked there, where about 50,000 pigs are cut up every day, while the other departments of the company were spared.

The media once again spread panic: The newspaper "Die Welt" compared the outbreak to Fukushima.[125] Politicians implemented tough measures such as quarantines and lockdowns, and Drosten congratulated the drastic crackdown.[126] - Miraculously, there were hardly any sick people among the "positive" ones, no deaths, and no spread in the surrounding area was registered either. What was going on?

Initially, there were apparently cross-reactions, because cattle and pigs are regularly vaccinated against corona animal diseases.[127] The vaccines naturally contain gene fragments of corona viruses, which may be ingested by the workers without them falling ill. Drosten's PCR test, in fact, also reacts to coronaviruses from cattle, as he himself admitted in his podcast. [128]

Secondly, this case shows how far apart the test results and the disease figures are. *"It may be true that coronaviruses from slaughter animals do not in principle infect humans... [but] PCR tests are highly sensitive procedures. They therefore respond to small traces of a (hereditary) substance, which does not have to be due to a viral infection either. Contamination, i.e. the simple fact of handling meat parts or being in a room where animals are cut up, can be sufficient to detect traces of a viral substance in the people concerned.*

A positive test does not necessarily mean that the person in question is infected, ill or even contagious. But this fundamental error of interpretation has always been made (with

---

125 "Die Welt" on 26.6.20

126 https://www.rnd.de/gesundheit/drosten-lobt-strategie-von-laschet-zu-corona-hotspot-tonnies-X3GCR4GHEZBGREOL52VORBC5W4.html

127 Message from 18.6.20 on http://www.wodarg.com/

128 https://www.youtube.com/watch?v=smhbENDRPOE

HIV/AIDS, Zika, swine flu, SARS, etc.) and also runs through the COVID-19 reporting." [129]

Journalist Johannes Kreis sums up:

"Comment 1: The topic of cross-reactions in PCR tests is usually lost, as most publications on this topic come from the manufacturers themselves. This has been the case for 20 years. And it is especially bad with the PCR protocols recommended by the WHO. The WHO seems never to have heard of the word cross-reaction. It is practically non-existent there.

Note 2: PCR cannot detect whether viruses are neutralised by antibodies. Likewise, PCR cannot detect whether viruses are reproducible. As a rule, it is also only fragments of the viral genome that are amplified by PCR.

Note 3: Whether you find something with PCR or not has nothing to do with the question of whether the species in question, to which the examined DNA (RNA) belongs, is causative for the disease.

Note 4: PCR diagnostics is a billion-dollar market.

Nobody knows what the set of all coronaviruses looks like. That is, no one can say whether SARS-CoV-2 has not existed before, because no one has looked for it with SARS-CoV-2 primers or whether SARS-CoV-2 has been measured along with other classical primers due to cross-reactions. It is naïve to think that biomedicine knows exactly what is inside cells. It is very far from that." [130]

Science journalist Peter Frey comments on the Corona tests as follows: *"At this point at the latest, the reader should become aware that the analysis of viral gene sequences in the human body is a delicate story, because what are we*

129 Oliver Märtens in:
   https://peds-ansichten.de/2020/07/pcr-test-correctiv-deutung/
130 https://www.rubikon.news/artikel/der-fluch-der-pcr-methode

actually extracting and how do we deal with the results, which we may not even have fully understood?" [131]

Biochemist Christine Johnson pointed out that one has to be very careful with PCR because it works with exponential multiplication and therefore errors in the experiment are also multiplied exponentially. [132]

After all this research, the only conclusion that remains is that **the PCR test cannot make any reasonable statements at all about any epidemic**. This makes it an ideal instrument of abuse and misleading. This is apparently exactly its purpose.

Is the coronavirus to blame for disease and death?

Let's move on to the question of whether the Drosten virus caused the disease it is accused of causing or whether the measured virus parts were simply present. In order to clarify something like this, there have been "Koch's postulates" for over a hundred years. [133] In short, a microorganism is considered a pathogen if four conditions are met (originally three, later one was added):

1 The pathogen must be detected in all sick people, but not in healthy people.

2 The pathogen must be isolated from the sick and cultivated in the laboratory.

---

131 https://peds-ansichten.de/2020/05/viren-angst-faszination-nutzen/
132 *"Viral Load and the PCR"*, Christine Johnson, Continuum Nov. 2001
 http://www.sidasante.com/themes/tests/pcr/viral_load_and_the_pcr.htm
133 Also called "Henle-Koch postulates", after the physicians Jakob Henle and Robert Koch.

3 If you infect healthy people with it, they must develop the same symptoms.

4 The pathogen must then also be detectable in the newly infected and identical to the first.

None of these Koch postulates have been fulfilled by the Covid19 virus to date, nor have the "Rivers postulates", which were later created specifically for viruses.[134] The virus has also never been clearly isolated and identified in the electron microscope. There are plenty of pictures of corona-viruses, but the clear description of how the pictures were taken, i.e. what exactly can be seen, is missing. And – what is even worse – the new infection with proof of the symptoms was also never made.

Science journalist Thorsten Engelbrecht and researcher Konstantin Demeter combed through the most important studies on SARS-CoV-2 and wrote to the authors. The result is sensational: none of the studies provided any evidence for virus isolation or for the postulates of Koch or Rivers. Thus, the coronavirus has never been found and isolated in a sick person, as the first postulate demands.[135]

There are a lot of publications about "virus isolates", and various complete genome sequences have been published, but no study shows that these were obtained by proper isolation, except by theoretical PCR-based computer analysis. The term "isolation" in some studies is misused there. In addition, all studies lack the control experiments that must show that nothing is measured with guaranteed virus-

---

134 https://off-guardian.org/2020/06/09/scientists-have-utterly-failed-to-prove-that-the-coronavirus-fulfills-kochs-postulates/

135 https://telegra.ph/Alle-führenden-Wissenschaftler-bestätigen-COVID-19-existiert-nicht-07-03 or https://telegra.ph/Die-Studien-der-Ärzte-klären-auf-weisen-SARS-CoV-2-nicht-nach-11-23

free material. This alone makes the studies worthless. You can find exact data on this on these sources. [136]

Incidentally, the head of the RKI, Wieler, opened his mouth during an interview with the TV station Phoenix at the end of October. He said that they had *"learned to lead society, whether the virus existed or not."*[137] Hear, hear! Does the virus perhaps not exist after all? What they have learned, however, is how to lead society – by the nose.

In any case, the coronavirus studies available so far would never hold up in a court case as proof of the existence of SARS-CoV-2. **Much less would the virus be proven to be responsible for the illnesses and deaths.** The prosecution therefore pleads for other causes of death to be considered.

Prohibited autopsies

At the beginning of the Corona crisis, the RKI banned the dissection of the dead. The last time this happened was in the Middle Ages, when the Church forbade such action as unchristian. Sending people to war and massacring them was OK, but opening up the dead for research purposes was severely punished. But back to today's Middle Ages: the "recommendation" of the RKI was supposedly meant to protect the pathologists according to the motto: *"We only want your best".*

Many pathologists felt offended in their professional honour, because after all they are trained to protect themselves effectively even with highly infectious corpses. The forensic pathologist Prof. Klaus Püschel from Hamburg wanted to

---

136 https://telegra.ph/Alle-führenden-Wissenschaftler-bestätigen-COVID-19-existiert-nicht-07-03 or https://telegra.ph/Die-Studien-der-Ärzte-klären-auf-weisen-SARS-CoV-2-nicht-nach-11-23
137 https://www.youtube.com/watch?v=-pxoXSFEqXA

know exactly what the "corona patients" had really died of and dissected 65 "corona" deceased. His result: *all of them* had suffered from serious previous illnesses. High blood pressure, heart attacks and arteriosclerosis. 46 alone had pre-existing diseases of the respiratory tract and lungs. In 28 cases, there was other organ damage or the patients had had transplanted organs.[138] Thus, those examined died *"with"* Corona, but not *"from"* it.

Prof. Püschel continued to perform autopsies and concluded after 167 autopsies that severe or fatal courses of Covid19 were rare and that the autopsied persons were significantly pre-damaged.[139] This is consistent with a study of 2,000 deaths by the Italian National Institute of Health (ISS). According to this, 99% of the deceased had one or more previous illnesses, 48.5% even three.

The RKI was probably not concerned with "protecting pathologists" but with covering up how insignificant the "new killer virus" really is. If we remember how one-sided the RKI's number acrobatics are trimmed to scaremongering, then the suspicion of criminal deceptive intentions by the RKI is not far off and should be worth further investigation.

Other causes of death found

From the beginning, "corona" was simply claimed as the cause, but no research was ever carried out to find out whether the virus found actually caused the atypical pneumonia, or whether it was simply present in the sick or the healthy. "Atypical pneumonia" can have a whole range of causes:

---

138 https://www.aerzteblatt.de/nachrichten/112189/Obduktionsberichte-Verstorbene-COVID-19-Patienten-hatten-alle-Vorerkrankungen
139 https://www.aerzteblatt.de/archiv/214070/Umgang-mit-Corona-Toten-Obduktionen-sind-keinesfalls-obsolet

- Inhalation of toxic substances, solvents or exhaust gases

- Penetration of food, drink or stomach contents into the lungs in cases of dysphagia or unconsciousness (aspiration pneumonia). Water is sufficient for this in the case of drowning.

- Immune system problems such as allergies and autoimmune diseases

- Radiotherapy in cancer treatment

- Water retention due to oedema during prolonged bed rest (congestive pneumonia) or due to cardiac or renal insufficiency. Older people are particularly affected by this.

These are all serious diseases that have nothing to do with bacteria or viruses. They are more likely to be fatal than "typical" pneumonias, i.e. those where the bacteria are known. Today, many doctors are so focused on infections that they first look for bacteria, and if they don't find any, then it "must" be viruses. For virologists anyway, because that is their daily bread. And those who look for viruses always find some fragment of influenza or, currently popular, coronavirus. All it takes is a few more cycles in the PCR.

The US health authority CDC confirmed the above on its website of 9.9.2020.[140] The most important statement is sensational: *94% of those who died with Corona had been diagnosed with an average of two to three (2.6) serious previous illnesses. Only in 6% nothing else was found, which is why these deaths were credited to Corona.*

---

140 https://www.cdc.gov/nchs/nvss/vsrr/Covid_weekly/index.htm?
fbclid=IwAR23vpHBFZcBVsoEQWKVE8yuy7md44tEr2yFcrHl0j92Lv
dZDa1ataE1tF8#Comorbidities

This means that instead of 161,000, only 9,600 Americans may have died from Covid-19. That would be about half a percent of the horror numbers predicted by US immunologist Dr. Anthony Fauci earlier this year. He was talking about 1.5 to 2.2 million corona deaths in the US. Fortunately, he was wrong by a factor of 200. This "expert" has advised all US presidents since Ronald Reagan - and extremely badly in the interests of the pharmaceutical industry. Some also call him the *"American Drosten"*.

If one compares the corrected figure of approx. 10,000 Corona deaths in the USA with the 80,000 deaths in the US flu wave of 2017/18,[141] then this puts the figures into perspective quite considerably.

In the meantime, it has become known that in Europe, too, all those who have died with a positive PCR are counted as "coronavirus deaths" in the statistics, regardless of what they actually died of. In Germany, even patients with pneumonia and a *negative* coronary test are counted as coronary patients if they had contact with a "positive" person at some point![142] That alone is a scandal.

Uwe Witt from the Health Committee of the German parliament quite rightly asked how many Corona deaths there really were in Germany. If one takes the CDC figures as a basis and subtracts 94%, only 558 would remain, but that would obviously not interest anyone here.[143]

Incidentally, the corona expert Prof. Drosten had still threatened 278,000 corona deaths in Germany in the spring of 2020. Anyone who was so far off the mark had better keep quiet in future.

---

141 https://www.statnews.com/2018/09/26/cdc-us-flu-deaths-winter/
142 https://twitter.com/QuakDr/status/1332601338514038784?s=20
143 http://alles-schallundrauch.blogspot.com/2020/09/94-der-corona-toten-sind-nicht-daran.html#ixzz6WpiGjP3J

Deceased due to the therapy

At the beginning of the corona virus panic, it was said that there was no cure for it. So, they experimented with all kinds of things in the hospitals: Antibiotics, paracetamol, cortisone, and all kinds of drugs that are actually there for completely different purposes. That's understandable, because many doctors also panicked, and so many mistakes were made.

In the renowned medical journal "Lancet" of 18. 2. 2020, an example of excessive medication use was reported:[144]

"It describes the case of a 50-year-old patient who suffered from fever, chills, cough, fatigue and shortness of breath and was classified as a COVID-19 patient.

He was then treated with a veritable armada of drugs consisting of the antiviral drugs interferon alfa-2b, lopinavir and ritonavir, the very harsh antibiotic moxifloxacin and high doses of cortisone (methylprednisolone) – substances that can have fatal side effects even when taken alone. In addition, tissue samples were taken at autopsy – and here the authors of the paper even concede that the observed liver damage could have been caused by the drugs. The conclusion that the patient died due to the toxic effect of the drugs is therefore compelling.

And if such a man, who was 50 and thus "in his prime" and had apparently suffered from no other illnesses than severe flu symptoms, dies as a result of the administration of such a "drug cocktail", then one can guess how such a highly toxic treatment affects people who are 70 or 80 years old and had previous illnesses up to and including cancer before they were classified as COVID-19 patients.

---

144 https://www.thelancet.com/action/showPdf?pii=S2213-2600(20)30076-X

The question is: Why did the doctors treat the 50-year-old in this way? And the answer is: out of a viral tunnel vision, out of the deeply rooted conviction that only medication can bring salvation as well as out of the fear typical of today's medical system, especially in times of pandemic panic, that something might have been left undone, which then often enough leads to medication excessive use. As in this case.

And so, for example, the pitiful 50-year-old, because he was short of breath, was given cortisone, a lymphocyte killer that slows down the inflammatory reaction. Everything then swells up, the fever drops. The patient temporarily feels better, he can breathe better again. At the same time, however, the defence reaction is suppressed, which can ultimately be fatal, as this case demonstrates, especially if other potentially fatal drugs are also administered.

Nevertheless, the Lancet paper actually concludes that "the patient died from a severe infection with SARS-CoV-2." In other words, it was claimed that the patient died only from a virus - and not from the drugs, despite the drug armada. And since this study was published in a journal whose content is de facto law, it served as a kind of blueprint for the treatment of COVID-19 patients".[145]

Several doctors from the USA and Europe, including from the University of Zurich, reported that many patients died of pulmonary embolism due to (micro)thrombosis in the lungs, which was initially overlooked because autopsies were not allowed in the beginning. Many of them could certainly have been saved by administering common blood thinners if this had been known.[146]

145 Source: https://www.rubikon.news/artikel/die-medikamenten-tragodie
146 https://www.berliner-zeitung.de/gesundheit-oekologie/wir-sehen-bei-corona-haeufig-stoerungen-der-blutgerinnung-li.82045

Artificial respiration

Another complication was breathing difficulties, which is why many patients were put on ventilators. This did more harm than good: Carl Diehm, a pulmonologist, pointed out that in New York the mortality rate of ventilated corona patients was 80%.[147] The overpressure with which the ventilators force the air into the lungs can injure the lungs, leading to immediate death or death from late effects within a year.[148]

The aforementioned New York nurse Erin Marie Olszewski experienced the suffering of the artificially ventilated as follows: "*They assigned patients who did not necessarily have Covid-19 to the wards. Possibly they were also connected to ventilators. The way they connected them was fatal.*

But the first response to everything at Elmhurst was immediately artificial respiration, even though it was killing people.

I think it was around the end of April when I noticed that there was not a single patient there who had been successfully taken off the ventilator. So, at that time, every patient connected to the machine was dying.

When artificial air is pumped into the lungs, it weakens them more and more. When they get weaker, the pressure of the ventilator has to be increased. This causes the human lungs to burst. In parallel, we gave the people sedatives. The Covid treatments these people were subjected to basically consisted of keeping them in a coma until they died.

What happened to the patients there means gross negligence and mishandling. Many of them need not have died. They were seen as disposable patients. Many of them

---

147 https://www.handelsblatt.com/meinung/kolumnen/expertenrat/diehm/
expertenrat-prof-dr-curt-diehm-es-ist-zeit-dass-wir-in-der-corona-
debatte-viel-staerker-auf-lungenaerzte-hoeren/25760524.html
148 This is officially called "ventilator-induced lung injury".

were low-income earners. They could not afford an expensive hospital."[149]

In the meantime, many doctors have largely moved away from ventilators and simply give supplementary oxygen through breathing masks.

The dangerous "miracle drug" hydroxychloroquine

Another complication is triggered by certain drugs. Dr. Wolfgang Wodarg noticed that the anti-malaria drug hydroxychloroquine (HCQ) has severe side effects, but specifically in people with a certain genetic defect. It is called "flavism", which is a deficiency of the enzyme G6PD.[150] This often occurs in the tropics, in malaria-infested areas, i.e. in Africa, South America and Southeast Asia.

The advantage is that flavism increases resistance to malaria. The disadvantage is that carriers of the genetic defect, especially men, can develop haemolysis (blood dissolution) if they come into contact with certain substances that are found, for example, in field beans, currants, peas and a number of medicines.[151] These include antimalarial drugs such as HCQ, the administration of which to such people can be fatal because of micro-embolism (blood plugs made from the remains of burst red blood cells) form in all organs. [152]

The trouble was that after an initial ban on the drug (it was not approved for this purpose), there was suddenly great hope that HCQ could help against Covid19. The WHO recommended it for the prevention and treatment of Covid19, and in April initiated three trials in which HCQ was dosed so high that it was in the toxic (poisonous) range. Many patients

---

149 https://www.compact-online.de/das-war-grob-fahrlaessig-panik-und-pfusch-in-new-york-2/
150 Glucose-6-dehydrogenase deficiency
151 Acetylsalicylic acid, metamizole, sulphonamides, vitamin K, naphthalene, aniline, antimalarials and nitrofurans
152 https://multipolar-magazin.de/artikel/Covid-19-medical-detectives

died, adding to the statistics of "corona deaths". Apart from the overdoses, the fatal risk for people with the G6PD defect has additionally been overlooked, although flavism has long been known as a contraindication.[153] This affects up to 30% of the population in Africa. No matter – HCQ and related chloroqins have been diligently used and studies done with them worldwide. President Trump praised the drug as a *"gift from God"* and said he was taking it himself for prophylaxis.

Only at the end of May, the Harvard Medical School and the University Hospital Zurich examined several studies on 96,000 patients in hundreds of hospitals worldwide and came to the conclusion that HCQ was not only useless, but even increased the risk of death due to severe side effects.[154] As a result, the WHO stopped all studies, but in Brazil they continued, and in the UK a new study was launched at the beginning of July 2020 in which around 40,000 healthcare workers are to take part. Oxford University is involved, too.[155]

Only Dr. Wodarg drew attention to the reports from the USA according to which mainly African Americans were among the alleged Corona deaths. Up to six times as many deaths were reported from the predominantly black counties as from white counties. Poorer health care was initially suspected as the cause, but then it was also heard from Great Britain that among the Corona deaths there were a disproportionate number of "ethnic minorities", i.e. immigrants, also among doctors and medical staff.

Dr. Wodarg points out that favism is also widespread in some areas of Italy. Malaria still existed in the Po Valley until the 1950s. Up to 71% of the test positives, but also doctors and

153 https://www.gelbe-liste.de/wirkstoffe/
Hydroxychloroquin_3297#Kontraindikation
154 https://www.who.int/emergencies/diseases/novel-coronavirus-2019/
global-research-on-novel-coronavirus-2019-ncov/solidarity-clinical-trial-
for-Covid-19-treatments
155 https://www.aerztezeitung.de/Nachrichten/Neue-Hydroxychloroquin-
Studie-in-Grossbritannien-410916.html

nurses had been treated with high doses of HCQ, and it was similar in Spain. Many large cities in Europe and the USA also have a high proportion of immigrants with flavism who, if tested positive, were treated with HCQ, which increased the mortality rate. Ignorant of the correlation, they were declared coronavirus deaths when in fact they were HCQ victims. The fatal thing is that the health authorities of all countries overlooked this serious "malpractice".[156]

There are also reports from doctors who have had good experiences with HCQ combined with zinc, if it is used early and provided that the dosage is not too high and flavism can be ruled out.

No figures are available on the mass use of HCQ worldwide, but there must be hundreds of thousands who have been treated with it. This may well explain the excess mortality in countries with high levels of flavism, such as Brazil. The pictures of dead people from the favelas were of course attributed to SARS-CoV-2 because the side effects are never discussed.

Dr. Claus Köhnlein suspects a connection between HCQ therapy and an unusual increase in excess mortality in Belgium, Holland, France, Italy, Spain and Great Britain. On the website with the official mortality statistics of most EU countries,[157] a strange phenomenon can be seen: The mortality rate drops continuously almost everywhere after the usual flu season. Only in the countries mentioned does it rise sharply at the end of March and fall again just as quickly in mid-April – a completely untypical course for an epidemic.

In neighbouring countries, this "jag" is not or barely visible. *"No virus can produce such "spikes", certainly not outside the usual flu season. Especially as there was no excessive mortality in Germany, for example, although it borders*

156 https://de.sputniknews.com/gesellschaft/20200505327031601-Covid-19-malaria-mittel-wodarg-warnt/
157 https://www.euromomo.eu/graphs-and-maps/

directly on France, Holland and Belgium. The same applies to Austria, which is a neighbour of Italy and Switzerland, and Portugal, which is next to Spain."[158] What was going on?

On 18 March, WHO proclaimed a major "trial-based drug offensive" to combat COVID-19, the "Solidarity Trial". The trial focused on the highly toxic drugs remdesivir, lopinavir/-ritonavir (Kaletra), interferon-β in combination with Kaletra, as well as HCQ and chloroquine.[159] The latter two drugs can cause cardiac arrhythmias, leading to death. *"This is especially true when administered in higher doses, as has occurred in the treatment of so-called COVID-19 patients not only in Italy, but also in Spain, France, England and the USA.* " [160]

And exactly such high doses were recommended by the WHO. The American doctor Meryl Nass wrote in an article that in the Solidarity study 2.4 g were administered on the first day and a total of 9.2 g up to the 10th day.[161] Since the active ingredient degrades slowly in the body, the quantities taken add up over several days. It has been known since 1979 that even a single dose of 1.9 - 2.6 g can be fatal. The limit of toxicity is therefore quickly exceeded.[162]

"Nevertheless, many countries around the globe participated in the Solidarity study, including Spain, France, Switzerland and Belgium – countries with noticeable excess mortality (limited to April).

Within three days, the researchers noticed cardiac ar-rhythmias in patients who had taken the higher dose (after three days, they had "had" 3.6 g of chloroquine). Neverthe-

---

158 https://www.rubikon.news/artikel/die-medikamenten-tragodie
159 https://www.immunopaedia.org.za/breaking-news/solidarity-trial-who-Covid-19-treatment-trial/
160 https://www.rubikon.news/artikel/die-medikamenten-tragodie
161 https://ahrp.org/Covid-19-has-turned-public-health-into-a-lethal-patient-killing-experimental-endeavor/
162 https://apps.who.int/iris/bitstream/handle/10665/65773/WHO_MAL_79.906.pdf?sequence=1&isAllowed=y

less, the patients obviously continued to take the doses. And on the sixth day, 11 and thus a considerable part of the test persons had died, which led to an immediate end of the high-dose part of the study.

"It appears that the Solidarity trials were not designed to test the benefits of hydroxychloroquine in Covid-19, but rather to see if patients could tolerate toxic, non-therapeutic doses," Meryl Nass criticises." [163]

There were other studies with HCQ in Europe and the USA. They were conducted in the countries where the death rate had the "jag" in the curve. One of them, *"the Recovery trial, co-funded by the Welcome Trust and the Bill & Melinda Gates Foundation, progressed at unprecedented speed and within a relatively short time had enrolled more than 11,000 patients from 175 hospitals in the UK."*[164]

For more info, see the Rubicon article in the last footnote and an interesting interview with Dr. Köhnlein. [165]

Antivirals as a "cure"?

The fixation of virologists and laboratory scientists on *"finding and destroying viruses"* is highly problematic. For what they find in the test tube ("in vitro") is far from being transferable to the human organism ("in vivo"). Thus, drugs are found that inhibit viral replication "in vitro", such as "Remdesivir" from Gilead Sciences, which has been on the market since February 2020 against SARS-CoV-2. Originally developed in 2014 against Ebola viruses, it was never approved. Now it got a new chance with Corona, it got special approvals against Covid19 in the US, EU and Japan for *"limited use in individual cases"*. Not a bad deal, since a 5-day treatment brings in between $2,300 and $3,100. The US government

---

163 https://www.rubikon.news/artikel/die-medikamenten-tragodie
164 ibid
165 https://www.youtube.com/watch?v=uijUzY4Prpw

has already ordered half a million doses for $1,170,000,000 (1.17 billion).[166]

A Chinese study on mice[167] found negative effects on the number and mobility of germ cells (sperm, eggs), the higher the dose, the worse.

So far, there has only been one study that showed some success with remdesivir treatment, but it was ambivalent. On the one hand, the drug is said to have reduced the ventilation time of intensive care patients from an average of 15 to 11 days; on the other hand, massive liver damage was observed.[168]

This moderate "success" is contradicted by a WHO study in more than 30 countries, announced in October, whose interim results showed clear trends. Treatments with remdesivir, hydroxychloroquine, lopinavir/ritonavir and interferon had little or no effect on Covid19, either against normal mortality or on treatment duration.[169]

The authors T. Engelbrecht and Dr. med. C. Köhnlein write in their book "Virus-Wahn" (Virus Delusion) that antivirals are not very "accurate", but rather comparable to a wide-area shot. Therefore, healthy cells are also affected and prevented from growing, comparable to chemotherapy That is why they are both immunosuppressing and carcinogenic.

Dr. Köhnlein expressed the assumption in the "Ärzteblatt" that Germany had come out of the crisis relatively well

166 https://de.sputniknews.com/wirtschaft/20200711327483285-us-pharmakonzern-corona-milliarden-profit/

167 https://www.biorxiv.org/content/10.1101/2020.04.21.050104v1

168 https://de.sputniknews.com/wissen/20201003328066671-wie-sicher-ist-remdesivir-eu-arzneibehoerde-prueft-moegliche-nierenschaeden-durch-corona-medikament/

169 https://deutsch.rt.com/international/107863-who-studie-vier-bekannte-medikamente-kaum-auswirkung-Covid-19-sterblichkeit/

because not as many antiviral drugs had been used there as in other European countries.[170]

Remdesivir, like almost all antivirals, incorporates a foreign molecule into the newly developing DNA during cell division, causing the cell to die. However, this does not only affect "infected" cells, but also healthy ones, which is reflected in numerous "side effects" that are often worse than the main effect. The organism pays a high price to get rid of the suspected virus. In the test tube this is not noticeable, but in the body it is very noticeable.

A similar failure had already been experienced decades ago with AZT (azidothymidine), also known as "Retrovir". The drug was developed in 1963 as a *"chain terminator"*. This means that the chain of cell divisions is terminated. That particularly affects cells that divide frequently, such as the cells of the intestinal mucosa or blood cells. This is why the idea came up to use it in leukaemia, where the leukocytes multiply particularly quickly. It's the same principle as chemotherapy: you damage all the cells as they divide, but the cancer cells die a little faster, at least in theory.

It's like trying to kill terrorists in a city by poisoning the drinking water because some scientist has found out that terrorists are more likely to react to the poison than all the other inhabitants. Of course, that has to go down the drain. When it was finally realised that patients were dying faster with AZT than from untreated leukaemia, it was withdrawn and disappeared into the poison cabinet for the time being. In professional circles, it was then called *"the drug in search of the right disease"*.

This was then found in 1986, when AIDS came on the scene. According to the motto *"give AZT a chance"*, it *was* now used against HIV, which supposedly worked – in the test tube. A first human trial spread hope to frightened AIDS patients, but

---

170 https://www.aerzteblatt.de/archiv/214539/COVID-19-Therapieansaetze-Therapeutische-Zurueckhaltung

on closer examination turned out to be "sloppy, fraudulent and completely worthless".[171] Nevertheless, AZT was approved, with nasty side effects that curiously coincided with the disease it was supposed to cure. One might think about that.

The fatal thing was that many healthy people were also treated with it, and they got AIDS symptoms much more often than untreated people. Why were they treated at all? Because the PCR test was positive for HIV, and nothing else. Kary Mullis, the inventor of the PCR, had protested strongly at the time against the misuse of his test.

In an interview, he vented his displeasure. Among other things, he complained that Anthony Fauci had no idea about anything, just like most people in high medical posts, they were just clerks without a clue, they changed the rules when they wanted to. The main problem with science in this century is that it is judged and funded by people who don't *understand* it.[172]

Mullis was ignored, the pharmaceutical business had to continue. History repeats itself when such disasters are forgotten and when the greed for profit drives the vaccine and drug manufacturers to once again accept injuries and deaths.

171 John Lauritsen: "The AZT-Story - Poison by Prescription" or: "raum & zeit-special" No. 4 or: "Weltwoche", Zurich, 25.6.1992
172 https://www.youtube.com/watch?v=c4bvAfeYXxc&feature=youtu.be

Interim report on the virus and the test

From all the evidence I have compiled so far, it is clear:

- The published infection figures are far too high and are never put into perspective to spread fear.

- The SARS-CoV-2 coronavirus as claimed has never been scientifically proven. It is probably a construct of other, known coronaviruses.

- It has not yet been proven anywhere that SARS-CoV-2 is the cause of pneumonia. Koch's postulates are all not fulfilled.

- The test with which the virus is supposedly "detected" delivers up to 90% false results and is therefore use-less for epidemiological statements and comparisons of "infection curves" or assessment of infection courses.

- The fact that 85% of so-called "infections" run without symptoms also rules out the virus as the cause. In any case, it is not a "killer virus".

- There was also no epidemic, apart from the usual wave of flu. The figures prove that: If we leave the RKI figure of just under 10,000 corona deaths in the season up to the summer[173] as it is and compare it with the flu deaths in the 2017/18 season (which were 25,000), then the 2020 figure certainly corresponds to a mild flu wave. Because no one has examined the deceased for other viruses, such as influenza. It is very likely that this was the usual flu mortality attributed to SARS-CoV2 only because of the new PCR test.

---

173 The flu season is always counted from October to May (in northern hemisphere)

- The age of those who died of corona also points to this: Their average age in Europe and the USA was between 80 (USA), 83 (Germany)[174] and 86 (Sweden), which corresponds to the otherwise usual average life expectancy, in Germany it is even higher (without "Corona": 81). This means: statistically, "Corona" did *not* cause people to die earlier, as would have been expected from a real pandemic.

- There was no excess mortality during the flu season, which can be proven by the official figures from the RKI and the Federal Statistical Office.[175]

- The number of tests has been ramped up from 350,000 per week to over 1,600,000 since May. This alone generated a multiple number of false positives. The extent to which the cycle numbers have been changed is being kept secret.

- "Positive" does not mean "sick", and "false positive" certainly does not.

- There was a lot of media hype around the so-called "hotspots" like in Göttingen or Garmisch, but nobody fell ill.

- "Positives" without symptoms are not contagious because the viral load is too low.[176]

---

174 https://de.rt.com/inland/110539-robert-koch-institut-87-prozent-der-corona-toten-sind-70-oder-aelter/

175 https://www.destatis.de/DE/Themen/Gesellschaft-Umwelt/Bevoelkerung/Sterbefaelle-Lebenserwartung/sterbefallzahlen.html

176 https://deutsch.rt.com/international/109526-studie-aus-wuhan-kein-beweis/
https://www.nature.com/articles/s41467-020-19802-w#MOESM1 (study of almost 10 million people)

- Hospitals cared for 12.8% fewer patients in the first 10 months of 2020 than in the same period of 2019.[177]

- The number of patients with severe respiratory illnesses (SARI cases) treated in the clinics even decreased by 15.6%.[178]

- The occupancy rate of the intensive care units (ITS) decreased by 6%.[179]

- The number of people who died in hospital and those who died from serious respiratory infections decreased by 4.8% compared to 2019.[180]

- According to the CDC study cited above, 96% of the alleged corona deaths must be subtracted who died "with" but not "from" corona.

- The head of Frankfurt's public health department also confirms that there was no excess mortality.[181]

So, there is no question of a *"possible overload of the health system"*. The increase in infections corresponds to that of the flu season of previous years and is lower than in 2017/18. Nevertheless, it is precisely this argument that is used to lie through one's teeth. On talk-show "Anne Will" in December, Uwe Janssens, head physician of an intensive care unit, said that the situation in intensive care units was dramatic because of Covid-19 and called for a hard lockdown.[182]

---

177 From a survey of 272 German hospitals:
https://de.rt.com/inland/110313-trotz-corona-kliniken-melden-weniger/
178 ibid
179 ibid
180 ibid
181 https://www.berliner-zeitung.de/news/keine-uebersterblichkeit-trotz-corona-amtsarzt-fordert-diskussion-ueber-die-mittel-der-pandemie-bekaempfung-li.108672
182 Source: https://reitschuster.de/post/parallel-realitaeten-bei-anne-will/

Heinrich Fiechtner MP then asked the Janssens' hospital in Eschweiler about the current occupancy figures and was told that there were currently no corona patients in the intensive care unit.[183]

Even if the intensive care beds of a clinic are full, the patients are easily transferred to other clinics that have free capacity. This has been common practice for many years, for example in the 2017/18 flu season, when many clinics were very busy.

Let's listen to Peter Haisenko again: *"Just as with the false data on "infected persons", the alleged threat of hospital overload is being dealt with. There are said to be 3,000 people with Corona in intensive care units. Most of them are not artificially respirated. I can't see a problem there. We have about 2,000 hospitals. That gives us 1.5 "corona patients" per hospital. If we subtract the false positives from that, there's not much left."* [184]

Conclusion:

If no more people died overall in the last 12 months than in previous years, even fewer than in the 2017/18 flu season, then this was not an epidemic, but a pure PCR "laboratory pandemic".

It's not the tested that are sick, it's the tests!

So similar pandemics could have been declared in the years before if the gene fragments claimed by Drosten had been searched for by PCR and found.

Even if they had not yet existed, which I doubt, the error rate of the test could have produced the same numbers at any

---

183 ibid

184 https://www.anderweltonline.com/klartext/klartext-20202/warum-gibt-es-akzeptable-und-inakzeptable-sterbefaelle/

time! The phenomenon that the numbers fluctuate with the seasons is found just as much with all other flu viruses.

Numbers must be put into context, otherwise they are misleading!

The trend of "higher numbers due to more tests with fewer deaths" can be seen worldwide. The WHO reported that positive test numbers (still called "infection numbers") had increased by 6% in mid-September, while the death rate decreased by 10%.[185]

No matter which statistics you look at, they all show the same thing: since the summer, "positive numbers" have been rising everywhere, while the numbers of "corona deaths" have not. If there really were a "2nd wave", then the death curves would have to rise, too. But they are not, which proves that this is a purely "test wave".

Mr. Drosten deplored people's growing loss of confidence in government statistics in an online interview, in which he remarked that we had rising case numbers but too few deaths.[186]

Worldwide, the numbers are far too low for a pandemic to be recognised. At the end of September, there was talk of one million deaths. If one applies to this the CDC statistics discussed above, according to which only 6% died of corona and all the others had serious previous illnesses that would have led to death even without corona, then 60,000 pure corona deaths remain.

---

185 https://de.sputniknews.com/panorama/20200922327986539-who-zahl-der-corona-neuinfektionen-auf-rekordhoch-/
186 https://youtu.be/uwGcgSDasZ0?t=1957 from minute 32

With a world population of 7.5 billion people, 0.0008% would then have died from "Corona". That is sad, but it is not a pandemic and in no way justifies ruining the world economy because of it.

Austria carried out voluntary mass testing in December 2020. The result should be cause for celebration, because out of 2 million tested, only 4,200 were positive, and most of them without symptoms, i.e. healthy! That is only *0.21% of the population*, who unfortunately can no longer do maths, otherwise they would realise that this *certainly cannot be a pandemic.* When will people finally wake up?

Or how does the CDC's report fit into a "pandemic" when only 40 (!) of 1.4 billion airline passengers worldwide have tested positive?[187] Or when the RKI reports 334,585 test positives in a population of 83,123,000? That only means that 99.589% of the German population is *not* affected. Where is the "pandemic" then?

There is a rule in science that says that among several theories, the one that generates the fewest contradictions and that requires the least theoretical contortions to explain these contradictions away must be accepted as valid.[188] If we apply this rule using the data available to us today, we come to the following conclusion: the fragments found by Drosten's PCR test are most likely parts of common coronaviruses that have always appeared in the course of flu in some sick people but were not detected before 2020.

This also explains the cross-reactions of the test with other coronaviruses, and it explains why about 85% of the test-positives do not get sick: they are probably immune, and the PCR finds the remnants of colds they have already had. More on this later in the chapter on immunity. The situation is

---

187 https://t.me/davebrych_public
188 called "Ockham's razor" after its inventor

similar with influenza: here, too, 80% of those infected do not get sick.

In recent years, the Federal Statistical Office has always reported at least 10,000 flu deaths per year. In 2020, there were only 411 flu deaths up to September - in words: four hundred and eleven. But there were more than 9,000 corona deaths. There is only one explanation for this:

The flu is now called Corona.

The government now claims on one hand that the flu is no longer present because isolation and spacing rules have helped. On the other hand, it claims that the number of Covid19 "positives" increases because the rules are not tough enough. So, anyone notices the contradiction?

At least it is due to the tests with their cross-reactions. They are primarily responsible for this immense shift in numbers. If only influenza were tested by PCR instead of corona in 2021, we would have the usual flu wave instead of a corona wave.

On 17.12. 2020, the French company "Biomerieux" reported that it has a test certified with which it is now possible to distinguish corona from flu infections.[189] This means nothing less than that was not possible before, and that therefore all flu infected people inflated the corona statistics! In other words, there were many more cross-reactions than initially suspected. The corona tests are useless.

"At the same time, fewer than 500 flu deaths are reported for the whole of 2020. So, did Corona kill the flu viruses? Oh yes, six cases of flu have just been cited in Munich. What are we to make of the letter to the editor from a doctor who has ten cases in his practice alone and refuses to report them as

---

189 https://www.wochenblick.at/bisher-nicht-moeglich-neuer-test-soll-corona-von-grippe-unterscheiden/

Corona cases as instructed and to collect the "Corona bounty"?

And it goes even further. Pharmacists have already been instructed not to inform customers about the dangers of the Corona vaccination under any circumstances. The media are joining in. They are refraining from any critical reporting. So, we are witnessing the biggest conspiracy in history." [190]

So, the "corona deaths" are largely the seasonal flu deaths that just got a new name. It is of no importance whether more corona or influenza viruses were involved. All numbers were statistically within the normal range. In other words, without Drosten's test, 2020 would have been a normal year, even with far fewer flu deaths than 2017/18.

It's not the virus that's the problem, it's the test and all the hype that's being created about it!

190 https://www.anderweltonline.com/klartext/klartext-20202/warum-gibt-es-akzeptable-und-inakzeptable-sterbefaelle/

A fat own goal by the RKI

There is another highly official source that confirms what I have said. It is the "Sentinel" system of the RKI. More than 20 years ago, they wanted to better assess the annual influenza waves and founded the "Influenza Working Group" (AGI).[191] The aim is to monitor the course of acute respiratory diseases.

About one percent of German medical practices regularly send samples (swabs) from patients to Sentinel, which is considered representative. The samples are then analysed in a special laboratory.[192] The RKI is very proud of this system and claims it on its website to be the top-ranking system in all of Europe. [193]

On its website, you can call up all the data under the "weekly reports". If you do this, you will be amazed: in 2020 the sentinel practices sent in 4,484 samples, of which 2,188 were virus-positive.[194] And now hold on to your hats: 2,175 were positive for influenza viruses and a whole 13 (in words: thirteen) for the coronavirus SARS-CoV-2. And the 13 detections were made from the 10th to the 15th calendar week. From week 16, i.e. 13 April, Corona did not show up at all in the super-representative sentinel practices! And before that, its performance was also more than poor, because of all flu patients with virus detection, 99.4% were infected with influenza and only 0.6% with Corona. And this is supposed to be a "dangerous pandemic"? If it weren't so sad, it could

---

191 https://influenza.rki.de/Arbeitsgemeinschaft.aspx
192 The laboratory of the "National Reference Centre for Influenza Viruses" (NRZ) at the Robert Koch Institute (RKI)
193 https://influenza.rki.de/
194 Week 40/2019 to week 36/2020, week = calendar week, i.e. from October 2019 to September 2020: https://influenza.rki.de/Wochenberichte/2019_2020/2020-36.pdf

pass for a joke: The RKI proves on its own pages that there was no epidemic.

This contradiction has been noticed by others, too. A concerned citizen asked the RKI for information. In its reply, the RKI scored another own goal by reporting that it was unlikely that people infected with corona had come to "these few doctors' surgeries" because there were so few infected people in Germany.[195] You have to let this sink in: either only a small number of people were infected or we have a pandemic. You can't have it both ways.

And so much for *"in these few doctors' surgeries"*: According to its own statement on the website, the sentinel system examines all courses of acute respiratory diseases,[196] takes, we remember, a *"top position" in* Europe and is thus *the* reference for epidemics in Germany. And if this reference doesn't find a single case for months, and only a few before that, then logically we don't have an epidemic. It is as simple as that. If it were otherwise, the RKI would do better to abolish its "top reference" right away.

Incidentally, this case confirms my observation: "test positive" is *not* = "infected"! While the PCR measures God knows what, the sentinel finds real infections through bacterial and viral laboratory tests. Here we are once again clearly shown the discrepancy between the two methods.

195 Source: https://telegra.ph/Bürgeranfragen-RKI-gibt-Ihre-Ahnungslosigkeit-offen-zu-08-12
196 Source: https://influenza.rki.de/Arbeitsgemeinschaft.aspx

The immunity

When the body is confronted with a pathogen, it reacts on several levels. On the one hand, there is the "cellular defence" in which certain cells are activated, so-called lymphocytes. These are found in the lymph, In the blood[197] and where they are needed, for example in wound fluid. There are B-lymphocytes and T-lymphocytes, with the latter being divided into "helper cells" and "killer cells". They attack foreign bodies and destroy them.

On the other hand, there is the "humoral defence", which are the famous antibodies that[198] are produced by the B-lymphocytes in response to very specific foreign substances. Antibodies are specialised and it takes a few days to produce enough to get a grip on an infection. Until then, the cellular defence takes care of the invaders.

Now the discussion about Corona and other viral diseases is all about the antibodies. If they have already been there, they can be produced much more quickly the next time and stop the infection in its early stages. This can happen without any symptoms at all, and the body is then said to be immune.

The antibodies can then be detected in the blood for quite a while with appropriate tests. But even if no more antibodies are found, this does not mean that immunity is lost, because the B-lymphocytes also have a "memory" and can quickly produce new ones.

It has now been discovered in recent months that in Covid19 the antibodies are not so decisive in immunisation.[199] Apparently, the T lymphocytes (T cells) play a much more

197 There they are called leukocytes
198 Also called immunoglobulins
199 e.g.: https://www.spiegel.de/wissenschaft/medizin/immunitaet-gegen-das-coronavirus-antikoerper-sind-nicht-alles-a-51bbb04f-cd0a-4f04-ac8b-5115c2059906

important role in the defence against infection. A study by the University Hospital of Tübingen compared blood samples from 180 patients who had undergone a SARS-CoV-2 infection with 185 blood samples from before the "pandemic". In the first group, as expected, all T-cells reacted to gene components of SARS-CoV-2, in the second group, which had never had to deal with the virus, an astonishing 81%.[200] The researchers explained this as a cross-reaction to gene components of other, already known coronaviruses. [201]Further studies confirm the existence of such cross-immunities. [202]

Be that as it may – the 81% immunity of the Tübingen study is close to the approx. 85% of the population who tested positive but did not get sick, such as in the "hotspot" of the Tyrolean ski resort Ischgl. Maybe this comes from T-cell immunity, even without antibodies? That would mean that only a fifth of the test-positive people could ever become infected, because all the others are already immune. In the blood of people who were infected with SARS in 2003, active T-cells against the virus can still be detected until now, which means that they are immune to Covid19, too.[203] A recent study[204] confirmed that Covid19 patients remain immune after recovery. This is in line with other study results.[205]

This T-cell immunity was even confirmed by Prof. Drosten in his blog. He said that this explains the many mild courses of

200 https://www.aerzteblatt.de/nachrichten/115217/T-Zellen-gegen-saisonale-Coronaviren-erkennen-auch-SARS-CoV-2

201 Another, better explanation would be that the virus is not so new. It has probably always existed.

202 http://www.cell.com/immunity/fulltext/S1074-7613(16)30160-1
http://www.cell.com/cell/fulltext/S0092-8674(20)30610-3
http://www.biorxiv.org/content/10.1101/2020.06.29.174888v1
http://www.researchsquare.com/article/rs-35331/v1

203 https://www.trendsderzukunft.de/corona-studie-stellt-fest-81-besitzen-kreuzimmunitaet-durch-schnupfenviren/

204 https://www.biorxiv.org/content/10.1101/2020.11.15.383323v1

205 https://de.sputniknews.com/wissen/20201123328428469-studie-anhaltende-immunitaet-nach-corona/

Covid19. He suspects that herd immunity could occur much faster because we have all been cross-immune for a long time. This would protect a large part of the population right now.[206] This quote contradicts his own panic statements, which he usually makes, just as he had also presented the PCR test as unsuitable for diagnosis in 2014. One wonders whether he is just forgetful or whether there is an intention behind it.

In obvious contrast to him, T-cells have a long-term memory. That is why every epidemic is more violent at the beginning than later on, the "herd immunity" of the population increases, and the infectivity of the virus decreases over time. This is observed in all viral epidemics. If viruses did not mutate until the next season, there would be no more flu epidemics. There has never been a "second wave" of the same pathogen, not even with the "Spanish flu" (explaining this in detail would take us too far here). The Covid19 flu wave also follows the same pattern, only the statistical tricks feign a second wave. Incidentally, there was never a "second wave" of influenza either, because in autumn a new season with new viruses always began and they started counting again from zero. The RKI has always done this, except with Corona, so that the numbers keep rising.

Dr. Friedrich Pürner, epidemiologist and head of a public health department, criticised the strategy of always using only test results as a basis; nothing is known about those who are really ill. He called the incidence rate of 35 or 50 per 100,000 inhabitants "arbitrarily chosen". He said he would risk his career as a civil servant for this statement,[207] and was promptly transferred for disciplinary reasons.[208]

---

206 Source: Drosten's blog at NDR, No. 58 of 30.9.2020 at:
https://www.reitschuster.de/post/drosten-wir-sind-doch-zu-grossen-teilen-schon-geschuetzt/

207 https://politikstube.com/gesundheitsamt-chef-zerreisst-soeders-corona-strategie/

208 https://www.youtube.com/watch?v=V1OEIHYnNtg

According to the Ministry of Health, by the way, a disease is considered *"rare"* if fewer than five in a thousand contract it. In other words, 500 out of 100,000, i.e. ten times the "magic limit" of 50 out of 100,000, above which the new Infection Protection Act provides for compulsory measures. Did you get the point? Below 500 it is a *"rare disease"* and above 50 a *"pandemic"?* That is complete nonsense. We are being taken for fools.

Vaccine manufacturers see it this way: for them, up to 100 per 100,000 side effects are considered *"rare"* (according to the package insert).

It would make sense to dispense with the typical antibody tests when asking whether someone is immune or not and instead develop simple tests that can find specific T-cells. Then the 81% of the population who have such cells would no longer need to be vaccinated. But that would be bad for the vaccination business.

There are also new findings on the question of infection with Covid19: Since every infection depends on the "viral load", i.e. the amount of viruses produced (as Mr. Drosten admits, too), only sick people with symptoms are contagious, but not supposedly "infected" people, which is somehow logical, because anyone who has so few viruses that they don't even sneeze or cough can hardly infect others with them. A WHO study confirms this, too.[209]

The largest study on this, with almost 10 million participants, was published in China in November 2020. With this enormous number of test persons, no evidence was found that anyone who tested positive without symptoms had ever infected anyone else.[210] Therefore, blanket restrictions such as quarantine or mask-wearing for symptom-free people are nonsensical and unjustified, even if they are "positive".

---

209 https://www.who.int/docs/default-source/coronaviruse/transcripts/who-audio-emergencies-coronavirus-press-conference-08jun2020.pdf
210 https://www.nature.com/articles/s41467-020-19802-w

Thus, even children are hardly ever infectious or at risk, because they are extremely rarely infected with SARS-CoV2.[211] Especially in children, the non-specific immune system, i.e. the one without antibodies, is particularly well developed. Only 1-2% of Covid19 sufferers are children, and they all have a mild course like any other cold. Pregnant women and infants also have no increased risk to worry about. The risk of death is zero for all people under 30 years of age. So far, only one child in Germany has died *with* Corona, but not *from* it. The three-year-old was already seriously ill beforehand and has been treated with immunosuppressants. [212]

It has nothing to do with immunity, but here's a curiosity on the side: At the medical faculty of the University of Duisburg-Essen, they found that smokers who smoked more than 10 cigarettes a day tested positive significantly less often. And a study by a Paris hospital found that there were only 5% smokers among the Covid19 patients. So compared to the 25% smokers in France, the risk of infection drops to a fifth.[213]

211 https://www.tagblatt.ch/leben/daten-aus-sechs-laendern-zeigen-kinder-sind-in-sachen-coronavirus-wirklich-weniger-ansteckend-ld.1229944
212 Source: https://www.martin-hirte.de/coronavirus/
213 https://www.compact-online.de/zitat-des-tages-raucher-stecken-sich-seltener-mit-corona-an/

What really happened in Italy?

One of the distinguishing features of the Corona Crisis is that it is accompanied from the beginning by a campaign that targets people's psyche. The main elements of this campaign are fear and panic. Its methods come from psychological warfare, which are very old,[214] but always evolving.

If emotions are to be aroused, for example in advertising, then one should appeal to primal instincts as much as possible, bypassing the mind. Images are better suited for this than words. One particular image particularly impressed and frightened people: the picture of the coffins in Bergamo and the army trucks that supposedly transported them. In retrospect, however, this turned out to be fake news, a perfidious advertising campaign for the lockdown. What really happened there?

Initially, the Italian Ministry of Health had decreed that all bodies that had tested positive had to be cremated. This created a traffic jam at the few crematoria in Lombardy, because there was not enough capacity. In Italy, as a Catholic country, cremations are rather the exception, and burying the bodies was not allowed. Moreover, almost all the funeral parlours in the region were closed, most of them for fear of infection, but also because many undertakers were in quarantine.[215] So the coffins were first stored in halls or churches.

One of the pictures with many coffins, which was circulating in the media, originally came from a ship sinking off Lampedusa in which many refugees had drowned. [216]

---

214 For example, the 36 stratagems (war lists) of the Chinese general Tan Daoji (5th century) or "The Psychology of the Masses" by Gustave Le Bons, 1895.

215 https://www.journalistenwatch.com/2020/12/18/tote-fliessband-wie/

216 https://correctiv.org/faktencheck/2020/03/20/dieses-foto-zeigt-keine-saerge-von-menschen-die-in-italien-durch-das-coronavirus-gestorben-sind

Regarding the military trucks, the chief virologist of the Milan University Hospital, Prof. Maria Rita Gismondo, said that a responsible military colonel had confirmed that the trucks had not transported a single corpse. She spoke of *"a psychological pandemic", "a worldwide panic strategy"*. Ambulances from her clinic had been requested to race back and forth through Milan with blue lights, but empty. Prof. Gismondo maintains to this day that Corona was *"a moderately severe flu"*. For this she has been publicly attacked and *"indirectly pressured"* by the government to stop talking about the real situation in Lombardy.[217]

Italy, especially the north, is a very special region, because here more people died of the "coronavirus" in spring 2020 than in Austria or Switzerland, for example. Did the virus mutate when it crossed the border? According to virology, the symptoms and the danger of a pathogen should be the same, no matter where in the world. So, what was different in Italy? On closer inspection, there are a lot of peculiarities there that have nothing to do with the virus, but all the more with the general health risks:

- The Italian health care system has been increasingly cut to the bone by the policies of recent years and has been working at its capacity limits for a long time.

- The hospitals are in poor condition, and in every flu season the occupancy rate in Lombardy is normally already 85-90%.

- Italy has the highest infection rate of resistant hospital germs (hospitalism) in Europe, ten times more than Germany. One third of all hospitalism deaths in Europe occur in Italy.

- Italy has the oldest population in Europe.

---

217 At a Berlin symposium https://www.compact-online.de/was-hat-die-elite-zu-verbergen-experten-packen-aus/

- Northern Italy has one of the highest rates of severe respiratory diseases. This is due to the extreme air pollution in this industrial region, where there is too little air exchange in winter due to the basin location between the Alps and the Apennines. Where high levels of air pollution are common, i.e. in Wuhan, northern Italy, Madrid, Paris, London New York, etc., one also finds higher Covid rates than elsewhere. Fine dust and nitrogen oxides logically promote and aggravate respiratory diseases, but also cardiovascular problems.[218]

- For cost reasons, the nursing staff of the old people's homes are almost all Eastern Europeans who fled en masse to their countries for fear of the coming lockdown. Many sick people were therefore transferred to the hospitals for lack of care, which made the situation there worse. In the old people's homes, which were nevertheless overburdened, many patients had to die prematurely, the families had been locked out and were not allowed to help with the care.

- Thousands of elderly patients were artificially ventilated in the hospitals. 5,000 respirators were used and the death rate was correspondingly high. On 18 September 2020, several doctors admitted to parliament that thousands of patients, especially the elderly, had died because of wrong medication and the use of ventilators.

- The treatment protocols encouraged the massive use of paracetamol, antibiotics and expensive antivirals, the cost of which was borne by the state. The many thromboses in the lungs were detected too late because of the ban on autopsies.

---

218 https://www.martin-hirte.de/coronavirus/

- In Lombardy, because of the panic in the homes and hospitals, many and strong medicines were given from 17 March onwards. Statistics from April showed that of the patients who died, 84% had received antibiotics, especially azithromycin, 55% antiviral drugs, 33% corticosteroids, and 18.6% had even received a mix of all three.[219]

- According to a study by the Italian health authority "Institutio Superiore di Sanità", 99.2% of coronary deaths had pre-existing conditions (cardiovascular, diabetes, cancer, stroke, chronic lung disease). The average age of the dead was over 80 years, only 0.8% were under 50.[220] In Italy, 500 people die every day from cardiovascular diseases and 400 from cancer. Finding enough test positives among these should not be a problem.

- In the province of Bergamo, 154,000 people were vaccinated against influenza in a large-scale vaccination campaign in the winter of 2019. 129,000 were older than 65. I will discuss the connection between Corona and flu vaccination in more detail later. [221]

- Another vaccination campaign took place in Bergamo and Brescia in January 2020. Here, 34,000 people had been vaccinated against meningococcus.[222]

We see, there were enough reasons to die of a lung problem in northern Italy in 2020. A virus was not required for this, but

219 https://www.epicentro.iss.it/en/coronavirus/bollettino/Report-COVID-2019_9_april_2020.pdf
220 http://alles-schallundrauch.blogspot.com/2020/05/italien-sagt-96-die-virustodesfalle.html#ixzz6Nf3rgYbc
221 http://alles-schallundrauch.blogspot.com/2020/05/italien-sagt-96-die-virustodesfalle.html#ixzz6Nf3rgYbc
222 https://www.bsnews.it/2020/01/18/meningite-vaccinate-34mila-persone-tra-brescia-e-bergamo/?refresh_ce

could still be found and held responsible thanks to the Drosten PCR test.

The mass graves of New York

There were more emotionally charged images sent around the world during the "pandemic". Drone footage showed mass graves being dug in New York, supposedly because there were so many coronavirus dead that the undertakers couldn't keep up. Creepy, one thought of the plague or other deadly epidemics.

In truth, Hart Island off New York has long been a huge graveyard. More than a hundred years ago, immigrants from Europe were quarantined there until it was certain that they would not bring in any epidemics. Later, the island was a prison and military base. For several decades, New York's dead who have no relatives or no money for a proper burial have been buried there. In the 1980s, the AIDS dead, whom no undertaker wanted because of the AIDS panic, were disposed of there. But there was no mention of all this in the media, only the gruesome pictures were used for the Corona fear campaign.[223] By the way, the published drone images were taken in 2016.[224]

The spectacle surrounding the hospital ship in New York harbour also turns out to have been blown up by the media. Only 71 of the 500 beds on the ship were occupied by Covid19 patients.[225]

---

223 https://wunderblog.daniel-deppe.de/hart-island-der-groesste-friedhof-der-welt/ http://www.faz.net/aktuell/gesellschaft/hart-island-die-verbotene-toten-insel-vor-new-york-12901789.html
https://www.nytimes.com/interactive/2016/05/15/nyregion/new-york-mass-graves-hart-island.html
224 https://kenfm.de/ein-zwischenruf-aus-dem-umfeld-des-bundestages/
225 https://www.cnbc.com/2020/04/17/nearly-90percent-of-the-us-navy-hospital-ship-in-new-york-is-empty-amid-coronavirus-fight.html

Sweden

Many Europeans looked longingly to Sweden this spring: There was no lockdown, hardly any school closures and no compulsory masks. People strolled through the streets, met in cafés and could move freely. Life went on as normal – but not completely. Sweden also imposed certain regulations, such as restrictions on nightclubs, gatherings and sporting events. Many Swedes refrained from travelling, and tourism from other countries also declined. Volvo and other factories closed down temporarily, there was an economic slump here too, although much less than in the rest of Europe.[226]

However, the approach in Sweden was not without flaws. Here, too, the austerity measures of earlier years · in the health and care sector had negative consequences.[227] The health authorities admitted that too little had been done in the nursing homes to protect those in need of care, which initially led to higher mortality. The profit-oriented use of poorly paid nurses ensured that they had to care for many patients and continued to work even when they were ill. This took its toll especially in nursing homes, as it did in other countries.[228] The official percentage of corona deaths in nursing homes was 37% in Germany, 51% in France, 62% in Ireland and 82% in Canada. [229]

Unlike the rest of Europe, however, the government opted for voluntarism, and enjoyed a high level of approval among the people. This is because the scientists of the health authority

---

226 Source: https://de.sputniknews.com/gesellschaft/20200610327348399-Covid-19-lockdown-analyse-teil-3/

227 https://deutsche-wirtschafts-nachrichten.de/503569/Schwedens-alternative-Strategie-im-Corona-Kampf-scheint-aufzugehen

228 Source: https://www.tagesspiegel.de/wissen/corona-tote-in-schweden-jeder-zweite-hat-zuvor-in-einem-seniorenheim-gelebt/25811204.html

229 Source: https://www.mopo.de/hamburg/corona-in-hamburg-uke-experte-lobt-schweden---und-fordert-oeffnung-der-schulen-36535890

are in charge there. The chief epidemiologist Anders Tegnell held his liberal course against the hostility of the non-Swedish media and succeeded. Admittedly, the Swedish economy also suffered losses in the first half of 2020, namely 3.5%, whereas the German economy suffered 6.75%, almost double.

The economic historian Prof. Dr. Christian Kreiß describes the situation as follows: *"Above all: Apparently no panic about rising Corona case numbers, no panic about rising death rates as in half of Europe and many other countries of the world. No anger, no aggression in the population, no denunciations, but trust and tolerance. At the same time, a much weaker economic crash than in the vast majority of industrialised countries that carried out harsh, state-imposed forced lockdowns, for example, only half as severe an economic crash as in Germany. Too good to be true? No, Sweden, mid-October 2020.*

Contrast this with the situation in Germany: fear and panic spreading on all channels about rapidly rising infection and death figures, denunciation calls and a denunciation portal, disputes about accommodation bans, children, even of primary school age, wearing masks in class, largely closed universities, threats of a new hard lockdown by politicians, compulsory wearing of masks outdoors, aggression, fear, threats, insults and an irritable mood in public life, an often disturbed daily interaction.

Which Corona way was and is the wiser one? The Swedish or the German?" [230]

Because the German government's Corona policy would look bad in a factual comparison of the two countries, the main-stream media try to badmouth Sweden's success and also use lies to do so: *"Sweden records economic slump compar-*

---

230 Source: https://kenfm.de/armes-schweden-der-schwedische-und-der-deutsche-corona-weg-im-vergleich-von-christian-kreiss/

able to Germany despite loose Corona measures" was the headline of the state-run media "Deutschlandfunk".

Prof. Kreiß disagrees: *"This is also simply not in line with the facts, but is an objective untruth and in my opinion a lie, i.e. a deliberate misrepresentation. In my opinion, the German state broadcaster is supposed to justify German government policy, and apparently at any price, even at the price of the truth. Now, one does not have to expect a state broadcaster to do anything other than court reporting.*

In the German mass media... the popular Sweden-bashing has been carried out excessively and with great glee for months."[231]

Particularly insidious was the report in the "Bild" newspaper and other media that Sweden had the most deaths in 150 years, allegedly because of Corona. The report came from the Reuters agency, but they had omitted the reference to the fact that the population has risen sharply in the last 150 years. It is the same trick as with the rising case numbers, without mentioning the rising test numbers. If one puts the numbers correctly into perspective, the hoax becomes clear: In 1869, Northern Europe suffered from a famine. The number of deaths in the first half of the year in Sweden was more than 1,300 per 100,000 inhabitants. In the first half of 2020, mortality was 501 deaths (all, not just because of Corona) per 100,000 inhabitants, less than 40% of the mortality in 1869.

"The real figures on Sweden therefore show pretty much the opposite of what the German leading media mostly reported: Contrary to the German media portrayals, there was and is no pandemic and no excess mortality discernible in Sweden, but quite normal mortality.

Why is Sweden reported so dishonestly in the German media? Well, assuming that the Swedish Corona way would

---

231 ibid

turn out to be right after all, despite all the permanent Sweden-bashing, then one would be admitting that the German handling of Corona was wrong. Then one would also have to admit that most of the panic-fuelling reports on Corona in the German mainstream media were wrong or misleading. That would raise some very uncomfortable questions about the German mainstream media and German politics after all. "[232]

The influence of flu vaccinations

In the 2017/18 flu season, a US study in the US military compared those vaccinated against influenza (flu) with those who were not vaccinated. It found that there were significantly more respiratory illnesses in the vaccinated group than in those who were not vaccinated. In addition, 36% more coronaviruses were found in the vaccinated.[233] Other studies, such as that of the University of Oxford among children, also showed that flu vaccination increased the risk of contracting influenza.[234]

In 2020, reports from Italy and Spain accumulated that among corona patients and deaths, most had previously been vaccinated against influenza, especially the elderly. The following graph allows a comparison of 17 countries: [235]

232 Source: https://kenfm.de/armes-schweden-der-schwedische-und-der-deutsche-corona-weg-im-vergleich-von-christian-kreiss/

233 https://www.sciencedirect.com/science/article/pii/S0264410X19313647

234 http://www.ncbi.nlm.nih.gov/pmc/articles/PMC3404712/

235 By Michael Kent, kindly provided by Sabine Hinz Verlag
    http://www.sabinehinz.de/

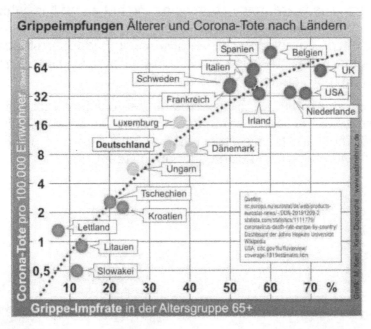

Grippeimpfungen Älterer und Corona-Tote nach Ländern

Grippe-Impfrate in der Altersgruppe 65+

Here it can be clearly seen: The number of corona deaths per 100,000 inhabitants (vertical axis) is proportional to the flu vaccination rate among the over-65s (horizontal axis)! This means: the more flu vaccinations had been given, the higher the death rate for "corona". Countries with low vaccination rates such as Latvia, Lithuania and Slovakia had the fewest deaths in percentage terms.

In the UK, authorities recommended that all newly flu vaccinated people stay at home for the next 12 weeks because they are particularly vulnerable and at risk in case of corona infection. This is consistent with the observation of many caregivers and naturopaths that a flu vaccination makes people more susceptible to respiratory infections. [236]

It has been known for some time that the flu vaccination does not deliver what it promises and weakens the immune

---

236 https://www.mirror.co.uk/news/uk-news/coronavirus-top-medic-warns-anyone-21708701

system. There are many sources on the net about this, which you can research yourself if you are interested.[237] A flu vaccination campaign with Sanofi vaccine had to be stopped in South Korea because 59 vaccinated people died.[238] You can find more sources on this here. [239]

The more people get themselves or their children vaccinated against flu, the more "corona cases" you will be able to find later. The calls for flu vaccination will drive up the positive rates and make the vaccinated more susceptible.

237 e.g.: http://www.impfkritik.de/ https://impfen-nein-danke.de/ as   well as various groups on telegram, bitchute etc.
238 https://www.fiercepharma.com/vaccines/sanofi-sk-flu-shots-halted-singapore-as-south-korea-post-vaccination-deaths-climb-to-59
239 https://telegra.ph/Die-Grippe-Impfung-ist-nicht-nur-nutzlos-die-beteiligten-wissen-über-den-Betrug-bescheid-11-11

The government's measures

Can masks protect?

The answer is "yes". Masks protect:

- from fines
- from evil glances of scared mask wearers
- from cheeky deputies (security)

However, masks do not protect against infection, whether of bystanders or the mask wearer himself. In both surgical and cotton masks, viruses pass through the fabric when coughed on, as has been shown in experiments in Seoul.[240]

Trying to stop viruses with masks[241] is ridiculous anyway. A coronavirus measures 0.08 micrometres. The pores in a mask may be small, 80 to 500 micrometres, depending on the model, but they are an open barn door for a virus. You might as well nail a fence in front of your window to keep mosquitoes out.

On 25.9.20, the US CDC retracted its previous claim that Covid19 was airborne. Chief Medical Officer John Brooks apologised for the error and said that the new guidelines stated that transmission was likely human-to-human.[242] Whatever that means.

On the website "Doctors Enlighten"[243] 44 studies from all over the world have been collected, all concluding that

---

240 https://www.aerzteblatt.de/nachrichten/111799/COVID-19-Patienten-husten-Viren-durch-chirurgische-Masken-und-Baumwollmasken-hindurch
241 I will not use "mouth-nose protection" or similar stupid terms, because it is not protection. A mask remains a mask.
242 https://bluntforcetruth.com/news/cdc-admits-there-is-no-proof-Covid-19-is-airborne-virus-and-they-have-been-misleading-the-public-all-along/

masks are completely useless, even for surgery! Comparisons were made of wound infections from operations with and without masks, and there was never a difference. Two studies even came to the astonishing conclusion that there were *fewer* infections in operations without masks than in those with. The rate of wound infections surprisingly dropped to half when no masks were worn during the operations.[244]

In another comparison of 1,537 operations with and 1,551 operations without masks, the wound infection rate was reduced from 4.7% to 3.5% – when masks were not used! [245]

The uselessness of masks becomes most obvious when comparing infection rates between countries with and without mandatory masks or between the phases of mask ban and mask-free in the same country. A comprehensive meta-study[246] by the National Bureau of Economic Research, one of the top research institutions in the USA, came to the conclusion: the Corona death rate fell regardless of the measures taken, and in fact in *all* countries studied. The spread of Corona could not be influenced by curfews, travel restrictions, quarantine measures or mandatory masking.[247]

In Germany, the RKI figures show that neither the lockdown nor the introduction of mandatory masks have influenced the typical course of infection in any way. When the first lockdown was imposed, the numbers were already in decline. Nor did the *"black lives matter"* demonstrations in the summer or the large demonstrations against the Corona measures in Berlin on 1 and 29 August, where almost no one

243 https://telegra.ph/Was-finden-wir-in-den-wissenschaftlichen-Studien-zu-Masken-10-28
http://www.aerzteklaerenauf.de/masken/index.php#520252ac490f56c02
244 https://www.ncbi.nlm.nih.gov/pmc/articles/PMC2493952/pdf/annrcse01509-0009.pdf
245 https://link.springer.com/article/10.1007/BF01658736
246 The results of several studies are analysed in an overall view
247 https://www.journalistenwatch.com/2020/09/08/weltweites-totalversagen-studie/

wore a mask or observed distance rules, result in an increase in the curve. The requirements for the latter "Querdenker" demos were pure harassment by the authorities, because at the more left-wing demos nobody cared about masks or distance and the police let them. Even Radio "Deutschlandfunk" reported that no increase in the number of cases could be detected as a result of the large demonstrations in Stuttgart, Berlin, Hamburg and Munich.[248]

The RKI data show that the "pandemic" in Germany was already in retreat before the first lockdown was imposed.[249] The university ETH Zurich determined the same for Switzerland.[250] A graph from Oxford University compares the Corona deaths with an index of government measures, and no correlation can be found.[251] This proves once again the ineffectiveness of the measures.

A meta-study by Tom Jefferson and his team was published in England, which retrospectively examined the influence of mask-wearing on the frequency of influenza infections. It came to the conclusion that no difference could be found, the infection rate was not reduced by mask wearing, neither in everyday life nor in health care. The different types of masks also made no difference.[252] Another meta-study by the US Centre for Disease Control (CDC) comes to the same conclusion [253]

248 https://www.deutschlandfunk.de/superspreader-events-massenveranstaltungen-haben-corona.1939.de.html?drn:news_id=1152418
249 https://advance.sagepub.com/ndownloader/files/22783862
250 http://www.luzernerzeitung.ch/schweiz/die-schweiz-haette-die-kurve-auch-mit-weniger-einschraenkungen-gekriegt-war-der-lockdown-uebertrieben-ld.1221111
251 https://github.com/tolex3/share/blob/master/20200727/lockdown_index_dead_per_M.jpg
252 https://www.medrxiv.org/content/10.1101/2020.03.30.20047217v1.full.pdf
253 https://wwwnc.cdc.gov/eid/article/26/5/19-0994_article

A Danish study tested the efficiency of masks with over 6,000 participants. For one month, they went out in public for three hours a day, half with, half without masks. After one month, there was hardly any difference, as 1.8% of the participants had been infected with a mask, and 2.1% without. The researchers were surprised by the small effect of mask-wearing.[254]

One has to bear in mind that most mask studies refer to the self-protection of staff in clinics. The conditions there are completely different from those in public: the distances between doctors and nurses and patients are smaller, the contact times are longer and the probability that airborne germs are present is greater than in school, in the supermarket or even outdoors. So if self-protection is already viewed with scepticism in clinics, it is no longer relevant on the street. There is no question of contagion without a mask; it is virtually impossible, if only because of the short contact times with strangers.

Of course, the RKI knows this too and therefore likes to argue in the subjunctive, it *"could perhaps..."*. Yes, of course, "could" can mean many things, an aeroplane could also fall on your head. The RKI also often uses the word *"plausibility"*. Why? Because there are no studies that provide solid evidence for protection by masks in public. However, there is evidence for the disadvantages and risks of masks. I refer you to the detailed, well-researched sources in the foot-note.[255]

In Austria, Prof. Dr. Franz Allerberger of the government-advising "AGES"[256] said that the compulsory use of masks in Austria, which had been mandatory twice until then, had no effect on the course of infection.[257] When asked by the

---

254 https://deutsch.rt.com/europa/109451-danische-studie-masken-bieten-nur/
255 https://telegra.ph/Der-Maskenbetrug-ist-entzaubert-06-26
256 The "Austrian Agency for Health and Food Safety".
257 on 19 August 2020 in an ORF interview

Austrian TV "ORF" interviewer whether this also applied to public transport, he replied that it did there too. There had been no outbreaks there either. Chinese studies had shown that even if you were sitting next to an infected person, infection could only occur in 1% of cases. You would have to talk to the infected person for at least 15 minutes at a short distance, sing or shout, or at least produce droplets. If you are yelled at for fifteen minutes on the train in China, you should probably change seats, otherwise the virus might fly in.

In the journal "Krankenhaushygiene up2date", Prof. Ines Kappstein wrote that wearing masks in public is scientifically unfounded and potentially counterproductive. It would also not be in line with WHO recommendations.[258]

When the mask requirement was reintroduced in Austria in July 2020, it was not for factual reasons but for psychological ones. The special representative of the Vienna Ministry of Health, Clemens Auer, explained that to date, relaxations of the measures had not led to an increase in the number of cases, even after the mask requirement had been temporarily abolished in shops. Nevertheless, the mask requirement makes psychological sense, as it signals to people that there is a danger. It is important that the policy measures always remain credible.[259]

Whether this serves the credibility of the policy, however, may be doubted. This shows once again that there are not epidemiological but political reasons behind the mask re-quirement.

In fact, neither in Germany nor in Austria have they found even one case of infection in a supermarket.[260]

258 https://www.thieme-connect.com/products/ejournals/pdf/10.1055/a-1174-6591.pdf
259 https://www.wochenblick.at/selbst-regierungsexperten-bestaetigten-die-sinnlosigkeit-der-maskenpflicht/
260 https://www.welt.de/wirtschaft/article211175829/Clemens-Auer-Es-gibt-keinen-Fall-bei-dem-sich-Menschen-in-Geschaeften-angesteckt-

It is well known that wearing masks does not prevent severe flu outbreaks, as this can be seen every year in East Asia. The Dutch Minister of Health did not initially introduce mandatory mask use because there was no evidence of medical benefit.[261] Apparently, there were still a few politicians at the time who would not let anyone stop them from thinking. And in our country?

If masks were protective, infections with other viruses, such as rhinoviruses, should also decrease. The opposite was the case: in the summer of 2020, these were significantly more prevalent than in the summer of 2019, as the RKI's sentinel report shows – despite masks and distance rules.[262] And why does the CDC report that 85% of test positives are mask wearers? That should give pause for thought.

By the way, the mask manufacturers know full well that their products are a farce. You should read the small print more often, even if you have to get out your glasses. On many packages there are instructions such as:

- These masks do not provide protection against viruses or bacteria.

- Do not reuse after use.

- The masks are not medically certified.

- No product liability is assumed

Very practical. Like arms deal worth billions (so don't reuse it!), without any risk. The main thing is that the frightened customer feels "protected" and not taken for a ride.

Two statements by a virologist on the question of whether the mask could help to stop the spread of the virus are interest-

haben.html

261 https://www.bfarm.de/SharedDocs/Risikoinformationen/
Medizinprodukte/DE/schutzmasken.html

262 https://deutsch.rt.com/inland/106478-keine-nachweise-mehr-im-rki/

ing. He said that the technical data was not good, that it would not stop the virus.[263]

And: it is not known whether masks reduce the virus dose and pointed out that even the constant wearing of masks could not prevent large outbreaks in many Asian countries.[264]

Now it only remains for me to say who expressed these doubts: it was Christian Drosten himself. Not even he is convinced of the sense of the masquerade, and yet the whole country is terrorised with it.

By the way: If it were as claimed that the viruses "stick" in the masks, then the masks would be contaminated and highly infectious after use. They would have to be incinerated as hazardous waste. But this is never mentioned – another illogic in this illogical drama.

There are jokers who annoy the health authorities or the police with calls along the lines of: *"I found a used mask on the floor, please take care of it". "Just throw it in a wastepaper basket!" "No, you mustn't touch it, you could get infected. Besides, it's hazardous waste."*

In one such case, a dialogue developed with a public health officer. She said that it was not dangerous, that it was not Ebola. The statistics clearly show that only very few people die from Corona. The caller knew this, of course, and said he only wanted to point out this madness with his little action.

The public health officer replied that she knew all this, but that she was only an executive body and could not do anything about it. She advised the caller to contact Mrs.

263 on 30 January 2020 on "Talk from Berlin" Source:
   https://youtu.be/Z3Zth7KYVHY?t=1552
264 at a hearing of the Health Committee on 9 September 2020, to be seen
   from minute 8:15 here:
   https://www.bundestag.de/dokumente/textarchiv/2020/kw37-pa-
   gesundheit-corona-709474

Merkel or, better still, the minister of health, Mr. Spahn, because he was the one who had come up with all this.[265]

Are masks harmful to health?

The answer is a resounding "yes", for the following reasons:

- The oxygen in the breathing air falls below the minimum permissible limit
- The carbon dioxide in the air we breathe rises *far* above the permissible limit
- Breathing becomes more difficult due to increased breathing resistance
- Germs accumulate in the damp environment with various consequences
- There are neither standards nor quality controls (except for medical masks), e.g. harmful formaldehyde can evaporate from new masks.
- The trigeminocardiac reflex (TCR) can lower blood pressure and heart rate
- Psychological perceptual disorders occur

Oxygen

Let's start with oxygen. Normally, the air consists of 21% oxygen, the rest is nitrogen and – only very little – carbon dioxide. In the occupational health and safety regulations, which are all similar internationally, the oxygen content in the breathing air must be at least 19.5%. If it falls below that, the

---

265 Retold from a posting on the internet, unfortunately without naming the author

room must be evacuated. If the level is permanently below that, the department or company is closed.

Various measurements[266] have shown that the oxygen content drops to 17-18% under the masks, depending on the model, because the inhaled air mixes with the exhaled air. What is not expected of workers in the factory is now being forced on all of us! **The masks are therefore illegal because they do not meet the protection standard.**

If the body does not receive enough oxygen ("hypoxia"), then various symptoms appear, such as clouding of consciousness up to fainting, bluish skin colour, shortness of breath and muscle weakness.

When there is a lack of oxygen, the brain is particularly affected, which is why dizziness, light-headedness and concentration problems often occur. Children in particular need a lot of oxygen for brain development. The neurologist Dr. Margareta Griesz-Brisson describes this impressively in a video that is worth watching, which has been censored by Youtube but can still be viewed elsewhere.[267]

She considers the coercive measures to be an absolute disaster at every level. She calls mandatory masking and distance rules inhumane and criminal. Health, she says, is largely in our own hands. Good food, good water, lots of exercise, sociability, joy, friends, love and plenty of fresh air strengthen the immune system. But that is exactly what the government forbids.

She said the hand disinfectants alone, which have all been thrown on the market, have caused a large number of allergies, skin diseases, immune reactions, and eczema. She said the spacing rules were unsurpassed in brutality, con-

---

266 http://www.antikrieg.eu/aktuell/2020_07_14_buerger.htm
267https://www.bitchute.com/video/WAQfkwwx8zs/
https://dein.tube/watch/3ywoAueWEnLK81e or:
https://ruhrkultour.de/margareta-griesz-brisson-zu-den-coronamassnahmen/
https://open.lbry.com/@KulturstudioTV:c/mask-madness-open:d

tempt for humanity and cruelty and were without precedent in the history of mankind.

As a human being, you can live for weeks without food, and for days without water but only a few minutes without oxygen. The brain in particular reacts extremely sensitively to a lack of oxygen. Some nerve cells, for example in the hippocampus, could not survive for more than three minutes without oxygen.

The symptoms start with headaches, drowsiness, dizziness, and even concentration problems, slower reaction times, i.e. restrictions of cognitive functions. Prolonged oxygen deficiency leads to gradual brain degradation. Even if the symptoms disappear again, the lack of oxygen in the brain progresses.

Neurodegenerative diseases have a lead time of years to decades. If you forget your phone number, for example, the degeneration in the brain has had a lead time of many years. Even if you think you have got used to the mask, the degenerative processes in the brain continue regardless. If, at some point, one is mercifully allowed to live without a mask again, the dead nerve cells will not grow back, what is gone is gone.

The neurologist stressed that she does not wear a mask because she needs her brain to think, she wants to treat her patients with a clear head and mind and not in a carbon dioxide anaesthesia.

The CO_2 poisoning

In addition to the lack of oxygen, there is another major problem, namely the rebreathing of carbon dioxide (CO_2). Normally there is 400 ppm[268] (0.04%) of carbon dioxide in the air.

"For example, the Federal Environment Agency states that concentrations below 1,000 ppm are harmless. The limit value for living spaces in Germany is 1,500 ppm. Values above 2,000 ppm, on the other hand, are considered "unacceptable". In a ministry paper from Austria "Guideline for the assessment of indoor air" it was stated that people start to perceive their breathing air as "unsatisfactory" at a CO_2 content of 1,000 ppm. At 3,000 ppm, it is already 50% of people who perceive the air as unsatisfactory.

From 40,000 ppm carbon dioxide is "numbing", from 80,000 ppm it is lethal, ... whereby the guideline values always apply to healthy people. People with health problems may encounter initial problems even at lower values. CO_2 is actually non-toxic for humans, but in too high concentrations it prevents the absorption of oxygen. The following applies: A concentration of eight or more percent CO_2 in the air we breathe over a period of 30 to 60 minutes can lead to death. Before that, headaches, lack of concentration and uncon-sciousness develop.

Dr. Helmut Traindl, a court-certified expert, measured the CO_2 levels under a homemade and two commercially available Corona protective masks in front of a running camera. It turned out that the maximum permissible values for workplaces were exceeded many times over. Not only does this mean that citizens were being subjected to an unlawful condition, such breathing air is also considered

---

268 ppm stands for "parts per million", so 1% is 10,000 ppm.

acutely anaesthetic and hazardous to health according to all medical findings."[269]

Dr. Traindl measured values of up to 50,000 ppm (5%) carbon dioxide under the masks![270] *"If the permitted limit values at a workplace were exceeded even briefly to the extent that occurs under the corona masks, one would have to reckon with serious consequences, up to and including the closure of the company.*[271]

Carbon dioxide is also produced during alcoholic fermentation and has led to many deaths in poorly ventilated wine cellars. It is known that fermentation gas (CO_2) causes drowsiness and lack of concentration from a concentration of 0.5%, increases breathing rate and pulse rate from 2% and causes blood circulation problems in the brain from 4%, often with dizziness, nausea or ringing in the ears. The dangerous thing is that you don't smell it, so you are not forewarned.

In Dr. Traindl's tests, the carbon dioxide levels exceeded the maximum limit of the factory inspectorate by up to 25 times![272] **Masks are illegal for the second time because the limits for CO_2 are far exceeded.**

An Italian study also measured too high values under the masks.[273]

The symptoms of too high CO_2 levels in the blood ("hypercapnia") are: Headaches, concentration problems, fatigue, sweating, dizziness, poorer fine motor skills, high

269 https://www.wochenblick.at/sachverstaendiger-beweist-live-co2-werte-unter-masken-gesundheitsschaedlich/

270 In some videos from the USA, similar measurements were shown with values up to 100,000 ppm, the maximum value that the respective device could display.

271 https://www.wochenblick.at/sachverstaendiger-beweist-live-co2-werte-unter-masken-gesundheitsschaedlich/

272 In Austria, the limit value is ten times higher than in Germany (2,000 ppm). In Belgium it is lower (1,200 ppm).

273 https://2020news.de/italien-studie-belegt-stark-erhoehten-co2-wert-unter-der-maske/

116

blood pressure, palpitations and cardiac arrhythmias, shortness of breath, confusion, dementia, unconsciousness, etc.... The immune system is also disturbed. As early as 2005, a study by the Technical University of Munich showed that hypercapnia already begins when surgical masks are put on.[274]

The medical newspaper "Ärzteblatt" writes that wearing masks measurably alters the gases dissolved in the blood and triggers physical impairments, especially in untrained persons.[275]

Paediatrician Eugen Janzen from Bad Salzuflen has proposed a study to see what happens to children when they wear masks all day, as they do at school. He would be willing to pay the costs, but no clinic has so far wanted to provide him with premises and equipment for one day.[276]

He points out that there is a space between the mask and the face where the exhaled air collects to be the first to flow back into the lungs when inhaling. This "dead space volume" measures about 70 ml, depending on the mask.

An adult exhales and inhales 500-700 ml, so first about 10% used air from the dead space until fresh air flows in. Children's lungs are smaller than those of adults. The breathing volume is 10 ml per kg of body weight. An infant weighing 7 kg breathes 70 ml, it would die under the mask because it can only breathe dead air. In children, the proportion of dead space air consumed per breath is always higher than in adults.

In addition, children have a higher oxygen requirement. If the oxygen level in the blood drops and the CO_2 level rises,

274 https://mediatum.ub.tum.de/doc/602557/602557.pdf
275 https://www.aerzteblatt.de/archiv/215610/Einfluss-gaengiger-Gesichtsmasken-auf-physiologische-Parameter-und-Belastungsempfinden-unter-arbeitstypischer-koerperlicher-Anstrengung
276 His video had a lot of positive feedback. The University of Witten/Herdecke now wants to conduct the study.

acidosis occurs. The blood vessels dilate and the blood pressure initially drops. In order not to faint, the adrenal glands produce more adrenaline (stress hormone) to keep the blood pressure up anyway. In measurements with and without a mask, Janzen found an increase in adrenaline levels of up to 300%.[277] In his case, the values even increased more than fourfold, which he attributes to the fact that in practice he wears an FFP2 mask all day, which makes the exchange of air much more difficult. Mask wearers are therefore under permanent adrenaline stress, with unknown long-term consequences.[278]

The initiative "Parents stand up" has conducted a nationwide survey among pupils on the compulsory wearing of masks at schools.[279] An initial evaluation of 2,300 questionnaires revealed a devastating picture: 44.1% of the pupils surveyed suffer from breathing difficulties, 73% from headaches, 86.4% from fatigue, 65.7% from concentration problems, 38% from dizziness and around 36% from anxiety. Forcing children and young people to wear masks, with or without PCR tests, is child abuse and simply a crime against humanity.

Deaths caused by wearing masks?

Considering that children and the elderly are particularly at risk, the mask requirement is nothing other than a vicious attack on the health and lives of those forced to wear masks. Time and again there are reports of people who have had breathing problems under the mask to the point of fainting on the street or while shopping.

---

277 https://youtu.be/9ZRYniOyZQI
278 https://youtu.be/0FD1tsUTL-o the video should be censored, search
   Eugen Janzen on other platforms
279 https://www.surveymonkey.de/r/Y9BV362

The following report comes from several sources on the internet and in the local press, but has not yet been fully confirmed. I am passing it on with reservations:

Near Wörth am Rhein on 7.9.2020, a 13-year-old masked schoolgirl fainted on a school bus and died shortly afterwards in the Karlsruhe Municipal Hospital. The girl was previously healthy. On 11.9. the public prosecutor's office announced that the autopsy had not yielded a clear result on the cause of death. On 16 September, the public prosecutor ordered further investigations. It would now also be investigated whether a lack of oxygen could be the cause of death.

On 19.9. it was announced that no medical reason for the girl's death could be found during the autopsy. According to a doctor and the cardiologist of the hospital, the respiratory drive had continuously reduced and probably led to a cardiac arrhythmia up to death by suffocation. *"No medical reason"* in this context means that no previous illnesses were found. An external effect (blow, strangulation or similar) was also ruled out. Thus, excluding all conceivable causes, only the mask remains as the cause of death. The autopsy result is available, but has not been published.

Meanwhile, the death of a second 13-year-old girl wearing a mask was reported from Eastern Friesland, she allegedly collapsed in the school secretary's office. Evidence or details of this are not yet available, so nothing can be said about the cause of death. There is a suspicion, however, if other causes can be ruled out, because according to the CO_2 levels measured by Dr. Traindl under the mask, this is certainly within the realm of possibility, especially in children.

Subsequently, a third case became known in which a child apparently died wearing a mask. I am also reporting this with reservations, as I do not yet have any reliable sources. Dr. Bodo Schiffmann[280] had reported in several videos that he

---

280 physician and corona critic

had researched the case and knew further details. In a letter,[281] someone who says he is friends with the girl's mother reported that on 28.9.2020, a six-year-old girl wearing a mask fainted on a school bus in Bavaria. The driver called the ambulance but did not dare to take off the mask. The paramedics then did so, immediately gave oxygen and took the child to hospital, where she died in the evening without having regained consciousness beforehand.

The attending doctor had informed the parents by telephone that no previous illnesses had been found and suspected CO_2 poisoning after the autopsy, which meant that it was not a natural cause of death. Therefore, a second autopsy was carried out in the forensic medicine department.

The girl had already reported a few days earlier that she always felt sick under the mask, could hardly breathe and saw "flickering images". However, she was not allowed to take the mask off at school, not even during sports lessons! She didn't want to go to school anymore, but she had to. She had been a healthy and sporty child.

In the meantime, the author of the letter added that the police had forbidden the parents to give further information to the public on the grounds that they could be liable to prosecution as there is an ongoing investigation. The bus driver is apparently under investigation for, among other things, not taking the child's mask off. The author of the letter has since publicly reported on the case.[282]

The journalist Benjamin Gollme from the podcast "Basta Berlin" researched the case.[283] A spokesperson for the Munich police confirmed to him that a six-year-old girl from the Rosenheim district died of natural causes in a Munich hospital on 16 September. What *"natural causes"* at the age

281 https://brd-news.de/maskentote-in-deutschland-3tes-kind-opfer/
282 https://youtu.be/cJ12wskLgso https://invidious.snopyta.org/cJ12wskLgso
283 https://de.sputniknews.com/podcasts/20201001328059656-basta-berlin-folge-56/

of six is supposed to be, the police could not explain. The name and place of residence of the family are known to Gollme, but he withholds them out of consideration. Markus Bayerbach, a member of the Bavarian state parliament, has also made several enquiries and has had Gollme's statements confirmed by the police.[284] Further enquiries are still ongoing.

Need I mention that nothing is reported in the mainstream media about such tragic cases? Usually there are vigils for deceased children with flowers and candles, but here the deaths of children are hushed up because the mere suspicion of masks being the culprit might prompt people to do their own research. Germany – how low have you sunk?

From a legal point of view, what is to be valued more highly: some undemocratic emergency ordinances such as compulsory masks, which are scientifically unsubstantiated, or the right to physical integrity protected by the Basic Law?

Prof. Dr. Sucharit Bhakti, former head of the "Institute for Medical Microbiology and Hygiene" at the University of Mainz, called for a stop to compulsory masks in an impressive interview. He called on all teachers and civil servants to remonstrate.[285] Masks should not be done to children and the elderly, as the increased CO_2 affects muscles, brain and psyche. This is "child abuse".[286]

This video was also deleted by Youtube after it had 120,000 views, but is back online after an injunction.[287] Prof. Bhakti is one of the best-known scientists fighting the corona craze with arguments. He and his wife are authors of the best-selling book "Corona False Alarm?", and his videos are very

---

284 https://t.me/BodoSchiffmann/283
285 The obligation to remonstrate is protected by the Basic Law. Please look it up yourself.
286 https://www.reitschuster.de/post/bhakdi-masken-fuer-schueler-sind-kindsmisshandlung/
287 https://youtu.be/YhLFfoDf1xk

informative.[288] In November, his entire Youtube channel was deleted.

One should realise that carbon dioxide is a waste product of our metabolism. The body has to get rid of it in order to function. Breathing it back in makes about as much sense as drinking your own urine.[289]

Masks are germ slingers

Exhaled air is warm and humid. The fabric of the masks is therefore an ideal place for bacteria and fungi to settle, because they are much larger than viruses and can collect in the fabric.

Dr. Wolfgang Wodarg writes on Facebook that the Swiss consumer magazine "K-Tipp" examined the masks of 20 commuters in the laboratory, and the results were devastating. They were full of bacteria and mould because the masks retain them when they are exhaled, because they are much larger than viruses and remain trapped. They thrive in the humidity and warmth. Staphylococci, which can cause lung and brain infections, were found on 14 of the 20 masks. Mould and yeast fungi had developed on 15 of the 20 masks, which can cause respiratory and eye irritation.[290]

What is normally released into the air and dies there if it does not find a new host immediately, is partly inhaled again with the next breath and increases the germ colonisation in the mucous membranes. This germ film leads to skin and mucous membrane problems, some of which are inflammatory and some allergic in nature – the so-called "mask mouth".

---

288 His video channel: https://www.youtube.com/channel/UCgjxQLDkeoa-uJu4sE0eNrg

289 Except possibly for therapeutic purposes in the treatment of autologous urine

290 https://www.facebook.com/83788386909/posts/10157087140196910/

New York dentist Rob Ramondi said in an interview with the New York Post that gum inflammation and tooth decay are now more common in mask wearers who were previously healthy. Under the mask, people breathe through their mouths more often, which makes the mouth drier and there is less saliva. However, saliva is otherwise responsible for cleaning the teeth and fighting bacteria. As a result, there is more bad breath. In addition, mask wearers generally drink less.[291] Fox News reported that 50% of patients are already affected by this.[292]

The US state of Kansas gave its 105 counties the choice of whether to adopt mandatory masks. This provided a perfect opportunity to compare health outcomes: In the counties with mandatory masks, 50% more people died from or with corona! If you only count the cases where "on" corona is likely, then even eleven times as many died from corona where masks were worn.[293]

The author of the article, Zacharias Fögen, explains it like this: The viruses in the mucous membrane of the upper airways sit in water droplets, and these get stuck in the mask when you exhale. There they dry and the viruses are inhaled again. But because they are much smaller without water droplets, they get into the lower airways, where they can cause pneumonia. An interesting theory that should be tested.

By the way, even new masks can be dangerous because of tissue particles that are inhaled. Peter Diener, a ventilation engineer, warns that both purchased and homemade masks have not been tested for filtering efficiency or safety. Tissues

291 https://kurier.at/wissen/gesundheit/mask-mouth-masken-tragen-bedecken-des-mundes-hat-uebelriechende-nebenwirkung/400992719

292 https://uncut-news.ch/2020/09/25/zahnaerzte-schlagen-wegen-maskenpflicht-alarm/

293 https://reitschuster.de/post/studie-erhoehen-die-masken-die-sterblichkeit/

release a very large number of fine particles, some of which enter the lungs. Only tested masks should be used. [294]

In the meantime, there have been first recalls of drugstore masks in which the dangerous dye aniline has been discovered.[295]

All masks for professional use, i.e. medical or for painters, farmers, craftsmen for sanding etc. go through strict testing procedures according to EU standards so that they do not cause any damage. But all of us, especially children, are fobbed off with cheap imports from Asia that have never been tested and are demonstrably unsuitable. Most people put up with this and harm themselves in the process. I think the cabaret artist Lisa Fitz is right when she says that Corona is an intelligence test.

The trigeminocardiac reflex

The trigeminal nerve is the facial nerve that makes the skin of the face sensitive. It exists on both sides of the face and is divided into three branches coming from the ear. The middle branch supplies the area between the upper lip and the eye up to the nose. When it is inflamed, it can be very painful. It has only been known for a few years that pressure or irritation of this nerve can trigger the "trigeminocardiac reflex" (TCR), which lowers the heart rate and leads to a drop in blood pressure, even to fainting. The phenomenon became known during eye operations, where it was initially called the "*oculo-cardiac reflex*".[296]

So what does this have to do with the mask? This reflex can also be triggered by irritation or the pressure of the masks

294 https://www.wodarg.com/fremde-federn/

295 https://www.hna.de/verbraucher/coronavirus-maske-gift-rueckruf-warnung-drogerie-mueller-mundschutz-lebensgefahr-kassel-hna-zr-90129285.html

296 https://flexikon.doccheck.com/de/Okulokardialer_Reflex

and thus lead to fainting. Especially in children, the reflex is more pronounced than in adults. Apart from hypoxia and carbon dioxide poisoning, this could be another reason for children fainting under the mask. You can find an explanation by Dr. Bodo Schiffmann here.[297]

Mental problems due to masks

People are used to reading other people's faces. How is the other person feeling? Is he relaxed, happy or annoyed, or is he picking a fight? Assessing the other person before making contact gives us security. The mask covers the mouth area, of all places, where most facial expressions take place. The reaction is caution, mistrust. One can observe that people become more fearful when masks are worn. And that is intentional, too.

Especially children who are much more dependent on assessing their surroundings, who are still in the process of learning the language of faces, are greatly unsettled. At the school enrolment in the new school year 2020, one saw many crying children and many who were afraid of school instead of looking forward to it. In addition, the mask compulsion signals *"Danger!"*. This is also intentional. A little girl wearing a mask told a reporter at her enrolment, *"I don't like the mask, I can't breathe properly. But still better than dying."* (She meant "on the virus").

What is being done to our children? What kind of generation is growing up to which danger, disease and death are suggested everywhere? What psychological damage does such a scenario cause, not to mention the developmental disorders of the brain due to lack of oxygen and CO_2 poisoning? If most people are too lazy to stand up for themselves, then they should stand up at the latest when they see these crimes against our children! This may sound

---

297 https://youtu.be/7ooGGoclVuE

very emotional for a non-fiction book, but here at the latest I lose my composure.

A new school booklet for first graders shows on the left in three comics what a child must observe: 1. keep distance, 2. disinfect hands and 3. wear a mask. On the right, they show what children must never do: 1. play together, 2. whisper and 3. sing. The children have to cut out the comics and paste them in the "right" place. This is mental cruelty, indoctrination and, as Prof. Bhakti says, child abuse!

Those who wear a mask out of sheer fear of infection, under the illusion that they are protected, are welcome to do so. But those who feel forced to do so and deprived of their free decision become angry. I also feel anger with masked people when I am out and about without a mask where it would actually be obligatory. *"He's just ignoring it!" is what* some people think. If looks could kill, we would already have more deaths than from a flu virus called Corona. This is how people who would otherwise be patient and friendly are turned against each other." Divide et Impera ".[298]

Another aspect is the uniformity through the masks. Wearing a mask has become a gesture of submission, the new Gessler hat. Accordingly, masks are already unpopular in wide circles. *"muzzle",* or *"face nappy"* do not suggest a joyful masked ball.

It doesn't help that the media would like to manipulate us into finding the whole mockery "chic". The newspaper "FAZ" wanted to push the mask on us as the "new black" of the fashion weeks, but the newspaper "Stern" took the cake when it declared the mask to be the "symbol of freedom". Yes, I know: *"War is peace! Freedom is slavery! Ignorance is strength!"* We already know all this from Orwell's "1984".

Basically, the mask only serves to make the presence of a "danger", i.e. the virus, which is invisible, visible. It is sup-

---

298 Divide and rule. The motto of the Roman Empire

posed to prevent us from returning to our normal lives out of sheer habit, because a "pandemic" is nowhere to be seen. The masks are a constant warning signal to keep us in a state of permanent stress.

The blogger Eric Peters is of the opinion that accepting the compulsion to wear a mask causes psychological changes. The ability to dissent is destroyed, he says, because the subjugation of everyone, similar to making people to be alike in Orwell's "1984", creates the impression that no one would contradict and consequently everyone would agree. Anyone who doubts must therefore be crazy and is questioning their own sanity.

No one will suspect that anyone else doubts the regulations, and this is tantamount to coercing submission. It seems as if everyone submits voluntarily, which creates enormous pressure to conform. The fact that all this was enforced without consent no longer matters at this point.

Should anyone still have doubts, they feel alone and out-numbered, because this is precisely the impression they want.[299]

The evil game could be taken even further: In Switzerland, considerations have been published to pay 2,000 francs to everyone who gets vaccinated, a small part at the time of vaccination, the larger part only when a majority of 60 or 70% has been vaccinated. This is intended to put opponents of vaccination under even more social pressure, because all those who have already been vaccinated are waiting for "their" money. If those who have been vaccinated are allowed to walk around without a mask, those who refuse to be vaccinated would be immediately recognisable by their masks.

A friend said to me: *"Don't write something like that, you'll give them ideas"*. My answer was: *"They have much worse*

299 https://krisenfrei.com/die-neue-partei-kleidung/

ideas, we wouldn't even think of them". Many of the things that were bad "conspiracy theories" a year ago have now come true and are called "new normality".

What is particularly perfidious is that the city of Munich, when enacting the mask requirement, expressly excluded any claims for damages of health that might arise from the forced wearing of the masks by deciding that the use of the masks is *"exclusively at one's own risk"*.[300] They are fully aware of the risk the masks pose to health. First endangering the citizens and then leaving them to pay for the damage. Thank you dear city council!

And what about the legal norm of the "ban on mummery" (except for Muslims)? Or the favourite slogan of left-wing activists *"show your face"*? All forgotten already?

The first step towards liberation will take place when the masks are publicly burned and we can see people, especially children, laughing again – if they haven't forgotten by then.

---

300 https://www.muenchen.de/rathaus/Stadtverwaltung/Referat-fuer-Gesundheit-und-Umwelt/Infektionsschutz/Neuartiges_Coronavirus/Mund-Nasen-Bedeckung.html

Dissociation and imprisonment without parole

That was the verdict for all of us, and the threat continues to hang in the air. That, too, is by design. *"There is no going back"*, the *"new normality"* and *"everyday mask"* are probably chosen Orwellian linguistic creations that suggest that the alleged "exceptional rules" are to be made permanent. It has always been a favourite trick of dictatorships to simply allow a state of exception to continue, thereby circumventing the official abolition of fundamental rights. Many dictatorships have started moderately and then gradually tightened the shackles. By which I do not mean that what is currently happening still falls under "moderate".

The "pandemic", which was not a pandemic, has been over since May 2020, there was no excess mortality, 410,000 doctors and nurses were on reduced hours, the threatened "overload of the health system" never happened,[301] and there was only a laboratory test "pandemic" in the autumn. Nevertheless, a second lockdown has been forced upon us, at any cost, especially livelihoods. All of this is being knowingly ignored by those in power (they're not that stupid) and bodes ill.

Let's pay attention to the words: politics wants to *"draw the reins"*, *for example*. Did we ask to be whipped like horses? What self-important arrogance speaks from such choice of words? Or the graciously granted *"relaxations"*. The term comes from the penal system and shows how the govern-ment sees the people: as delinquents who can be locked away at any time. In October, one could read that Merkel had declared that there must be a "brutal crackdown". This is the language of dictators and tyrants - not of democrats.[302]

---

301 https://www.heise.de/tp/features/Corona-Lockdown-Droht-tatsaechlich-eine-akute-nationale-Gesundheitsnotlage-4942433.html

With the empirical data of the last few months, we can assess the effect of lockdown and distance rules and conclude: *they have brought nothing.* The infection curves have declined similarly in all countries, if you take out the increased test numbers, regardless of whether and when the individual countries introduced compulsory measures. Sweden and Belarus, both without lockdown or mandatory masking, even came through the crisis better than countries with strict measures like France, Italy or Spain.[303]

In three countries with lockdowns, Corona mortality rates on 8 November 2020 were: 0.00014% (Germany), 0.00036% (Austria) and 0.00061% (Switzerland). In three countries without lockdowns it was even lower: in Sweden less than half of Germany (0.00006%), in Belarus less than a third (0.00004%) and in Japan almost zero.[304]

Incidentally, in December 2020, there were only 13 corona patients in Swedish intensive care units.[305]

Prof. Gunnar Jeschke from ETH Zurich examined statistics from the Blavatnik School of Government at Oxford University. There it was clearly shown that "social distancing" could not reduce the mortality rate in any country.[306]

The same conclusion was reached in an NBER study[307] of 25 US states and 23 countries.[308] Other studies also confirm that

302 https://www.focus.de/politik/deutschland/die-verschiedenen-vorschlaege-der-minister-ampel-andere-kriterien-einheitsregeln-um-diese-vorschlaege-gehts-bei-merkels-corona-gipfel_id_12480484.html
303 https://deutsch.rt.com/inland/109491-gesundheitsministerium-zu-Covid-19-keine-belege-fuer-positive-wirkung-lockdown/
304 https://deutsch.rt.com/inland/109155-laut-statistik-lander-mit-lockdown/
305 https://www.achgut.com/artikel/fundstueck_schweden_nur_still_13_corona_sick_in_intensive_care_units
306 Source: https://de.sputniknews.com/politik/20200627327426019-panik-politik-katastrophen-journalismus-corona-krise/
307 National Bureau for Economic Research
308 https://www.nber.org/papers/w27719.pdf

lockdowns and mandatory masks have failed to reduce infection and death rates.[309]

Lockdown and mandatory masking have been shown to be a scientific error, with no benefit but all the more harm. The government continues under the motto: *"The lockdown didn't bring the numbers down, so let's do more of it to bring the numbers down."* Logic has never been part of propaganda. The measures are being tightened for purely political reasons, namely as blackmail to get vaccination through. But would vaccination be the solution, medically speaking?

We need to take a closer look.

---

309 https://www.aier.org/article/lockdowns-and-mask-mandates-do-not-lead-to-reduced-Covid-transmission-rates-or-deaths-new-study-suggests/

Vaccination - curse or blessing?

Since their discovery, vaccinations have been celebrated as medicine's great victory over infectious diseases. What is not discussed, however, is the fact that the history of vaccinations has always been accompanied by failures and vaccine damage that far dwarf the alleged benefits.

When it became known in London in 1714 that the pus of smallpox patients was being transferred to healthy people in Turkey to protect them from smallpox, many doctors in Europe began experimenting with the new method. The most famous was Edward Jenner (1749 - 1823), who did not abandon the idea despite tragic failures.[310] On his deathbed, he is reported to have said, *"I don't know whether I haven't made a terrible mistake and created something monstrous."* Not a good start, but vaccination became popular and was extended to other diseases.

I could present you with pages and pages of examples from history to today and studies showing that:

- Vaccination **does not** prevent the disease against which it was used. Often enough, epidemics were only triggered by vaccination campaigns.

- Vaccinated people are often more infectious than non-vaccinated people, even if they do not fall ill themselves.

- The decline in infectious diseases in the last century is **not due** to vaccinations, but to improvements in living standards such as hygiene, clean drinking

---

310 His first victim was his ten-month-old son, who was developmentally retarded by Jenner's experiment and lived as an imbecile, as they said at the time, until he died at 21. A 5-year-old boy also died after vaccination, and a pregnant woman miscarried. The foetus was covered with smallpox blisters.

water, nutrition and medical care. Statistics show that many diseases disappeared *before vaccines* were available.[311]

- *All* vaccinations have side effects, which vary in severity depending on the vaccine. These are sometimes worse than the disease (not) being prevented. Of course, vaccine damage is statistically distributed, so that most get away with no or few symptoms. But the fate is all the worse for those who are affected.

I can prove all this with sources, but this would go far beyond the scope of this book. I therefore refer you to sites on the internet that are critical of vaccination.[312] I recommend the site of Robert F. Kennedy Jr.[313] The nephew of the assassinated US President John F. Kennedy has been fighting for the rights of vaccine victims, especially children, for 30 years and has provided a wealth of information. He spoke at the big anti-Corona demo in Berlin on 29.8.2020,[314] but this was kept quiet in the media.

Something fundamental about vaccination is often over-looked: Pathogens usually find their way via the mouth/nasal mucous membranes or via the stomach or intestines, rarely via the skin. Nature has "built in" special protective mechan-isms everywhere, for example in the mucous membranes, where a rapid reaction of the immune system and swelling with lymph is prepared. The pathogens are expected there, so to speak. If they are injected under the skin, into the muscle or directly into the blood, this is not the natural way. The immune reaction starts more slowly, the pathogen has

---

311 https://telegra.ph/Der-Impf-Mythos-Die-Statistiken-08-16
312 e.g.: http://vactruth.com/ http://www.impfkritik.de/ https://impfen-nein-danke.de/ as well as various groups on telegram, bitchute etc.
313 http://childrenshealthdefense.org/
314 https://youtu.be/GHBzjfS3PdU

the surprise advantage. If you do this with infants, whose immune system has yet to develop, the risk is even greater.

But that's not all, the danger can be increased even more: Instead of one foreign substance, two or three, up to six different foreign substances can be given at the same time. For a doctor this is a practical solution. You could have several vaccinations in one "shot". But the immune system faces a big problem that does not exist in nature. It is actually logical that many things can get out of hand.

By the way, it turned out that since 2018 there are no more pure measles vaccines in the EU. Children who now have to be vaccinated for school or day care nurseries get the MMR triple vaccination, i.e. mumps and rubella, on top. If desired, even with an extra bonus: Chickenpox.[315]

---

315 https://www.rki.de/SharedDocs/FAQ/Impfen/MMR/
    FAQ_Uebersicht_MSG.html

Comparison study vaccinated – unvaccinated

The Center for Disease Control CDC, the top US disease agency, has the largest database on vaccinations in the US.[316] In 1999, a staff member, Thomas Verstraeten, was commissioned to conduct an internal meta-study comparing fully vaccinated children with unvaccinated children. The results were so explosive that the study was not published in a "*post-processed* (cleaned) *version*" until four years later.

The CDC blocked public access to the database and has since blocked all requests from scientists who want to do similar comparative studies. Only the four largest vaccine manufacturers in the USA[317] were given the results. Nevertheless, it was possible to obtain the data of the original study, and they are worrying.[318]

Before looking at the results, it is important to mention that there has been a huge increase in chronic diseases among children and adolescents over the last thirty years, especially in the USA, but also in Europe. During the same period, the number of vaccinations increased: In the early 1980s, children in the USA had received 12 vaccinations by the age of 14 with the triple vaccines DPT (diphtheria, pertussis, tetanus) and MMR (measles, mumps, rubella), plus polio. Vaccinations started at the age of two months. Today, children receive 54 vaccinations with 70 different vaccines such as hepatitis, influenza, meningitis, HPV, Rotavirus and many more. It starts the day after birth, continues in the 2nd, 4th, 6th, 7th, 12th, 15th, 18th month, then once a year until the 18th birthday. [319]

---

316 Vaccine Safety Datalink (VSD)
317 Pfizer, Merck, GlaxoSmithKline and Sanofi
318 https://childrenshealthdefense.org/child-health-topics/exposing-truth/
   fully-vaccinated-vs-unvaccinated/
319 https://childrenshealthdefense.org/child-health-topics/known-culprit/
   vaccines-culprit/cdc-recommended-vaccine-schedule-1986-vs-2019/

That there is a connection between the many vaccinations and the increase in chronic diseases, not just a coincidence, has been suspected for some time. The concealed CDC study clearly proves this connection. The evaluation of the statistics revealed the following picture: [320]

- Hepatitis B vaccination in new born baby males leads later to a threefold risk of developing autism

- Flu vaccination increases the risk of non-flu infections 4.4-fold

- DTP vaccination increases infant mortality 3.9-fold in boys and 10-fold in girls

- The risk of neurological developmental disorders increases[321] 3.7-fold with vaccination, and 6.6-fold in vaccinated premature babies

- Among 6 to12 year olds, vaccinated children were found to have: 3.1x more allergies, 4.2x more ADHD,[322] 4.2x more autism, 2.9x more eczema, 5.2x more learning disorders and 30x more hay fever.

- HPV vaccination[323] increases the risk of asthma 8-fold

- Hepatitis B vaccination in the first six months leads to premature puberty twice as often later on

- Children vaccinated with MMR are 2.5 times more likely to develop ulcerative colitis (inflammation of the colon) and 3 times more likely to develop Crohn's disease (chronic inflammatory bowel disease).

- H1N1 flu vaccination leads to miscarriages in pregnant women 7.7 times more often in the following

---

320 https://childrenshealthdefense.org/wp-content/uploads/Vaxxed-Unvaxxed-Full-Presentation-Parts-I-VII.pdf
321 This refers to the mandatory vaccinations according to the vaccination schedule
322 Attention deficit disorder with hyperactivity
323 HPV=Human Papillomaviruses

four weeks if the woman had also been vaccinated with the same vaccine in the previous year.

These data show that vaccination risks are much greater than officially admitted. They also confirm the long-suspected link between vaccinations in young children (especially DTP and MMR) and autism risk (4.2 times more common than in the unvaccinated). Despite knowing its own data, the CDC denied this connection in public for years – an outright lie. Only the lawsuit of a child protection organisation[324] at a US federal court forced the CDC to admit that there was no scientific proof, no study, that autism had *nothing* to do with vaccination. [325]

324 Informed Consent Action Network von Del Bigtree
https://www.icandecide.org/
325 https://www.icandecide.org/wp-content/uploads/2019/12/001-COMPLAINT-against-Centers-for-Disease-Control-and-Prevention.pdf

Sudden infant death syndrome

SIDS is the abbreviation for "Sudden Infant Death Syndrome". The frightening phenomenon of infants suddenly being found dead in their cots with no apparent cause or illness has given rise to much speculation. It is the second most common cause of death in children between one and twelve months. American and Australian studies show that about half of the SIDS children had been vaccinated within four weeks before their death. The shorter the interval between vaccination, the more deaths occurred.

This is consistent with other observations, according to which one third of the vaccinated children develop mild to severe symptoms of illness, such as fever, vomiting, seizures or listlessness, during the same period. This mostly concerns the DPT triple vaccination, but can also occur with other vaccinations.

Now, US statistical death data from early March to mid-April 2020 showed a sharp decline in infant deaths. Normally, about 700 infants die per week in the US, but during that period there were only 500, almost 30% fewer. Why? Research by doctors revealed that the WHO and CDC reported a sharp drop in childhood vaccinations starting in March, due to closed doctors' offices or supply problems with vaccines during the lockdown.[326] This is another indication of the danger of vaccinations, especially for young children.

---

326 https://needtoknow.news/2020/07/infant-deaths-decrease-30-during-lockdown-coinciding-with-sharp-drop-in-vaccinations/
https://healthchoice.org/lessons-from-the-lockdown/

The planned Corona vaccination

The CDC meta-study on vaccine damage is just one of many that have been produced in recent decades. They all relate to conventional vaccinations. So far, there are three ways to induce the immune system to produce antibodies or, less frequently, specific T cells:

- Vaccination with the live but attenuated antigens
- Vaccination with inactivated (dead) antigens
- Vaccination with certain proteins that are typical for the pathogen

The production of such vaccines is complex and therefore relatively expensive. In the case of viruses, such as influenza, they are grown, extracted and purified in chicken eggs or other cell cultures. In the case of some vaccines, tissue from aborted human foetuses is used in the production process. All active vaccines against hepatitis A, rubella and chickenpox available in the EU are produced with cell lines from aborted children. Japan has developed alternative, neutral vaccines, but these are not licensed in the EU.[327]

But despite intensive research, there are no vaccines against many viruses. The virologist Prof. Hendrik Streeck points out that there has not yet been a vaccine against most viruses, neither for HIV, nor for dengue, malaria, tuberculosis or hepatitis C. And, I might add, not even against SARS-CoV-1, although they had 17 years to develop one.[328]

And with SARS-CoV-2, this is supposed to be achieved in eight months? Only if one follows the brazen demand of Prof.

---

327 https://aerzte-fuer-das-leben.de/fachinformationen/
schwangerschaftsabbruch-abtreibung/impfstoffe-und-abtreibung/
#zusammenfassung
328 https://www.tichyseinblick.de/kolumnen/aus-aller-welt/corona-in-
suedostasien-aehnliche-methoden-noch-fatalere-oekonomische-folgen/

Drosten, who calls for the safety regulations for vaccines to be suspended.[329] A scientist who simply wants to ignore scientific safety rules is not a scientist, but a lobbyist for foreign interests.

The approval of new vaccines takes about ten years, because regulated procedures have to be followed, each of which takes time. This includes laboratory experiments that prove an immune reaction in vitro (in the laboratory), followed by animal experiments and toxicological studies, until human trials in various phases are approved, which are also accompanied by pharmacological, toxicological and safety studies. Because of possible long-term effects, the test persons must be observed for years in order to be able to recognise or exclude such effects.

This cannot be shortened even if you pump a lot of money into the industry. Even with a lot of money, you can't reduce a pregnancy to a few months. It took five years to develop a vaccine against Ebola, the shortest time so far; tuberculosis took 13 years, rotavirus 15 years and chickenpox 28 years.

But even if everything should go well, it is not yet said that there really is protection against infection. Because the vaccine manufacturers only have to prove that antibodies are produced by the vaccination. Whether these antibodies prevent the disease to be fought – that does not need to be proven.[330]

Here is another argument against vaccination: Vaccination is supposed to protect by stimulating the formation of antibodies. Even if this succeeds without major damage, it is still questionable whether or to what extent they protect. The virologists are still arguing about whether the detection of

329 https://www.handelsblatt.com/politik/international/sars-impfstoffe-virologe-drosten-wir-muessen-regularien-fuer-impfstoffe-ausser-kraft-setzen/25657800.html?ticket=ST-894597-tTNCxszw6CbNO2CvDwlM-ap4
330 https://youtu.be/iRYsN9IL1As

antibodies, for example with antibody tests, means that one is also immune. Perhaps they should first clarify this question before conducting vaccination experiments with us. But that would be bad for business.

The latest from the gene lab: RNA / DNA vaccinations

Nevertheless, the manufacturers claim that they will soon be able to launch vaccines on the market that are "proven and safe". They are relying on a new method that has never been tested on humans: mRNA vaccination,[331] which was developed at MIT in 2016.[332] In this process, a protein of the coronavirus, which is typical for the "spikes", the little arms of the virus, is to be produced in the body itself. The mRNA is introduced into the cell, where it causes the ribosomes (cell corpuscles) to produce the protein. This then migrates out of the cell to the membrane, where it is recognised as hostile by T cells. These in turn attack the cell, destroy it and produce antibodies to be prepared when the real coronavirus comes along one day. So much for the theory in a nutshell.

The mRNA is normally a messenger that tells the ribosomes of the cell which proteins the body needs for its growth and metabolism. It copies the genetic information, i.e. the blueprint of the proteins, from the DNA in the cell nucleus. The vaccination therefore introduces a false blueprint into the cell so that it has to produce the antigens itself, which then trigger the immune reaction.

This is very practical, especially for the vaccine manufacturers, because the complex protein synthesis is simply "outsourced" from the factory to the body of the vaccinated person. The previous cultivation of vaccines in chicken eggs,

---

331 "m" stands for messenger
332 https://news.mit.edu/2016/programmable-rna-vaccines-0704

bacteria or cell lines is costly, whereas mRNA vaccines can be produced much cheaper and faster.[333]

That would all be wonderful if it worked in practice and, above all, did no harm. The two main problems are that the procedure is so new that, apart from a few animal experiments, there is still no experience with it, and that, because of the "rush", many safety tests will be omitted.

Instead, "exposure studies" are proposed. Vaccinated people are deliberately exposed to the infection in order to test whether the protection works. This would shorten the years-long phase II and III studies.[334] Measures such as exposure studies in humans have so far been classified as ethically questionable. But here too, thanks to Corona, the criteria are simply reformulated and the ethics are adapted to the needs of the pharmaceutical industry.[335] Exposure studies are therefore ethically questionable because at this stage the negative consequences are not yet foreseeable. With the Corona vaccination, the exposure studies are done "live", i.e. on the population, which is unaware of them and trusts the regulations that are currently being suspended.

The WHO launched the *Access to COVID-19 Tools (ACT) Accelerator* campaign in April 2020, which is working to shorten vaccine development. The Gates Foundation and GAVI are among the organisations involved. We will come across these names later.[336]

It is also problematic that the genetic events of the cells are interfered with. This is because the same method, using mRNA, pDNA[337] or viral vector vaccine,[338] is used in genetic engineering to change the genetic material. It is a paradox:

333 https://www.pharmazeutische-zeitung.de/issue-212018/vaccinate-with-genes/
334 https://de.wikipedia.org/wiki/SARS-CoV-2-Impfstoff#cite_ref-Shah_113-1
335 https://science.sciencemag.org/content/368/6493/832
336 https://www.who.int/initiatives/act-accelerator
337 pDNA (plasmid DNA) enters the cell nucleus and alters the genome

people are fighting against meat and soya from genetically modified production, but are calling for a vaccination in which they themselves could be genetically modified!

"No," say the manufacturers, *"only pDNA can do that, mRNA does not penetrate the cell nucleus."* Oh yeah? Are you sure? There are indeed pDNA vaccination projects for SARS-CoV-2.[339] And why should we believe an industry that for decades has suppressed all studies that provide evidence of countless vaccine harms around the world? Who knowingly accepts the suffering and death of their clients in order to pay dividends?

No, because who knows what is really in the syringes afterwards, mRNA, pDNA or whatever else, and what it does to us. Maybe we will be sterilised, which would solve the problem of overpopulation in the medium term. This is not a fantasy, but has already been practised in Africa and India, by the "humanitarian" Gates Foundation. I will come back to this later.

But we need not be afraid of walking around as a "genetically modified organism" (GMO). In 2001, the EU wisely ensured that the term can be applied to all living beings – except humans. So, we can rest assured: even if we are genetically modified, we do not fall under the GMO directives. After all.[340]

Why not vaccinate with attenuated or dead viruses as before? Is it because no complete SARS-CoV2 isolate has ever been found and propagated?

---

338 A vector is a genetically modified virus (usually adenoviruses from monkey kidneys) that is no longer infectious but carries other substances into the cell, where the same programme then runs as with mRNA or pDNA. All three methods work similarly.

339 https://de.wikipedia.org/wiki/SARS-CoV-2-Impfstoff

340 Directive 2001/18/EC of the European Parliament and of the Council of 12 March 2001 (Release Directive)https://www.bfr.bund.de/de/a-z_index/gentechnisch_veraenderte_organismen_gvo_-4749.html

Risk assessment

Genetic vaccinations are highly interesting for research and industry; they promise a brave new world with good earning opportunities. Worldwide vaccination programmes require worldwide pandemics. But if there are no pandemics, then they are made. And if they turn out (fortunately) to be just another variant of the flu, then the mass psychology of the media makers ensures that everyone believes in them anyway. According to the motto of the US-led industry: *"If you can't make it, fake it.*

But even enthusiastic genetic researchers realise that in reality it is not so simple with genetic vaccinations. We do not know how toxic many of the individual substances are. Moreover, it is not clear what the immune response looks like; it can be excessive (allergy) and possibly directed against the body's own cells (autoimmune diseases).[341]

Vaccination reactions as with conventional vaccinations have been observed. It is unclear how the antigens artificially produced by the vaccination are distributed in the body (whether they can still be stopped) and how toxic they are. [342]

RNA vaccination in particular has shown in animal experiments that it can trigger excessive immune reactions up to anaphylactic shock.[343] The phenomenon is known, it is called "cytokine storm".[344]

---

341 https://www.trillium.de/zeitschriften/trillium-immunologie/archiv/ausgaben-2019/heft-32019/aus-der-grundlagenforschung/design-und-funktionsweise-von-mrna-basierten-impfstoffen-zum-schutz-vor-infektionskrankheiten.html

342 https://www.pharmazeutische-zeitung.de/issue-212018/vaccinate-with-genes/

343 https://en.wikipedia.org/wiki/RNA_vaccine

344 https://www.aerzteblatt.de/archiv/60056/Lebensbedrohlicher-Zytokinsturm

Fine, say the manufacturers, let's just give it a try. Currently (November 2020) there are about 170 Corona vaccine projects and 30 are already in phase III testing. In Russia, the state Gamaleya Centre has already finished its vaccine *"Sputnik V"* and is selling it all over the world, even before the market launch in early 2021. According to the WHO, there are 167 vaccines in development worldwide.[345] The vaccine project of the British manufacturer *AstraZeneca* in cooperation with Oxford University is hotly debated. Despite strong side effects in test phase II, such as headaches, high fever, muscle pain, up to the loss of white blood cells, test phase III was recently released. In Brazil, two volunteers aged 28 and 33 from the AstraZeneca and Chinese Corona-vac vaccine trials died. The latter trial was subsequently halted by the authorities for the time being.[346]

The EU Commission ordered 400 million vaccine doses from AstraZeneca for 1 billion euros at the end of August. At the same time, it guaranteed the company exemption from any liability. [347]

You order 400,000,000 vaccines that have not yet been tested, let alone approved. Taxpayers' money for risks that citizens have to pay for, both health-wise and financially. Respect for so much chutzpah!

In order to be able to vaccinate soon, the regulatory authorities are being put under pressure. The chairman of the German Drug Commission, Wolf-Dieter Ludwig, sits on the EMA [348] and said that Health Minister Spahn has put pressure on the EMA to speed up the approval.[349] Ludwig

---

345 https://de.wikipedia.org/wiki/SARS-CoV-2-Impfstoff approx. 20 are in phase I, II or III.   Status August 2020

346 https://deutsch.rt.com/international/109010-nach-tod-eines-freiwilligen-brasilien-stellt-test-eines-chinesischen-Covid-19-vakzins-ein/

347 https://www.anti-spiegel.ru/2020/Covid-19-was-der-spiegel-ueber-die-bestellung-von-impfstoffen-durch-die-eu-kommission-verschweigt/

348 European Medicines Agency, responsible for vaccine authorisation

349 https://de.rt.com/inland/110813-chef-arzeimittel-kommision-spahn-hat/

went on to say that the vaccine had not been sufficiently tested, that nothing was known about its long-term effect and that he would not be vaccinated with it.

Someone who is extremely competent in the field of vaccines is the immunologist and toxicologist Prof. Dr. Stefan Hockerz.[350] In a very interesting podcast[351] he explains the problems of mRNA vaccines in general and the AstraZeneca trials in particular. I briefly summarise the most important points from the podcast:

- The vaccination study is to be carried out with 30,000 test volunteers, the usual number is up to 200,000; 500 have participated so far.

- Among the 500, there were already two participants who had transverse myelitis, an inflammation of the spinal cord similar to multiple sclerosis, an immune reaction directed against the spinal cord.

- Only selected healthy people take part in these studies. To what extent can this be transferred to older, weakened people, the main target group for vaccination?

- Experience shows that side effects are to be expected in about 5% of all vaccinations, and about 0.1% of those vaccinated die.

- This means that if 80 million Germans were vaccinated, 4 million would suffer from mild or severe side effects. One would have to reckon with 80,000 deaths. That would be a medium-sized city wiped out to prevent "9,000 coronavirus deaths", 95% of whom would have died even without the virus.

---

350 http://www.tpi-consult.de/index.php?site=content&contentid=29
351 https://youtu.be/RJue8CKkD8M
   Should youtube censor again, you can find it at http://bitchute.com/

- There are no toxicological studies for mRNA vaccines yet.

- Coronaviruses trigger two types of antibodies: neutralising and binding. The latter amplify the infection, but it is not known to what degree.

- "Challenge experiments" are prescribed for vaccination studies: You vaccinate half of the test subjects and then infect all of them. This was done in an animal experiment with 40 ferrets (20 vaccinated with mRNA, 20 not). The non-vaccinated ones became ill with corona symptoms, the 20 vaccinated ones all died directly after the infections (so-called "paradoxical immune reaction" or cytokine storm).

- It is completely unclear to what extent mRNA alters the germline, i.e. whether the offspring are damaged. There are no studies on this yet.

- Normally, toxicological data must be available before human studies. Prof. Hockerz asked several times at the Paul Ehrlich Institute, which is responsible for the approval of vaccines. Although he knows some of the colleagues there well, he never received any information and suspects that this data is not available at all.

- **Vaccinations make healthy people ill so that a feared disease may be easier to contract. Therefore, a particularly careful assessment must be made between the disease produced (vaccination reaction) and the risks of the actual disease.**

- Vaccination is therefore only indicated in the case of serious and fatal diseases such as smallpox or Ebola. **In the case of Covid19, which is similar to influenza, vaccination is not necessary or appropriate.**

- In 46% of the test persons, there was a drop in white blood cells, i.e. a dampening of the immune defence.

Prof. Hockerz complains that in the Corona vaccination studies, regulations have been sacrificed on the altar of politics. The people are being led to believe things that he would not have thought possible in the worst science fiction films. He calls the planned vaccination **"a mass intentional bodily harm. "**

Regarding the PCR test, he says that every product sold normally has to be CE-certified. The PCR is not certified and for that one normally goes to prison. The government measures are justified with a criminal test that cannot detect a virus or infections. Koch's postulates are not fulfilled either. He calls it an "absurdity" that happens nevertheless. Robert Koch and Paul Ehrlich would turn in their graves if they saw what the institutes named after them are doing today.[352]

The American physician and internist Dr. Carrie Madej said in an interview that this vaccine is different from those that have been produced in rapid processes so far. Safety tests and animal trials have been skipped, so it is not a safe vaccine.

Together with other colleagues, she suspects that the animal tests were skipped because all such vaccine projects have failed in the last 20 years. The test animals initially made a good impression, the antibody level in the blood rose, the T-cell response was improved. But when the vaccinated animals were then exposed to the virus, there were cytokine storms, violent immune reactions. Pneumonia, liver problems and deaths occurred. This is why RNA vaccinations have never been approved.[353]

---

352 Quotes from: https://youtu.be/RJue8CKkD8M
353 https://www.kla.tv/17550

In the meantime, severe vaccine damage has become known with the new corona vaccination.

- A staff member at Bartlett Regional Hospital in Juneau suffered anaphylactic shock shortly after vaccination, with rash on her body and face, shortness of breath and increased heart rate.[354]

- Two staff members at a hospital in Alaska had to be admitted to intensive care just minutes after being vaccinated with the BioNTech vaccine, the New York Times reported.[355]

- A nurse from Chattanooga, Tennesee had herself filmed being vaccinated with the BioNTech vaccine and collapsed on camera. When she felt a little better, she got up to explain that this happens to her often when she is in pain, and fainted again.[356]

- Four study participants from the same manufacturer suffer from facial paralysis, some of them for six months already.[357] This is called "Bell's palsy syndrome", it resembles a stroke when one half of the face hangs down.

- The vaccination trials of an Australian project were terminated after several subjects tested positive for HIV.[358]

- In addition, up to 84% of the BioNTech subjects suffered from side effects such as vaccination site reactions, fatigue, headache, muscle or joint pain, chills

354 https://www.epochtimes.de/gesundheit/alaska-krankenpfleger-nach-corona-impfung-auf-intensivstation-a3405607.html?telegram=1

355 ibid

356 https://reitschuster.de/post/us-krankenschwester-bricht-nach-impfung-zusammen/

357 https://snanews.de/20201216/toxikologe-corona-impfstoff-187459.html

358 https://snanews.de/20201211/impfstoff-hiv-122989.htm

or fever.[359] French epidemiologist Prof. Eric Caume was appalled by the high figure. He said he had never seen so many side effects with a vaccine.[360]

Infertility possible

Dr. Wodarg pointed out to the Corona Committee that not only cytokine storms, i.e. immune overreactions that get out of hand, pose a serious danger, but that mRNA vaccinations can also make women infertile.[361] This is due to the fact that the immune defence is directed towards the "spikes" of the viruses. They contain syncytin, a protein that is responsible for building the placenta at the beginning of pregnancy. If the syncytin is also attacked by the immune system as a result of the vaccination, the placenta will not grow and the woman will no longer be able to have children.

"Under syncitin deficiency, the pregnancy does not go on, and the vaccinated woman can never have a child again, because she is virtually allergised with syncitin by the vaccination. Any syncitin formed in the body is then immediately destroyed by the corona antibodies ".[362]

The British authorities know this because they ordered that this vaccine should not be given to any woman who is pregnant or thinking of becoming pregnant. This is clear from the package insert, which also states that there are no

---

359 https://www.epochtimes.de/gesundheit/biontech-pfizer-bis-zu-84-prozent-nebenwirkungen-gesichtslaehmung-bei-vier-testpersonen-a3401040.html
360 https://uncut-news.ch/franzoesischer-experte-fuer-infektionskrankheiten-warnt-vor-den-gefahren-des-Covid-19-impfstoffs/
361 https://youtu.be/EbSXV7rzxtE from 1:50 h
362 https://www.compact-online.de/corona-impfung-fuehrt-voraussichtlich-zur-unfruchtbarkeit/

studies yet on interactions with other medicines and no findings on whether the vaccination makes people infertile.[363] *In Germany, however, pregnant women are also to be vaccinated.*[364] *All safety standards are completely ignored here!*

Now, the risk of becoming infertile was not communicated to the participants in the test studies, as Dr. Wodarg has researched. This raises the question: is this just sloppiness, or are they aware of the risk? It is irresponsible to allow something like this without having clarified this important point. Or do they want to misuse the Corona vaccination for population control? We may find the answer later, in the chapter on Bill Gates.

The hasty market introduction amounts to the fact that the most important part of the studies, the long-term observation, is done directly "on the object", i.e. on us. This is so obvious that even a TV presenter notices it.

On 20.11.20, Prof. Stephan Becker, head of virology at the University of Marburg, was interviewed on TV "Heute-Journal". He said that after the vaccinations, one wanted to observe very closely what side effects occur. The presenter asked in astonishment whether the vaccination was given first and the side effects registered afterwards.

Prof. Becker replied that this was precisely the purpose of an emergency approval, which should then lead to a normal approval when sufficient safety data is available. The moderator then described the many jubilant reports about the "successes" of the vaccine manufacturers and asked how much of all this was scientifically proven. Prof. Becker hesitated and stuttered around, saying that this was exactly

363 https://assets.publishing.service.gov.uk/government/uploads/system/uploads/attachment_data/file/941452/Information_for_healthcare_professionals.pdf

364 https://www.n-tv.de/politik/Antworten-die-verunsichern-koennten-article22217016.html

what the scientists were still missing a bit, namely the exact results of the studies so far. The authorities will get them, the scientists don't have them yet, but he hopes that they will get them in the future.[365] And we hope that such "scientists" will at some point be held responsible for the consequences of their human experiments.

Assuming that Gates' dream was to vaccinate everyone on the planet, and that the new mRNA vaccines were no more dangerous than the conventional ones, which is optimistic, then according to Prof. Hockerz we have to reckon with 5% side effects, which would be 350 million people affected, about the same as the population of the USA, and with 0.1% vaccination deaths, i.e. 7 million, somewhat less than the population of Switzerland or Austria.

The British government, which wants to start vaccinating as early as December, expects so many side effects that the Medicines and Healthcare products Regulatory Agency (MHRA)[366] has issued a call for tenders for artificial intelligence software to be able to sufficiently document the high number of expected damages.[367] As already said: studies on the object.

In an interview with Radio Munich, Prof. Bhakdi predicted autoimmune reactions, the extent of which no one knows. If that should happen, then God have mercy on the one who allowed it.[368]

RKI head Wieler apparently also expects deaths due to vaccination. He said in front of the camera that people will also die in connection with the vaccination, and then one

365 https://www.zdf.de/nachrichten/heute-journal/problem-nebenwirkungen-100.html
366 Medicine and Healthcare Products Regulatory Agency
367 https://ted.europa.eu/udl?uri=TED:NOTICE:506291-2020:TEXT:EN:HTML&src=0
368 https://www.compact-online.de/westliche-pharmariesen-beantragen-zulassung-fuer-mrna-impfstoff-bhakdi-warnt-vor-katastrophe/

would have to investigate whether the vaccination or another disease was to blame.[369]

In the meantime, the vaccination propaganda has made a small course correction: While all along it was said *"once the vaccination is in, you are all free again"*, now they talk about a *"temporary immunity"* that has to be refreshed again and again – of course through further, regular vaccinations. That, in turn, is good for business.

It seems like déjà vu to me after I came across a text in Johann Wolfgang Goethe's "Faust":

> *"Here was the medicine, the patients died,*
> *and no one asked: Who recovered?*
> *So, we have with hellish latwergen[370]*
> *in these valleys, these mountains*
> *far worse than the plague raged.*
> *I myself have given the poison to thousands:*
> *They withered away, I must experience,*
> *that one praises the insolent murderers."*

---

369 https://clubderklarenworte.de/der-atem-stockt/
370 disease-causing, mercury-containing "plague medicine" on a syrup basis

Dangerous "little helpers"

Doctors judge the "success" of a vaccination by the reaction. The "antibody titres", i.e. the amount of antibodies produced, are measured. If the immune system reacts too weakly, then the dose was too low or an additional stimulus is missing. To create this stimulus, so-called "adjuvants"[371] are added to the vaccine. They have nothing to do with the vaccination, but they provoke the immune system so that it becomes aware of the vaccine. An "appropriate reaction" usually results in reddening of the vaccination site, local pain, possibly fever and other inflammatory symptoms. But this can also get out of hand, because the adjuvants certainly have their share of vaccine side effects. The most dangerous adjuvants are:

- **Thiomersal** contains 50% mercury. This is not only a neurotoxin but also damages the liver, kidneys and other tissues and increases the risk of autism. It is supposed to "preserve" the vaccine.

- **Aluminium** (for example in aluminium hydroxide) damages the brain, has been found in increased numbers in Alzheimer's patients and can trigger muscle inflammation.[372]

There are other controversial adjuvants such as formaldehyde, phenol, polysorbate 80 or squalene,[373] but their individual effects are difficult to prove because they are only ever given in combination with vaccines. Only in the case of

---

371 "Helper", from Latin, in English also called "booster".
372 MMF (macrophagic myofascitis)
373 Is extracted from shark liver. Animal rights activists fear that up to half a million more sharks will be slaughtered if this adjuvant is used for vaccinations worldwide.

mercury and aluminium do we know the individual effects, and they can be severe. It is even suspected that the adjuvants alone could provoke the formation of antibodies without a vaccine.[374] However, to my knowledge, such an experiment has never been carried out.

Business without risk (for the manufacturers)

Now that it is clear that the hastily cobbled-together Covid19 vaccine threatens to be a disaster, the question arises as to who will pay for the expected vaccine damage? In the USA, vaccine manufacturers have been exempted from paying damages in the case of vaccine damage since 1986. The lobby at the CDC, the FDA and in Congress has done a great job.

In Europe we are almost there, thanks to corona panic. A spokesperson for the EU Commission said that everything had already been settled and that compensation clauses had been built into the preliminary contracts in case the manufacturers were sued for damages.[375] The reason given is the time pressure the unfortunate manufacturers are under. Instead of ten years, they only have 12 months to develop the vaccines.[376] Therefore, the EU would have to assume the cost risk.[377]

A great deal for the companies, because the states not only buy the expensive vaccines, they also pay for the damage

374 https://www.impfkritik.de/adjuvans/
375 https://www.berliner-zeitung.de/wirtschaft-verantwortung/corona-impfung-wer-zahlt-fuer-moegliche-schaeden-li.101215
376 https://www.compact-online.de/eu-kommission-pharmaindustrie-fuer-nebenwirkungen-bei-corona-impfung-nicht-haftbar/
377 https://www.berliner-zeitung.de/wirtschaft-verantwortung/corona-impfung-wer-zahlt-fuer-moegliche-schaeden-li.101215

that will be caused by hastily throwing the vaccines onto the market.

Normally, ten years are calculated for the development of a new vaccine so that possible late effects can also be recognised in long-term studies. This is now to be dropped.

The vaccination business is extremely lucrative, because:

- Medicines can only be sold to the sick, vaccinations can also be sold to the healthy (that is to everyone).
- Epidemic warnings in the media can create demand.
- Mostly the states or health organisations pay, not the client.
- Some vaccinations are compulsory in some countries.
- Manufacturers are exempt from liability in the event of damage (in the USA, Europe is almost there).

In the case of Corona, development costs are also generously reimbursed. For this, the EU has allocated almost €16 billion at a donor conference for tests, treatments and vaccines. The EU will still pay for the vaccines.

The vaccine industry can therefore make even more profits than the pharmaceutical industry. The profit margins are said to be similar to those of arms or drug deals. Therefore, vaccinations have gone from a well-intentioned precaution for public health to an embattled business model – lobbying and corruption included.

Dr. Wolfgang Wodarg describes it this way: *"Vaccine development was initially done in state care and solely from public funds.... However, there was a complete paradigm shift when vaccination was deregulated from a burden within the framework of public services to a business idea of commercial enterprises of the pharmaceutical industry.*

For about two generations, the state has only been able to make sure that the industry does not sell us anything harmful. But even that is being made increasingly difficult by a greedy industry whose primary interest is not health but profit, through corrupting influences on regulatory and health authorities, and more and more directly on politics. And since the invention of "pandemic preparedness", vaccine development and marketing has mutated into a global business with the fear of epidemics.

Virologists directly or indirectly dependent on the bio-tech industry have taken on the role of creating fear of hostile pathogens at ever shorter intervals. In this "fight against viruses", the companies are helped by the "war correspondents" in cooperating mainstream media, who stir up the necessary fear and political pressure. They repeatedly create a public mood under the influence of which our governments have been blackmailed – or even encouraged? – to ignore all critical voices and buy in large quantities the quickly cobbled together medicines or vaccines of the pandemic profiteers.

In any case, the commitment of the responsible governments to exempt the vaccine industry from any liability is already completely irresponsible. This virtually invites the neglect of the otherwise so often invoked precautionary principle and turns the vaccine industry into a responsibility-free zone, in which masses of speculators and virological harebrains are already cavorting."[378]

---

378 Source: https://www.rubikon.news/artikel/unter-falscher-flagge-5

The Swine Flu "Pandemic

Pandemics come and go, people forget about them. Yet a lot can be learned from them, especially from the mistakes that were made. That's why the comparison of the 2009 swine flu "pandemic" with Corona is very interesting; in a way, it was a trial run for what is happening today. I don't want to tell you the whole story now, because a good film does that better: The ARTE documentary *"Profiteers of Fear - The Swine Flu Business"* from 2009 is very informative and can still be found on the internet.[379]

You should watch it, today such honest documentaries would be impossible in the mainstream. When you watch the film, you often think it is from today.

In spring 2009, a new influenza virus of the type H1N1 made the news, especially in Mexico. The media declared that a "new epidemic" called "swine flu" was on the way, although the numbers of sick people were no different from other flu seasons. Only, the virus was "new" and "potentially danger-ous". The WHO threatened a possible pandemic in April, but the numbers did not support it. So, the WHO simply changed the definition of a pandemic in order to be able to declare one again. In April 2009, it simply deleted the requirement that there must be "a substantial number of deaths" for a pandemic. It was now enough to find a pathogen in several countries, which is not difficult. In fact, when the swine flu pandemic was declared, there were only a few deaths world-wide.[380]

The declaration of a pandemic was the prerequisite for the worldwide vaccination programme that was now underway.

379https://www.youtube.com/watch?v=ECO4FzFP6Nk
https://invidious.snopyta.org/watch?v=ECO4FzFP6Nk as well as on bitch-ute.com several times via search function, in case it is censored on youtube
380 https://www.arznei-telegramm.de/html/2010_06/1006059_01.html

The newspaper "Arznei-Telegramm" complained that pharmaceutical lobbyists were allowed to influence the guidelines of the WHO in favour of the companies that profit from a pandemic.[381]

What happened next looks familiar: The media made a huge hype about "the new virus" that could wipe out humanity. The RKI warned with increasing numbers of cases: *"Swine flu is spreading ever faster in Germany. According to the RKI, a total of 29,907 cases of the new flu have been registered across Germany so far. "The wave has begun," said the President of the RKI.*

The Federal Institute for Vaccines and Biomedical Medicinal Products (known as the Paul Ehrlich Institute) – marching in lockstep with the Robert Koch Institute – was not above filling out safety declarations for their vaccines to pharmaceutical companies in 2009 and, unsurprisingly, they are doing so again today."[382]

And Mr. Drosten, at that time still a virologist in Bonn (yes, him again), threatened that swine flu had considerably stronger side effects than one could imagine from the worst vaccine.[383] I didn't know that diseases also have *"side effects"* lately, but I don't want to contradict the great expert.

Incidentally, Drosten, who at the time strongly recommended vaccination to all Germans from the vaccine manufacturer GlaxoSmithKline, had received a scientific sponsorship award in 2004 – from GlaxoSmithKline.[384] Coincidences do exist...

In the USA, it was then as now Anthony Fauci who fuelled the panic. The WHO warned that at least two billion people,

381 https://www.arznei-telegramm.de/html/2010_06/1006059_01.html

382 https://peds-ansichten.de/2020/05/christian-drosten-verantwortung-schweinegrippe-sanofi-glaxosmithkline-ehrung/

383 https://peds-ansichten.de/2020/05/christian-drosten-verantwortung-schweinegrippe-sanofi-glaxosmithkline-ehrung/

384 https://www.rubikon.news/artikel/der-sundenbock-4

i.e. one third of the world's population, could be infected with swine flu in the next two years. Unfortunately, how this figure was arrived at remained obscure.

Then as now, Dr. Wolfgang Wodarg, a member of the parliament in 2009 and spokesman for the "Enquete Commission on Ethics and the Law of Modern Medicine", also chairman of the Council of Europe's Health Committee, warned against the whole panic. In the newspaper "Welt" he criticised the WHO for making common cause with the pharmaceutical industry. He also warned that the vaccine was *"unnecessary and perhaps even dangerous"* and said that swine flu was *"more harmless than seasonal flu"*.

However, the fear propaganda continued to be stoked and vaccines came onto the market in a hurry. Germany bought for € 500 million, France for over a billion euros. In total, the manufacturers made $ 7-10 billion from the "pandemic".[385] But it soon came out that the German government had bought 50 million doses of "Pandemrix" (fancy name) from GlaxoSmithKline and 200,000 "Celvapan" from Baxter. Pandemrix contained the adjuvants thiomersal, squalene and polysorbate 80, at least in the European version (at home in the US, the version had no adjuvants). Celvapan had no adjuvants at all and was intended for government, federal officials and the armed forces. This came out, the scandal was big and went through the press.[386] There was talk of a "two-class vaccination", and in the end only 17% of Germans had themselves vaccinated. Worldwide, however, 31 million people were vaccinated with Pandemrix.

But the vaccination had terrible side effects: allergic shocks, convulsions, facial paralysis and, above all, narcolepsy, a disturbance of the sleep-wake rhythm. People suddenly fall asleep, are therefore unable to work and are not allowed to drive. 900 children are affected throughout Europe, the

---

385 According to investment bank JP Morgan
386 e.g. the "Süddeutsche Zeitung" from 19.10.2009

disease is incurable. Especially in Sweden and Norway there were many cases, the government paid compensation (instead of the manufacturers) and the drug was withdrawn. In Germany, the 28.3 million unused vaccine doses worth €239 million were disposed of in the Magdeburg incinerator. Never mind, the pharmaceutical companies had already done their business.

When the WHO then ended the "pandemic" in August 2010, in retrospect it proved to be a storm in a teacup: it had been milder than the flu outbreaks of previous years.[387] In Germany, 252 people had died from the "pandemic". The newspaper "Der Spiegel" reported astonishingly critically in March 2010 under the title "Chronicle of a Hysteria".[388]

Nothing but expenses? Yes, it has − the victims of vaccinations, most of them children and adolescents. The WHO will continue in 2020 as it did then, as will the RKI and the PEI. Christian Drosten, who was completely wrong with his prognoses on the course of the swine flu, becomes an advisor to the federal government, and Dr. Wodarg, who assessed the situation correctly, is ignored and slandered as a "corona denier".

That's why I believe: Swine flu was a staging and a test, a precursor to the Corona plot. History repeats itself, especially when no lessons are learned.

---

387 https://de.wikipedia.org/wiki/Pandemie_H1N1_2009/10
388 Well worth reading: https://www.spiegel.de/spiegel/a-682149.html

Alternative therapy and prophylaxis

Covid19, like all viral diseases, is an inflammation, and the immune system plays the key role. Instead of fighting the virus as such, for example with antivirals, one can also strengthen the immune system to such an extent that it can better cope with infections itself, both before and during an illness. I would like to point out and explain a few interesting approaches here.

Plasma therapy

Plasma therapy[389] is a variant of "passive vaccination". One does not wait until the body produces antibodies against the virus, but gives such antibodies directly into the blood. With passive vaccination, the antibodies are produced synthetically. Such projects are already underway worldwide.[390] Plasma therapy uses the purified blood plasma[391] of people who have survived the disease and donate their blood.

The procedure has been used successfully in other diseases, such as corona infections like SARS and MERS. Several studies are also underway for Covid19, with Russia and China reporting good results. Moscow's mayor, Sergei Sobyanin, said that half of those who needed intensive treatment had recovered with this therapy.[392] But in the West,

---

389 Discovered by Emil von Behring at the end of the 19th century.
390 https://de.wikipedia.org/wiki/SARS-CoV-2-
   Impfstoff#Passive_Immunisierung
391 The liquid part of the blood without the blood cells
392 https://de.sputniknews.com/panorama/20200615327379547-russland-
   moskau-corona-infizierte-blutplasma-transfusion/

the success is controversial among doctors.[393] They prefer to wait for the vaccination.

In Mantua in Lombardy, a doctor had apparently been able to prevent further deaths using this method. The media censored the report and the government had intimidated him with the police so that he would not pursue it.

US President Trump, on the other hand, swears by the method and had it applied to himself when he was infected in October 2020.

Vitamin D

It is known that vitamin D plays an important role in calcium metabolism and is necessary for bone formation. Less well known, however, is its immune-stimulating function: vitamin D activates the T-cells, promotes the formation of antibodies and animates the mucous membranes of the respiratory tract to produce "antimicrobial peptides", which are something like the body's own antibiotics that protect the lungs from infections.[394]

In the meantime, official bodies are also opening up to consider the therapeutic function of vitamin D, unfortunately not here, but in France. The "Académie Nationale de Médecine" announced in a press release of 22 May 2020 that a clear connection between the vitamin D level in the blood and mortality from corona had been established. They are now looking into the possibility of improving the condition

---

393https://www.dw.com/de/hilft-die-plasma-therapie-wirklich-bei-Covid-19/a-54676888
https://www.apotheken-umschau.de/Coronavirus/Dank-Spenden-Plasmatherapie-gegen-COVID-19-558589.html
394 https://dr-kersten.com/corona-virus-praevention-und-therapie-durch-vitamin-d

of patients through vitamin D administration.[395] The Academy recommends testing all senior citizens over 60 and treating those suffering from vitamin D deficiency with high doses of 50,000 - 100,000 units of vitamin D.[396]

Other studies found that 80% of corona patients were vitamin D deficient.[397] A study in French nursing homes found an 89% reduction in Covid19 mortality, and in a Spanish study it was as high as 96%.[398]

Vitamin D is produced by the body itself in the skin when exposed to sunlight. People in areas with a lot of sun have developed dark skin to protect themselves from too much radiation. However, if they live in areas with little sun, i.e. in central and northern Europe, they suffer from chronic vitamin D deficiency, especially in winter. But even fair-skinned Europeans are usually undersupplied, since the modern way of life no longer takes place in the fields and meadows, but indoors.

It has long been suspected that there is a link between lack of sunshine in winter and the rising cases of flu with higher mortality rates. Studies have shown that most people in central and northern Europe have low levels of vitamin D in their blood.[399] This is increasingly true of dark-skinned immigrants. You can improve this to some extent by eating fish, but vitamin D should still be taken as a food supplement.[400] But not as a permanent solution. Anything that the body produces itself can be supplemented in case of

---

395 http://www.academie-medecine.fr/communique-de-lacademie-nationale-de-medecine-vitamine-d-et-Covid-19/
396 https://www.heise.de/tp/features/Covid-19-und-Vitamin-D-4787490.html
397 https://www.cosmopolitan.de/neue-erkenntnis-80-prozent-der-corona-patienten-hatten-vitamin-d-mangel-101086.html
398 https://swprs.org/wunder-von-elgg-vitamin-d/
399 Under 30ng/ml
400 https://dr-kersten.com/corona-virus-praevention-und-therapie-durch-vitamin-d

deficiency. If you do this for too long, the body gets used to the "supply" and therefore reduces its own production.

"With the strict curfews in Italy and Spain, the situation has been exacerbated. People have only been allowed to leave their homes for a short time, if at all. Inside the flats, however, the sun does not shine, and so the curfews have led to a widespread vitamin D deficiency. This has deprived the body's own defences of their weapons, and if there has been any excess mortality at all, it is probably due to this. We also need vitamin D to defend ourselves against normal flu and other types of virus. Without it, we are almost defence-less against the attacks.

Yes, people should be protected, but this has had exactly the opposite effect, including on us."[401]

Now, vitamin D is not a specific medicine against Covid19 , nor is vitamin C or the trace elements zinc, magnesium and selenium, which are also often deficient. But these sub-stances help the immune system to cope better with an infection, whether Covid, flu or whatever.

There has never been a cure for viral infections comparable to antibiotics for bacterial infections.

Ultimately, the immune system has to cope with the disease, medical assistance is necessary in severe cases, but only to alleviate and prevent complications. Only the body itself can heal. Vitamins and trace elements support it in both therapy and prophylaxis. Everyone is responsible for the condition of their own body and should give it what it needs to keep its immune system fit.

---

401 https://www.anderweltonline.com/klartext/klartext-20202/
corona-shows-who-takes-migrants-from-africa-to-europe-puts-them-in-life-
threatening/

CDS

The following method is hotly contested, especially its opponents are very active with warnings and opposition. We will see why. On the other hand, it holds great potential and should therefore be discussed objectively. It is chlorine dioxide, ClO_2, taken in very low concentration with water. But let us start from the beginning.

Chlorine dioxide was discovered by chance. The story could be from a movie: In 1998, an American businessman and gold prospector named Jim Humble was travelling with his workers in the jungles of Guyana. Far from any civilisation, they were stuck in the constant rain and his men fell ill with malaria. The medicines were soon used up, the roads impassable, no supplies possible. When the sick had a fever of over 40° C, Humble decided to take a desperate step. He still had a remedy to disinfect drinking water and gave his team five drops each with water to take. After a short time, the men were fit again.

Humble then also fell ill, but cured himself with the same method. Back home, he continued his research and developed MMS[402], which is "activated" (mixed) with citric acid and taken diluted. Humble wrote a book about it and has since had many fans all over the world who swear by the remedy.

Chemically, MMS is sodium chlorite ($NaClO_2$), not to be confused with sodium chloride ($NaCl$ = table salt). When mixed with acid, chlorine dioxide ClO_2, the actual agent, is formed. This is a gas, which dissolves completely in water. This solution is taken in small amounts. The dosage had to be taken gradually, as overdoses could lead to side effects such as nausea, diarrhoea or vomiting.

---

402 "Miracle Mineral Supplement"

The German biophysicist Andreas Kalcker succeeded in eliminating the side effects, even at high doses, through a further development. He replaced the citric acid with hydrochloric acid, which produces common salt as a residual product of the reaction, and called the solution CDS.[403] It contains 0.3% chlorine dioxide gas, which, unlike MMS (which was taken directly but activated, in dilution) is dissolved in water by diffusion. It is diluted 1:100 before ingestion.

Since MMS and later CDS have been used, doctors, authorities and pharmacists have been up in arms against the remedy with the argument that it is a corrosive bleaching agent. This is true, but it depends on the concentration and the type of application. For bleaching paper, it is enriched with methanol and a concentration 60,000 times higher than CDS is used. Most household cleaners or swimming pool chlorinators contain completely different chlorine compounds[404] than CDS, so they are completely different substances. Nevertheless, critics lump them together – ignorance or intention?

In toxicology, one must differentiate between 1. quantity 2. concentration and 3. type and place of administration. The fact that quantity can turn a remedy into a poison has been known since Paracelsus. Would you like to have nitroglycerin as a medicine? No problem, it is given for heart diseases. Or rat poison? Works as an anticoagulant under the name "Marcumar". Many poisons are used in homeopathy – but highly diluted.

Chlorine dioxide as a gas is corrosive to the mucous membranes, and if inhaled for a long time it is also toxic. If you make it yourself from sodium chlorite and acid, you must not inhale the vapours. However, there are methods to prevent the vapours from escaping. Under no circumstances

---

403 Chlorine Dioxide Solution
404 Sodium hypochlorite, sodium dichloroisocyanurate, etc.

should sodium chlorite (MMS) be used undiluted, as this would actually corrode the mucous membranes.

CDS, on the other hand, is chlorine dioxide dissolved in water in a low concentration of 0.3% and is diluted to 0.003% before ingestion. This concentration is non-toxic and has no side effects even at ten times the dose. There has also been no known case of death from chlorine dioxide poisoning *after ingestion* in the medical literature for 100 years, no damage to pregnant women or unborn children and no carcinogenic effect.

The cases cited by opponents all relate to poisoning *when inhaled* at high concentrations, e.g. in animal experiments, or to the ingestion of the precursor MMS at too high a concentration. Five cases of severe poisoning with MMS have been documented, including three failed suicide attempts with hundreds of times the amount originally recommended. Kalcker ironically recommends that if one wants to kill oneself, one should better choose another substance.[405]

The critics also do not differentiate between MMS and CDS, lumping the two together. In addition, they argue that the effect is *"not scientifically proven"*. How could it be, when so far no pharmaceutical company and no university has been willing to conduct studies on it? But hundreds of well-documented cases are not accepted, it is only *"anecdotal"*.

Chlorine dioxide is an excellent agent against bacteria and viruses. That is why it is officially used in the treatment of drinking water.[406] It is also used for mineral water bottles. Blood bags are disinfected with chlorine dioxide to kill HIV, among other things.[407] It is also used as standard in dental

---

405 Lin JL, Lim PS. 1993.:
   "Acute sodium chlorite poisoning associated with renal failure"
   at: https://andreaskalcker.com/de/toxizitaet/
406 https://de.wikipedia.org/wiki/Chlordioxid
407 https://www.ncbi.nlm.nih.gov/pmc/articles/PMC7158349/

practices, so it cannot be that dangerous. It is quickly broken down in the body.

CDS is an oxidant, i.e. it supplies oxygen for biochemical processes, which is also the basis of its virus-killing effect. In addition, it reduces acidosis (over-acidification) of the blood, which is caused by deficiency respiration and too high a CO_2 concentration. It inhibits viral activity, which is stronger in an acidic environment.[408] Kalcker explains the exact process here[409] and in a video.[410] In this video, Kalcker also gives a possible explanation why children rarely get Corona.

Is CDS now illegal? No, the product is approved, but only for water treatment. It has not (yet) been approved as a medicine, except in Bolivia. Andreas Kalcker, who founded a centre in Switzerland to research CDS, is working on this. To be clear: CDS must not be offered or advertised as a medicine or food supplement. I expressly do not do that. For legal reasons, I have to advise against experimenting with it.

As a chronicler, however, I pass on the experiences that others have had with it. And, of course I have formed an opinion about it, namely that these experiences are so promising that medically controlled studies should definitely be done on it.

Such studies are legal because the Declaration of Helsinki of the World Medical Association explicitly allows, in paragraph 37, the use of unproven interventions if the doctor believes that they can save lives, restore health or alleviate suffering,

---

408 https://www.apotheke-adhoc.de/branchennews/alle-branchennews/branchennews-detail/ipev-einfluss-des-ph-werts-auf-virenaktivitaet-wissenschaftlich-belegt-7/

409 https://andreaskalcker.com/wp-content/uploads/2020/04/chlordioxid-im-einsatz-gegen-das-coronavirus-de-v.2.1.pdf

410 https://lbry.tv/@Kalcker:7/why-ClO2-works-for-Covid-19:2
    also on the website: http://andreaskalcker.com/

especially if there are no official cures yet.[411] This is the case with Covid19 and applies to CDS.

Studies and large-scale trials

The first large-scale trial, at that time still with MMS, took place in a malaria area. From 11-16 December 2012, a trial was conducted in a village in Uganda with the International Red Cross, the Uganda Red Cross, the health authorities and Ugandan scientists. 154 malaria patients received MMS under medical supervision after extensive pre-tests. The success was astounding, as almost all of them were malaria-free the next day, as confirmed by the laboratory tests. Only eleven patients needed a second dose, then they were also cured.

All this was documented, but the Red Cross withdrew from the project, several senior doctors in the investigation were dismissed, and the initiator, Klaas Proesmans, who had co-financed the project, parted ways with the project under pressure from the pharmaceutical industry.[412]

According to the report, 75,000 malaria patients in Africa have since been cured with MMS, with a cure rate of 99%.

There are 2,000 children dying of malaria every day worldwide whose lives could be saved with CDS.

The video about it has disappeared from Youtube, but has been saved on Kalcker's website.[413]

---

411 https://www.bundesaerztekammer.de/fileadmin/user_upload/downloads/pdf-Ordner/International/Deklaration_von_Helsinki_2013_20190905.pdf
412 https://secure.avaaz.org/community_petitions/de/Stoppt_die_Unterdrueckung_des_guenstigen_Heilmittels_MMS/
413 https://andreaskalcker.com/de/videos/

The first large clinical trial with CDS was conducted in Guayaquil in Ecuador in May 2020. There, a great many people died of or with corona, and medical staff were also affected. The conditions were similar to those in northern Italy during the "hot phase". The medical association "AEMEMI"[414] had already heard about CDS and some doctors tried it on themselves – with very good success.

When the president of the medical association, Dr. Mauricio Quiñonez, fell seriously ill, a diabetic at that, and was almost dying, he had himself treated with CDS intravenously. The success was that he was able to get up again after two days and quickly recovered. Since then, he has been jokingly called "Lazarus" by his colleagues.

That was the beginning of the study in which many doctors in Guayaquil participated. They treated 104 seriously ill Covid19 patients. 97% of them recovered in a short time. This is a success rate that is usually never achieved in such studies, which is why it is also doubted by the CDS opponents. Normally, a success rate of 30% with drugs is already considered very good. For a vaccination to be approved, it is sufficient to prove a rate of 25%.

The results of the study have all been legally documented and are to be published soon. If you want to know more, you can find some reports of healed patients on video.[415] Of course, this study was spontaneous and born out of necessity, which is why it does not meet the standards of usual medical studies. The doctors did not want a double-blind study where half of the patients get a placebo when it comes to life-threatening situations. That would be unethical.

But a second, larger study on "CDS in Covid19" has started, decentralised, in seven Latin American countries and with

---

414 Asociación Ecuatoriana de Médicos Expertos en Medicina Integrativa
415 https://cdn.lbryplayer.xyz/api/v3/streams/free/Covid-19-Finally-defeated-!!/6aeffef414fb66b417c39040242dc4b3f7855cc3/5c064d
   auch auf der Webseite: http://andreaskalcker.com/

over 500 patients. The goal is to get CDS approved as a drug worldwide. [416]

In Bolivia, on 14.10.2020, the preparation, marketing, supply and use of chlorine dioxide for the prevention and treatment of coronavirus[417] was permitted by law, and at the same time the dosage was prescribed.[418] The reason was that word of the success of CDS had spread in South America among the people and, as it was illegal, many people had obtained sodium chlorite, i.e. MMS, and used it themselves. This had resulted in damage to the mucous membrane because some people thought they could take it undiluted. To prevent un-controlled use, the government saw fit to legalise chlorine dioxide and regulate its production, marketing and use, although the official opinion of the Ministry of Health is still against the drug.

Why is chlorine dioxide so fiercely opposed? On the one hand, out of ignorance and because of the disgusting propaganda of the opponents (*"chlorine bleach", "corrosive",* etc.). On the other hand, the pharmaceutical industry is afraid of losing sales. The market for antimalarial drugs alone, which only help to a limited extent, such as HCQ, is a billion-dollar business. If a corona cure were to become known that cannot be patented (because it is well known) and costs only a few cents to produce, then the corona vaccinations would also become pointless and the beautiful business would be spoiled. Because CDS can be made easily and cheaply in any pharmacy, and some people make it themselves, at home in the kitchen. It works even for non-professionals, all you need is a big jar of pickles. I know many people in my circle of acquaintances who have been using it for years, and

416 https://www.mediarebell.com/watch/lxNitVRGzgXTkz1

417 *"Law regulating the Production, Marketing, Supply and Consensual Use of Chlorine Dioxide Solution (CDS) for the Prevention and Treatment of the Coronavirus Pandemic (Covid19)" from* 14.10.2020

418 https://eldeber.com.bo/pais/pese-a-advertencia-de-la-ops-gobierno-publica-ley-para-el-uso-del-dioxido-de-cloro-contra-el-Covid-1_210738

I have never heard of any side effects. On the contrary, I have been told of amazing healings where "normal" medicines failed. A small animated video on Telegram explains the history and function of CDS.[419]

So, I repeat: it is high time for a scientific investigation. If the successes are confirmed, then CDS must not be withheld from humanity.

---

419 https://t.me/dmso_archiv/28

The social impact of the anti-Corona measures

There is no need to ask whether the coercive measures such as curfew, contact bans, masking, travel bans, quarantine and stand-off rules do harm to our society. They do, I don't think anyone will disagree. The extent of the damage is only gradually becoming apparent, but we can certainly take stock. I will look at the different areas individually, but first I will devote myself to the campaign that makes it all possible.

Psychological control

Big projects require good planning and long preparation. If you want to impose something on someone that they would otherwise never accept because it would be against their interests, then the Hegelian dialectic helps: thesis - antithesis - synthesis. The thesis is health, the antithesis is death, and the synthesis is vaccination or coercive measures.

The recipe is simple: create a problem, real or imagined, it doesn't matter. It just has to be perceived as threatening. Then simmer on low heat and stir until the sauce is "cooked through". Then, when the victim is so annoyed that he says, *"Anything better than this!"*, it is time to present an exit. This is, of course, the pre-planned "solution". The victim is softened up and reaches for the apparent salvation. Mission accomplished.

Seen precisely, Corona follows exactly this pattern: a threat suddenly arises out of nowhere, whether the virus is dangerous or not is irrelevant. It fulfils its purpose and fills the people with fear, which is increased to panic. Politics strikes hard, worldwide. Then there are "relaxations", people go on holiday and hope for better times. Then the noose is tightened again, loosened again, and so on. The phase of soft-boiling is a rollercoaster of emotions, until at some point the "rescue" is presented. But what exactly is the goal? There are several, one of which is already steadily suggested: *"It won't end until the vaccination is there."* The other goals are not yet stated, but are visible to those who look closely. We do that in the next part of the book.

"Phase 1", the shock phase, we have experienced. "Phase 2", the soft boil, we are experiencing. "Phase 3", the planned "solution", is still in the future. Everything is proceeding according to the Hegelian dialectic. This fact alone shows that the whole thing is planned.

Phase 1: Fear and terror

Every year, medicine discovers new pathogens. Viruses in particular mutate frequently, thereby improving their chances of success. The range of possible "threats" to humans is large. As we have seen, it does not take a pandemic to declare a pandemic. In SARS 2003, there were a total of 774 deaths *worldwide,* which was about 0.00001% of the world's population.[420] When the WHO declared the swine flu pandemic in May 2009, the virus was almost only present in Mexico with 97 deaths.[421] That is sad, but not a pandemic. At Covid19, the numbers were far below those of the usual flu waves when it was once again "Pandemic Day" at the WHO headquarter on 11 March 2020.

---

420 https://www.who.int/csr/sars/country/table2004_04_21/en/
421 https://en.wikipedia.org/wiki/2009_swine_flu_pandemic

Seen in this light, one could have chosen any virus for any pandemic every year. Note: Flu epidemics do not become "pandemics" through particularly high mortality rates, such as in 2017/18, but through consistent PR, i.e. media relations. And this has been developed to perfection in 2020.

I have already reported on the method of working with images, such as coffins in Italy and mass graves in New York. In addition, there were daily news reports with pictures of intensive care patients on tubes, some staff in protective suits, crying and desperate relatives. Fearful, worried people were interviewed, and their fear was transmitted to the viewer. The presenters all made worried faces and demanded in a warning tone not to underestimate the danger. And all this in a continuous stream. Many couldn't stand it anymore and switched the TV off – and then on again, because they wanted to be *"informed"*, i.e. *"formed: brought into shape"* – language is revealing.

In addition to the exaggerated case and death figures, which I have already explained at length, selected "experts" threw around completely exaggerated "estimates" that were meant to frighten, even if none of them materialised later. Hardly anyone remembers the 278,000 corona deaths that Drosten predicted for Germany as recently as spring.[422] If anyone does remember, they say we owe it to the government's tough measures that we were spared that. But the case numbers in Sweden, Iceland and Belarus, which had no lockdown or mask requirement, prove otherwise. They are far below the figures for Spain, Italy and France, the countries with the toughest measures. And I have already presented the studies on the futility of the measures above.

It would be bad enough if people only believed the statistics. But it is much worse: the hysteria orchestrated by the media has multiplied the numbers in people's minds. A survey by an opinion research institute in five countries asked people what

---

422 https://www.rubikon.news/artikel/die-medikamenten-tragodie

they thought the number of people infected with Covid was in their country.[423] The results were shocking when compared to the (already too high) official figures:

- The British estimated four times the number of infected people
- The Swedes and US Americans estimate 20 times the official number
- The Germans and French estimated the 46-fold

Then they asked about the estimated death toll. Here the difference between perception and reality was even more glaring:

- The French, the British and the Swedes estimated 100 times the official number
- US-Americans estimated 225-fold
- Germans estimated 300 times the official death toll.

The German media have done a great job! If one takes into account that, according to the CDC, 94% of the "corona deaths" died of other diseases,[424] i.e. *with* and not *from* corona, then this increases the incorrect estimation of the death figures by a factor of 16.

This shows that very few people even look up the official figures, which are on the net, let alone do the math. In Spain, TV propaganda exaggerated with the statement: *"Today 180 people died from Corona. It's a great tragedy, as if a plane*

423 https://www.kekstcnc.com/media/2793/kekstcnc_research_Covid-19_opinion_tracker_wave-4.pdf
424 https://www.cdc.gov/nchs/nvss/vsrr/Covid_weekly/index.htm

crashed every day." Neutral journalism would add: *"Today, as every day, 1,400 people died in Spain, 700 of them from cardiovascular diseases or tumours, 40 from suicide. Of the 180 "corona deaths", 175 suffered from heart failure and other serious illnesses, and the remaining five were over 70. Today, no healthy person under 70 died of corona."*

The problem is that the relation is lost. For example, the WHO reported that according to new estimates, about 10% of the world's population, i.e. 760 million, are infected with the virus.[425] That sounds bad at first. But if you take the WHO figure of about one million corona deaths worldwide (yes, I know, according to the CDC, this figure should also be reduced), the mortality rate is 0.13%.[426] And that matches the flu mortality rate, which according to the WHO is 0.1 - 0.4%. I told you: the flu is now called Corona, regardless of whether it is caused by influenza or coronavirus.

The WHO is thus revising its estimate from March, which assumed a mortality rate of 3.4%, i.e. 26 times higher! Interestingly, Prof. John P. Ioannidis already gave the figure of 0.13% mortality in March, which he had calculated from the data of a cruise ship on which Corona had broken out. Prof. Ioannidis from Stanford University is one of the most renowned epidemiologists and the most cited scientist worldwide. He is one of the first and most competent corona critics. He called the corona pandemic a once-in-a-hundred-years evidence fiasco. The predictions of 40 million corona deaths worldwide were only "science fiction" for him. As early as March, he called the damage caused by lockdown and social distance much worse than anything the virus could cause.[427] He was completely right.

---

425 https://www.politaia.org/gegengift-gegen-steigende-panik-mit-einer-ber-uhigenden-zahl/?source=ENL
https://deutsch.rt.com/international/107733-who-bestatigt-indirekt-sterblichkeit-durch/
426 One million dead divided by 760 million infected people
427 https://de.wikipedia.org/wiki/
John_Ioannidis#points_of_view_on_the_COVID-19_pandemic

All this shows how little people deal with the numbers, it is probably too exhausting. They prefer to consume the dark-coloured media reports, and in their minds it grows into a monstrous misjudgement of the situation, which is character-ised by emotions instead of reason. This is the high school of disinformation of the media, the WHO, the RKI and politics, and it is used worldwide.

You can only get out of this whirlpool of emotions if you look at the real facts. That is why I am doing all the work, for myself and for my readers, to bring some light of reason into the darkness of fear.

Phase 2: Carrot and stick

This is the phase we were in from summer 2020. The first lockdown had been lifted, the borders opened, the prisoners had free access. Although there were masks when shopping and on buses and trains, we were allowed to relax a little. But there were regular threats of the "second wave". Sure, there is a new wave of flu every autumn, but there has never been a second wave with the same pathogen, at most with muta-tions. But the citizen doesn't know that, no one has told him.

But now it did not want to come, the second wave, so the tests were increased with the desired result. The false positives alone are enough to increase the "number of cases"; the result can be "adjusted" with the number of tests and the number of cycles (ct value) in the tests.

Only a few people noticed that the intensive care units were almost empty in the summer and that the hospital staff was working short-time. No matter, the wave was conjured up, there was talk of "exponential growth" in the numbers in the certainty that no one would do the math anyway. There were closures of regions, re-openings, masks yes, masks no, a jumble of regulations, quarantine sometimes short, sometimes long, sometimes not at all, absurd regulations galore and complete confusion.

You live between hope and fear, and that drains you and makes you tired. And then there's the uncertainty about what's going to happen professionally. Pubs open, pubs close, they have closing hours, depending on the federal state, the virus is active at night from 10 or 11 p.m., it is more active with alcohol, and in Hamburg it orients itself on house numbers. It's a glorious time for regulation-minded officials. One employee reported on the hair-raising conditions in the health offices.[428] The aim is to annoy people so much that they are more likely to accept unpleasant "solutions" in the bitter end.

We'll talk about phase 3 later, it's still in the future.

---

428 https://www.reitschuster.de/post/es-ist-ein-wahnwitz-was-da-geschieht/

The division of society

Even before Corona, deep rifts ran through society, not only in Europe, but in the entire Western world. They were fuelled by politics and the media. While in the 1970s and 1980s there was still a pluralistic society in which topics were discussed controversially, this changed after the fall of the Soviet Union, creeping at first, and accelerating since the turn of the millennium.

Politics and the media are increasingly propagating a uniform opinion that is predetermined. The discussion is no longer about content, but about *who* said something and whether they belong to the "right" side. Those who disagree are ostracised, some are even criminalised. Either one follows the guidelines or one is defamed. For example, as *"deniers"*, first there were the *"Holocaust deniers"*, then the *"climate deniers"*, now the *"corona deniers"*. The label is particularly perfidious because it means *"denying against one's better judgement"*. It implies that the *"denier"* actually knows that he is wrong, and thus what he denies is declared to be "right". The word *"denier"* has become a signal word: *this opinion is "evil"!*

How about a new word, like "conspiracy denier"? Well, that would only apply to those who are privy to a conspiracy, and that is only a few. For most people, "conspiracy ignorant" would be more accurate, because they don't know anything. They have been taught that there are no conspiracies in this world.

Today, you only need to label people to prevent their opinions from being taken seriously. Popular labels are *"conspiracy theorist"*, *"aluhat carrier"*, *"right-wing"*, *"populist"* or *"crude"*. Anyone labelled in this way is automatically excluded from any social discourse. They are forced to constantly justify themselves, saying they are *"not right-wing"* or *"not anti-vaccination"*. But that doesn't help at all, the stigma sticks.

But the same fighting words wear out and become stale. The well-known Corona critics Dr. Bodo Schiffmann and Samuel Eckert were to receive the *"Golden Aluhat"*, a defamatory negative award, but to the annoyance of the award organisers, they were looking forward to it and wanted to collect it personally. This was too much for the awarding bodies and they were summarily disqualified, even though they had the most votes.[429] So you can also turn the whole thing around if you have a sense of humour.

I myself have no problem with being called a *"conspiracy theorist"*. On the contrary – it is an honour for me to expose conspiracies and the theory behind them. It is the conspiracy practitioners who should be condemned.

Most people find it too much of a nuisance to deal with controversial opinions. They prefer to stay within the delimited framework of the mainstream. In the end, they also don't care whether 11 September 2001 was an inside job or not, or who is behind the Syria war. That is far away. With Corona, that has changed, because it affects everyone. This makes the rifts in society even deeper: those who are afraid of contagion, and most of them are, rally around the government because they expect help from there. The authorities are supposed to save them. That is always the case in times of crisis. The crisis is used to ostracise critics all the more harshly.

Wisely, a new bone of contention has been introduced: the compulsory wearing of masks. This is practical, because deviants are immediately recognisable because they do not wear the mask correctly or are completely "topless". This causes bad blood, and there have already been fights over it.

---

429 https://de.sputniknews.com/videos/20201013328152351-goldener-aluhut-eklt/

The return of denunciation

The authorities are adding fuel to the fire by encouraging people everywhere to denounce. Many municipalities have already printed forms or set up internet portals where people can denounce their neighbours for violating the Corona rules – even anonymously. Schools are asking children to denounce their classmates!

The public broadcaster WDR encourages its viewers to denounce all doctors who have doubts about the dangerousness of the virus or who do not consistently apply the mask requirement. Downplaying or denying the virus could result in severe fines or consequences for the profession. The patient should observe and report "deviations", such as whether everyone wears masks, spacing in the waiting room is maintained, whether there are Plexiglas walls, etc. Should the doctor play down Corona, he should be contradicted and reported to the medical association, which would then investigate the matter.[430]

Instead of arbitrating or mediating, the citizens of our country are turned against each other. The country is to be turned into a denouncer state. Corona is probably just a test run to see how far people can be pushed. Once denunciation is established, it can easily be transferred to political opinions in the planned dictatorship.

In addition, feelings of guilt are stirred up: those who do not comply with the measures are allegedly to blame for the possible death of those infected. It is irresponsible to "talk down" the number of corona victims or disrespectful "towards those who die". One can only say: Which politician has had respect for the victims of hospitalism, for example, which is twice as many every year? Who has been closing hospitals

---

430 https://deutsch.rt.com/inland/108034-was-nicht-passt-wird-passend/

and cutting back the nursing sector?[431] Who mourned the 25,000 deaths in the 2017/18 flu epidemic or called lockdowns at the time? Who cares about the misery caused by redundancies and company bankruptcies, the jump in the number of suicides, the surgery cancelled because of Corona, the mental suffering of the elderly in solitary confinement?

The state propaganda is so cynical and hypocritical that it can only bring most people into line by inducing feelings of guilt. It tries to turn the tables by declaring critics "thought criminals", as in "1984", who are to blame if everyone has to go into lockdown. Merkel already recommends sending critics to psychiatric treatment. That was one of the methods under socialism and is probably a relic from her communist cadre training. Some professor from the ethics committee wants to ban all those who don't want to be vaccinated from taking life-saving measures in hospital, should they themselves fall ill one day.[432] Could it be any more cynical?

There is something malignant in the whole Corona conspiracy. This is the only way to explain completely senseless rules, up to and including complete indifference to the suffering of children. Doctors' mask exemptions are ignored or, at demos, simply confiscated by the police. Doctors who issue "too many" of them lose their licence to practise and have to tolerate house searches to get hold of patient data.

A friend described to me how he perceives the mood in his small town: *"Only the "own people" are valid. Everyone else is an opponent. Dissenting opinions are not valid, the truth is not valid. There is no reconciliation of interests, only one's*

---

431 In Germany, twenty hospitals with 2,144 beds and about 4,000 jobs are scheduled to close by the end of 2020, twice as many as the average in recent years. https://snanews.de/20201222/buendnis-klinikrettung-schliessungsstopp-von-krankenhaeusern-254745.html

432 https://reitschuster.de/post/kanzlerin-erklaert-kritiker-zum-fall-fuer-den-psychologen/

own advantage, optimised by adaptation to the point of toadyism. "If you live in slavery, get on well with your masters". You can feel that the vast majority, in their fear, crave to obey rules, right or wrong. Obedience as a value in itself and a drug against fear."

The Stockholm Syndrome

The measures take an entire people hostage and dictate the conditions under which they will (or will not) be released. This has triggered a "Stockholm syndrome" in many people.

It's called that because in 1973 bank robbers in Stockholm held four hostages for over five days. What was amazing was that the hostages developed positive feelings such as sympathy, gratitude and care for their tormentors, which lasted even after their release. Thus, they even visited the perpetrators while still in prison. This phenomenon has been observed more often, for example in the Gladbeck hostage crisis in 1988 or in Algeria in 2003.

A psychological analysis brought to light three basic patterns that can trigger the syndrome, namely when the perpetrator makes demands that are somehow understandable, then the hostages support them. And when the perpetrator credibly presents himself as a victim, for example of society, and asserts that he does not want to use violence. In addition, there is "voluntary" submission and collaboration, since resistance is pointless anyway. This creates an alliance between perpetrator and victim.[433]

If we transfer this to the Corona situation, the parallels are clearly visible. This explains, among other things, the behaviour of the majority of the people who stand behind their tormentors.

---

433 https://www.lecturio.de/magazin/stockholm-syndrom/

The strategy of fear

Fuelling fear is an important aspect of the Corona plot. The German Institute for Economic Research produced an internal paper on the subject, which states that the willingness to vaccinate increases if the virus can be assessed as particularly dangerous. To do this, the (alleged) risks posed by the virus must be presented as precisely as possible.[434]

However, the intimidation of citizens through disinformation sometimes comes to light unintentionally. For example, internal minutes of the Austrian Coronavirus Task Force at the Vienna Ministry of Health became public on 12 March 2020. Ministers, health experts and Federal Chancellor Sebastian Kurz were present.

Chancellor Kurz regretted not yet sensing any real concern among the people, whereupon an expert held up the UK as a good example of how to successfully play on people's fear. Kurz then stressed that people should be afraid of the death of their parents or grandparents, but not of a shortage of food.

The minutes stupidly became public and were initially denied by the Chancellor's Office as a "forgery". However, this could be refuted, so that a spokesperson then placated that Kurz had only wanted to say that he understood the fear of contagion, but not the fear of food shortages.[435]

The fear strategy was also recommended in Germany: As of 18 March 2020, the Federal Ministry of the Interior sent a strategy paper to the Chancellery and other ministries that was supposed to remain secret. It bears the note: *"Classified matter - for official use only"*. It is called *"How to get COVID-*

---

434 https://de.sputniknews.com/deutschland/20201026328273535-corona-massnahmen-alternative-impfpflicht/

435 https://deutsch.rt.com/europa/101989-menschen-sollen-angst-haben-internes-protokoll-bringt-sebastian-kurz-in-bedraegnis/

19 under control" and gives recommendations on how to deal with the crisis. Somehow it got to various media outlets and sparked discussion.[436] It conjures up a "worst case scenario" with over one million corona deaths by the end of May in Germany. Various measures were proposed to contain it. It is interesting to note that although the "worst case" did not materialise, the measures were nevertheless taken.

The following strategies were recommended:

- Extending the tests to as many citizens as possible gives those locked in the curfew the image of active crisis management by the state.

- Apart from massive tests, everything that is not essential for survival, such as sports, culture, education, gastronomy, shops and even small social occasions, must be stopped.

- The "worst case" must be made clear.

- The case mortality rate should no longer be communicated, as it seems insignificant. Especially with regard to the elderly, people would think that this way they would *"get rid of the elderly"*, because they only burden the economy, since there is overpopulation anyway, so *"with a bit of luck"* one could inherit earlier.

- The *"desired shock effect"* can be achieved with concrete examples, such as the fact that hospitals are full and seriously ill people die at home struggling for air. It is a primal fear to die by suffocation or to get too little air. Just like the fear of the relatives of not being able to help, as in the disturbing pictures from Italy.

---

436 https://fragdenstaat.de/blog/2020/04/01/strategiepapier-des-innenministeriums-corona-szenarien/

- It must be shown that children can easily become infected and then infect their parents. If a mother or father then dies in agony at home just because the children did not wash their hands after playing, then this is the most terrible thing that can ever happen to a child.[437]

This cynicism is hard to bear. The technocrats play on fears and feelings of guilt for their propaganda, not only of children, without thinking about the consequences. This includes banning everything that makes life worth living: travelling, going out, celebrating, singing, closeness, visiting friends and relatives, big weddings, cultural events, sports, football matches, Christmas markets, carnivals, discos etc..

The consequences are isolation, insecurity, fear and stress. All this is known to be immunosuppressive. So everything is done to make people more susceptible to infections. Then there are the masks with oxygen deprivation and CO_2 exposure.

In the meantime, word has even reached the WHO about the psychological damage caused by the staged pandemic. The WHO chief pointed out that about one billion people suffer from mental disorders, but only a small minority can afford medical help.[438]

All this happens under the pretext of wanting to save lives. Psychologist Wilfried Nelles says: "*The virus kills, they say. Our mortality is made drastically clear to us. The shock leads to the fact that virtually the whole life is paralysed in order not to die. Thus, the global lockdown has unintentionally made something very fundamental clear: If you cannot or will not die, you cannot live! The price of unconditionally avoiding*

---

437 https://fragdenstaat.de/dokumente/4123-wie-wir-Covid-19-unter-kontrolle-bekommen/

438 https://de.sputniknews.com/panorama/20200828327818020-corona-wirkt-sich-negativ-auf-psychische-gesundheit-von-millionen-menschen-aus--who/

death is the loss of life. The price is the death of alive-ness."[439]

In "Ped's Ansichten" you can read: *"First the dead are invented, then politics is made with these fictitious victims and finally – trapped in fear and madness – people actually die. In the background, however, people continue to "arrange". Power uses fears to implement its own agendas by breaking down resistance for its own interests or those of others.*

However, this pathological behaviour alone would hardly have any chance of success. Therefore, the masses to be ruled must play along, play along more than just a mere submission to their masters. The subjugated must become the mouthpieces of the rulers".[440]

One scaremonger that has received little attention so far is the strict measures taken by governments themselves. *"If the authorities are cracking down so hard, then the virus must be dangerous!"* The conclusion is obvious, but it is a fallacy because most have not understood the aims of the Corona crisis, which I will discuss later. Psychologically, this is a brilliant move: bully and disenfranchise people, thus increasing their fear in order to be able to bully and disenfranchise them even more through their fear. The only way to break this vicious circle is to see through the lies and expose them publicly. That is the intention of this book.

The fear is increased by feelings of guilt. It is not the government that is to blame for the hardships of the measures, no, it is all of you because you were not consistent enough! Too careless with the contacts, with the masks, with the partying. This is the only way to increase the number of infections, and now you have to pay for it in the harsh lockdown.

This is nonsense and has been refuted by the many studies I have researched, but it is subliminally planted in people's

439 Source: https://www.rubikon.news/artikel/der-verlust-des-lebens
440 Source: https://peds-ansichten.de/2020/10/der-student-und-der-tod/

minds. So deeply, in fact, that almost no one notices the illogical nature of the measures: too many parties cause more and more deaths – not among the young, but among the over-80s. They shouldn't have been partying every night in the old people's home. That's why there are now curfews and alcohol bans.

This also creates scapegoats: the mask and vaccination refusers, the critical doctors, the sceptics and the "Querdenker" (lateral thinkers). Merkel cheekily calls criticism of her measures an attack on our entire way of life.[441]

This is particularly perfidious because here the cause complains about the effect. After all, it is the government's measures that are destroying *"our whole way of life"*, not the critics who are still trying to save some of it.

The old and the young

The elderly, who miss their family and grandchildren, are hit very hard. In the homes they were locked up, sedated with medication and treated like lepers, partly due to a lack of staff, partly due to excessive caution. Social gatherings were cut back or cancelled altogether.

Before the Corona Committee of Inquiry, nursing staff from the old people's homes reported that the mental situation in the nursing homes was partly catastrophic. The hygiene measures and the many tests had caused more psychological damage than they had helped. The obligation to wear masks impedes various therapies. The residents were literally locked up, they were not allowed to leave their rooms, not even in the corridor, and visits were forbidden.

441 https://www.welt.de/vermischtes/article222525488/Angela-Merkel-zu-
Corona-Leugnern-Angriff-auf-unsere-Lebensweise.html

They felt totally helpless and at the mercy of others, like in prison, and totally abandoned. Such people simply die of loneliness because they have given up on themselves.[442]

It is sad that the people in need of care in the facilities are not asked for their opinion. The mother of an acquaintance who lives in a nursing home said: *"I'm old, I'm going to die soon anyway, I don't care from what I'll die. But I don't want to die alone, I want to be able to say goodbye to my loved ones. That is important to me. It's not worth prolonging this life of loneliness."*

However, it is the children who are most affected. They grow up in this oppressive atmosphere, understand the situation even less than their parents and cannot defend themselves.

Once again Wilfried Nelles:

"I wonder what it does to a child when it is now drilled into them that the others are dangerous and you have to keep your distance from them; how much the present children and later adults internalise this. Will they ever be able to hug another person unsuspectingly? If they are now programmed for "social distancing" and constant hand washing, the schools will be the neurosis breeding grounds for the next generation of adults."[443]

The conditions in schools and day-care centres are very bad. Most schools insist on the mandatory use of masks, even if they are not mandatory in some federal states, probably because they are afraid of being held responsible if a test is positive. Legal exceptions such as medical certificates are usually ignored, and students therefore become unfocused, suffer from dizziness and headaches or simply keel over, as has been reported several times, although not in the mainstream media. There, such cases are covered up. You

442 https://de.sputniknews.com/politik/20200728327583781-corona-untersuchungsausschuss-kein-killer-virus/
443 https://www.rubikon.news/artikel/der-verlust-des-lebens

can find the testimony of a paediatrician in this video.[444] In another video[445], children talk about their school experiences.

Hair-raising conditions in some schools were described before the Corona Committee, for example from letters from concerned parents who reported that anger and panic were instigated in children against *"antisocial people"* because they *"wanted to kill others" if they did* not comply with the measures. This went so far that children were physically attacked who walked outdoors without masks.

Children who question the hygiene rules have to do punitive work, even asking is an offence.

Several cases of child isolation have been reported from the state of Baden-Württemberg, not only in the home but in room confinement. Contact with parents and siblings is restricted, and if it is not, then only with a mask and distance. The health authorities can check this at any time, and violations can result in incarceration in a closed institution as well as prison sentences of two years. This does not only affect (falsely) tested positive children, but also those in whose school/class another child was (falsely) tested positive. Currently, about 300,000 children and 30,000 teachers in Germany are in quarantine, each for a fortnight.

Speaking to the Corona Committee, Ms Tina Romdhani from the civic group "Parents Stand Up" remarked that all the measures were, in her opinion, made for the purpose of teaching children to be submissive and to accept rules without questioning them. This would also undermine and damage the children's sense of right and wrong.[446]

To call these unspeakable conditions a "hygiene dictatorship" is still far too kind.

---

444 https://youtu.be/tj1RtxaYYeg https://fb.watch/1sfSQycdlS/   or:
    https://dlive.tv/p/davebrych+g9pOtRhMg?ref=davebrych
445 https://youtu.be/zkqoWQ1aqoU
446 https://kenfm.de/corona-untersuchungsausschuss-teil-14-von-jochen-mitschka/

The international study "COVID KIDS", conducted on 3,000 children and adolescents by the universities of Tübingen and Luxembourg, found that before Corona, 95% of German children had been "satisfied to very satisfied" with their lives; during the crisis, the figure was only 53%. What they complained about most was the lack of friends and family members.[447]

The regulation to ventilate classrooms so extremely in winter that children need winter coats is also complete nonsense. The change in temperature makes them even more suscept-ible to colds. And something else was overlooked that the alleged physicist Merkel should actually know: cold air can absorb less moisture than warm air. When it is heated by the heating, it becomes very dry. The result: the mucous mem-branes in the throat and nose dry out, and this weakens the immune defence. In this way, a "2nd wave" can also be ventilated.

Maria Eing, a paediatric nurse who works in a day-care centre, spoke about her experiences at a demonstration for basic rights in Münster/Westphalia:

"All these measures inflict serious damage on our health and especially on the health and development of our children. It is a creeping loss of our humanity, in all its diverse expressive and creative capacities. The facelessness in our society triggers insecurity and fear in children. The vital possibility of reassuring oneself through facial expressions and the sound of the voice – "am I in good hands and safe here?" - has been taken away from children for months in their first early years of development.

This has devastating consequences that often only find expression years later. Their trust, their protection, being accepted – this vital space of experience is severely restricted for our children. The orientation in oneself is visibly

447 https://de.rt.com/inland/109859-neue-normal-studie-lebenszufriedenheit-kinder/

steered further away from one's own perception to a perception that shifts more and more to the evaluation by other people. In this way, the child becomes more and more alien to itself. At some point it no longer knows who he/she is.

A loss of joie de vivre, of deep hearty laughter, of the joy of play and discovery, with the ability to feel timeless, carefree and secure in experience, becomes more noticeable. But the loss of the ability to deal with conflict is also becoming increasingly visible.

The number of children who become deeply sad, sometimes desperate, at the smallest triggers is growing. The number of children who literally fight for their survival at the slightest altercation is growing. The number of children who quietly withdraw is growing. In school age, many children signal an instability of their health, name numerous symptoms.

I don't want to carry on with this development, which also leaves its mark on me!

Our humanity is increasingly reduced to the observance of rules, to control, to keeping our distance, to experiencing excessive demands and permanent stress. There are numerous examples in the day-care centre that prove the futility of these measures. For me and the children, these directives are incomprehensible. There is still no end in sight to these measures. For weeks I have been working with the knowledge that I am harming the children and myself, and this ambivalence of doing things that I cannot justify makes me ill in the long run. My job is still my livelihood for the moment. When I ask around, a lot of people are feeling the same way as me right now.

Together, let us continue to peacefully resist and inform people. Let's support and protect our children together. Let us go our own ways together in our togetherness ".[448]

---

448 https://www.rubikon.news/artikel/der-alltagliche-schrecken

Those who see the light of day for the first time and their mothers also have to suffer. Several heavily pregnant women came forward in Instagram chats and were told that they have to take a test shortly before delivery, which has to be negative, otherwise the new born child will be taken away and quarantined for 14 days![449] The info is not official, but it's something to keep in mind. That would be complete nonsense, because new born children of mothers with corona develop in the same way as those of healthy mothers.[450]

In France and Belgium, but also in other countries, women have recently been forced to give birth with a mask, and the fathers are no longer allowed to be present. Giving birth is as strenuous as competitive sport, and the woman has to breathe hard to push, otherwise she may have to have a caesarean section. The reason given is the risk of infection for the obstetricians. But they could wear one of those masks that are supposed to provide such excellent protection – couldn't they?

The author Kathi Garnier rightly says: *"And whoever thinks that the woman giving birth has to bear joint responsibility for her fellow human beings, for the 'common good', then I'll give him or her the bird. The woman giving birth doesn't have to do anything! The only thing she has to do is make sure that she and her child are doing well. And that's why I would advise all my friends to whom something like this should happen: "Resist! Tear the mask off your face. Breathe, pant, moan and scream as loud as you can."*[451]

Not only the masks, but also the lockdown claims victims among the new born babies. In Adelaide, Australia, four new born babies died within a month because the necessary operations for congenital heart defects could not be

449 https://t.me/davebrych_public
450 https://ntk-institute.org/node/167124/
451 https://www.rubikon.news/artikel/tief-durchatmen

performed there. Due to travel restrictions, they were not allowed to be transferred to other hospitals.[452]

In South Tyrol, too, a six-month-old girl died who should have been operated on four months after birth at the latest. Because of Corona, the surgery date was postponed again and again until it was too late.[453]

The desperate

Studies have been made all over the world on the mental state of people in 2020 and compared with the previous year. I could now present individual studies, but that would be too extensive. The article in the footnote gives a good overview.[454] The results of the studies show that mental health problems have increased significantly worldwide: Depression, anxiety, learning difficulties, stress, addictive behaviour, aggression, domestic violence, etc.

Children and young people as well as carers are particularly affected. The main reasons are stress, isolation and economic worries. There are long waiting lists in psychological counselling centres, pastoral care telephones are overloaded, the consumption of alcohol and tobacco has increased and that of drugs probably too. According to an Allensbach survey, only 20% of 30- to 59-year-olds are still hopeful about the future.[455]

---

452 https://nitter.net/9NewsAUS/status/1318632532716457986
453 https://www.unsertirol24.com/2020/10/15/suedtiroler-maedchen-stirbt-weil-operation-zu-spaet-kam/
454 https://www.rubikon.news/artikel/angriff-auf-die-seele
455 https://www.welt.de/wirtschaft/article221566080/Allensbach-Studie-zu-Corona-Die-Generation-Mitte-versinkt-in-der-Depression.html

The health insurance scheme "Kaufmännische Krankenkasse" in Hanover, with around 1.7 million insured persons, recorded more than 26,700 sickness notifications due to mental illness in the first half of 2020. Compared to the previous year, this is an increase of 80%. [456]

Suicide rates have also increased significantly in all countries; the extent to which the increase is related to the severity of the interventions is being investigated. The numbers of suicide attempts and suicidal thoughts have also increased. At a congress in Italy, it was reported that men were particularly affected. Apart from existential worries because of the Corona policy, fear of infecting others is a reason, as well as overwork and stress among health workers. In addition, care for the mentally ill almost came to a standstill during the lockdown.[457]

The Berlin fire brigade announced on request that in 2020 there was an extreme increase in calls under the keyword *"near strangulation/hanging"*. In 2018, there were seven call-outs, in 2019 three. In 2020, there were already 294 deployments by October. That's an increase of 9,800%! But not only the suicide rate increased, but also domestic violence cases.[458]

Doctors at John Muir Medical Center in California reported that in the first four weeks of the lockdown, there were as many suicide attempts there as there usually are in an entire year. [459]

456 https://de.sputniknews.com/panorama/20200803327627258-deutschland80-prozent-mehr-psychische-erkrankungen-in-corona-krise-studie/
457 Source: https://kurier.at/amp/chronik/welt/corona-krise-psychiater-beklagen-suizidwelle-in-italien/401023949
458 https://www.berliner-zeitung.de/news/berliner-feuerwehr-zahl-der-einsaetze-wegen-moeglichem-suiziden-steigt-massiv-an-li.117723
459 https://www.dailymail.co.uk/news/article-8347011/Doctors-California-say-people-killed-four-weeks-YEAR.html

Australia registered one and a half times as many suicides as coronavirus deaths since March.[460] This shows once again that the damage caused by coercive measures is worse than what the virus is said to have caused.

It is even worse in Japan. There, the number of suicides rose to 2,153 in one month (October), which is more than the number of official corona deaths in the whole year, namely 2,087! Only a few countries, like Japan, publish such figures. There, young people are also strongly affected: Japan is the only country in the G7 where the main cause of death among 15 to 39-year-olds is suicide! [461]

Even if the coercive measures were stopped immediately, the wave of suicides would not be stopped yet, because the economic crisis is still to come. At the moment, governments are still distributing aid money and paying short-time allowances. If that stops, then the insolvencies and waves of redundancies will come, which have been postponed until now. A rule of thumb of the trade unions says that with every one percent increase in unemployment, the number of suicides rises by one percent.

I will not attempt an estimate of the economic damage caused by the lockdown and travel restrictions in this book. Most of the damage is not even foreseeable yet, but it is already clear that the consequences will be far worse than any other crisis since 1945.

460 https://www.aier.org/article/madness-in-melbourne/
461 https://de.rt.com/gesellschaft/109888-japan-mehr-tote-wegen-selbstmorde/

The destruction of culture

One little-noticed sector that is taking a big hit is culture. With 1.5 million people, the cultural sector is one of the largest industries in Germany. More than 100,000 ensembles, theatres, concert halls, cinemas, organisers, technicians, etc. are facing ruin. While authors have had to give up readings but can continue to publish, actors and musicians are deprived of work opportunities. The slow opening in summer has done little good, because the Corona harassment such as distance rules dictate that the halls can only be filled to a fraction and thus generate losses. It is like in gastronomy: for a few visitors it is not worth opening because the costs exceed the income.

Classical music is particularly hard hit, as the audience is mostly older and hardly dares to leave their home. For example, Hamburg's Elbphilharmonie, which is usually sold out, is only allowed to sell 800 of its more than 2,000 seats, and even those are rarely reached. In Germany, singing together is also forbidden, choirs are no longer allowed to meet. That did not exist in the 3rd Reich or under Stalinism!

Very few musicians have fixed employment contracts in orchestras and depend on their own pension schemes. Savings are melting away in the lockdown, and there is no improvement in sight. Thus, creative artists will soon lengthen the queues at the social welfare office, and the country will become even more culturally impoverished. What is currently taking place in Western world is a silent cultural revolution. Unlike in China, cultural workers are not being killed, but their work is being banned and their livelihoods destroyed. And we are all losing the opportunity to enjoy culture live – they want to nail us in front of the TV and computer screen, there we can be controlled.

What is surprising, however, is how few artists are standing up against the Corona regime, at least verbally. With a few exceptions, they keep a low profile, presumably because they are afraid of being ostracised if the business should run again at some point. Yet their prominence could have much more impact on the public than the protests of scientists. There was a tired attempt where they politely asked the government to be classified as "systemically relevant" after all. No, dear artists, you are obviously not, at least not in the eyes of the powerful. You have to act more violently.

There has never been a closure of churches and bans on worship in Germany before either, not even in the darkest of times. The faithful can no longer even seek comfort where they usually do. One may stand by religion as one likes, but it too is part of our culture and history. However, with a few exceptions[462], the churches and the priests have failed by not only accepting all this without protest, but for the most part playing along with the evil game.

---

462 For example, the courageous sermons of Pastor Jakob Tscharntke
http://www.pi-news.net/2020/12/pastor-jakob-tscharntke-die-macht-des-boesen-tobt-sich-aus/

The Corona Religion

The title may seem a little strange to you, but religion and "Corona" certainly have a lot in common. In both cases it is about an invisible being whose existence is not proven and in which one can believe or not. In both cases there are "experts", here priests, there virologists, whose task it is to explain this being to believers and non-believers alike and to bring them closer to it. In both cases, non-believers are proselytised and, if they do not play along, ostracised and sanctioned.

The "Corona's Witnesses" consider themselves to be in possession of the only truth revealed by their revered prophets (Drosten, Fauci etc.). Anyone who questions this is committing blasphemy. Heretics cannot count on tolerance, they cannot take part in discussion, because their arguments must be false by definition. The particularly stubborn are put down by the Inquisition in the pulpit of the mainstream media.

Those who are employed are fired, those who are not are deprived of their livelihood (licence to practise), because examples must be made as a warning. *"Punish one, educate thousands,"* Mao Tse Tung allegedly said. It's all been done before – the strategy is well known.

Now you would think we would have overcome such nonsense long ago. Enlightenment seemed to be a secure good, but this is a fallacy. There are also quite irrational views in modern science that must not be questioned, driven by business interests and a desire for prestige. Medicine in particular has become a coveted object of those who earn extraordinarily well with their treatment methods and medicines. I won't go into this now, but it is obvious that there are not only losers in Corona, but also winners, and on a very large scale. The millions of tests administered worldwide and the profits from the billions of planned vaccinations alone are beyond comparison.

Of course, no one stands up and says that he wants to rip us all off and therefore we have to follow him. No, there has to be a "higher goal", a morally sound one. How about "health", that's what everyone wants, isn't it?

After all, the priests only want what is best for their flocks. As I said, the thesis is health, the antithesis is death, and the synthesis is vaccination or coercive measures. The virus has the role of evil, of the devil who wants to destroy us, and whoever is possessed by it can only be saved by the priest-doctors.

Anyone who doubts this belief is evil, too, and *"endangers others"* if, for example, they do not wear a mask or go out partying – a case for the Inquisition. The whole system follows the pattern of a bigoted Puritan religion. As with the Puritans, the most fanatical believers are those who follow the priests under fear and renunciation (*"then I'll just stay at home, then I'll just wear the mask"*) in order to be saved if possible.

Then someone comes along who blithely ignores the whole spell and afterwards – oh sacrilege! – doesn't even fall ill as a punishment, then envy is great. Someone like that has to go, because he would expose the futility of this theatre, if one thought about it. Then it's better not to think about it, but to follow the herd. That is more comfortable.

Merkel used the pseudo-religious dressing up of the corona virus when she called it a *"calamity"* and a *"visitation"*.[463] By the way, the name "Corona" is well chosen: the "crown" of viruses, the royal class. And now please all get on your knees and pray along: *"Corona is almighty and Drosten is his prophet. And deliver us from the virus. Amen."*

---

463 https://deutsch.rt.com/inland/108178-fuerchtet-merkel-strafe-gottes-corona/

The legal aspect

Many people have asked themselves in recent months whether the government is allowed to interfere so strongly with our fundamental rights. After all, lockdown and quarantine are de facto deprivations of liberty, travel bans are restrictions on freedom of movement, compulsory masks endanger our health, i.e. our "physical integrity", the ban on religious services violates the free exercise of religion, and the forced closures of entire sectors such as gastronomy, tour operators, hotels, artists, freelancers, etc., prevent the free exercise of one's profession and in many cases threaten one's existence.

The German Basic Law contains many articles that are well-intentioned and sound good, but there are backdoors. Many articles on fundamental rights state that they *"may only be restricted by a federal law"*. In short: they may be restricted.

This is exactly what the federal government practices with the help of the Infection Protection Act.[464] This was approved by the parliament, and since then it has no longer been consulted. The Chancellor, the Health Minister and the Minister-Presidents of the 15 federal states now govern "in the manner of a lord of the manor" in closed rounds of talks. The results are then announced to the people on public TV.

Liberal party FDP leader Lindner criticised the method as *"secret diplomacy"* and said that parliaments should no longer be bypassed. He probably only says that because he is not member of the deciding committee.

The "lonely decisions from above" also include the completely arbitrary "incidence rate" of 35 or 50 test positives per 100,000 inhabitants. It has no scientific background whatsoever, and here again the reference value is missing: how many tests, pray tell? It is easy to exceed this number, you

---

464 https://www.sozialgesetzbuch-sgb.de/ifsg/1.html

just have to increase the number of tests until the false positives become statistically significant. Some doctors have seen through this trick and complain about it, but they stubbornly continue to test. The main thing is that the politicians can once again unleash harassment on the people.

The many absurdities of bureaucracy are further enriched by number games as they are currently practised in Austria: *"Example: In the municipality of Hüttschlag with 900 inhabitants, there were seven people who tested positive. Extrapolating the seven-day incidence to 100,000 inhabitants, 780 people tested positive are then reported as the official number. But 773 of them do not exist, they were only statistically calculated. So you have a "contaminated" village. And since Austria consists mainly of small communities, the country quickly becomes a super-spreader.*

In international comparative statistics for states, where even one million inhabitants are used as a reference value, small states such as Qatar, Andorra or the Vatican are consequently at the top of the infection figures. For example, about 800 people live in the Vatican City State, 26 of whom have tested positive for Corona since March. Extrapolated from this, there are 32,000 cases, i.e. more than there are inhabitants." [465]

But one thing is often forgotten: All coercive measures are only regulations and not laws.[466] But they would have to be because of the serious encroachments on fundamental rights, which may only be restricted by laws, if at all. Ordinances cannot stand above the Basic Law and thus fundamental rights – a legal principle that is constantly ignored.

In their decrees, the authorities refer to § 28 of the Infection Protection Act, which allows *"protective measures in the case of infected or suspected cases"*, such as quarantine, surveil-

---

465 https://www.compact-online.de/statistik-wie-man-corona-zahlen-ins-riesenhafte-hochrechnet/
466 I will come back to the amendment of November 2020

lance and, since the amendment in June, also restrictions on freedom of movement. However, this refers to specific individual cases and not to the population as a whole.

A whole nation is put under general suspicion here - everyone is *suspect*.

Furthermore, § 28 allows restrictions on fundamental rights only *"to the extent and for as long as necessary to prevent the spread of communicable diseases"*. This is interpreted extremely freely and sweepingly, without any evaluation of the proportionality of the measures. There is also no professional evaluation (assessment) of the measures taken so far to see whether they have achieved anything at all. The government and the RKI simply ignore this. It is very convenient to be able to simply pass regulations without having to justify or discuss them. That no longer has anything to do with democracy.

In addition, the courts rarely oppose government policy. This is due to a peculiarity of the German judicial system that few people are aware of: the Federal Republic of Germany is the only country in Europe where the judiciary is not independent, not even formally. The public prosecutors' offices here are subordinate to the interior ministries of the States or the federal government and are thus bound by instructions. This means that the interior ministers can prevent charges from being brought at all at any time, and "where there's no accuser, there's no judge." No matter how convinced a judge is of a person's or authority's guilt, without a public prosecutor's office there will be no trial at all.

Why do you think the many criminal charges against Merkel and her minister of the interior in 2015, which involved numerous breaches of the law in the great opening of the border, all ended up in the wastepaper basket? Because the public prosecutors were not allowed to take action on the instructions of the Ministry of the Interior. It's that simple in Germany – the judiciary is subordinate to the executive. There is no real separation of powers in the FRG. For this reason, the European Court of Justice has barred the FRG from using the European arrest warrant until the problem is fixed at some point, but I doubt it will.

Nevertheless, opposition is growing among lawyers, too, many judges are concerned about the presumptions of the executive. More than 60 decrees issued by the authorities have been "overturned" by courts all over Germany because they were unlawful. [467]

But all this is not enough for the Minister of Health, who wants to extend and even tighten his special rights. The liberal MP Konstantin Kuhle criticises that a self-confident parliament should not allow this shift of power. [468]

The unlawful exclusion of parliaments is criticised by many lawyers. Many are of the opinion that the Infection Protection Act is actually an enabling law that can be used to undermine basic civil rights. The President of the Constitutional Court of Rhineland-Palatinate, Lars Brocker, warned that the special rights regime of corona ordinances is not constitutional because only the executive acts. The most severe restrictions of fundamental rights since the end of the Second World War lack any democratic legitimacy. The government is aware of the unconstitutionality of the Corona coercive measures. [469]

The former president of the Federal Constitutional Court, Hans-Jürgen Papier, says that civil liberties are in danger. It is not the relaxation of measures that must be justified, but

---

467 https://kopp-report.de/wie-politik-und-medien-die-ganze-wahrheit-ueber-corona-tests-verschweigen/

468 https://de.sputniknews.com/deutschland/20201019328218325-parlament-sonderrechte-spahns-kontrollieren/

469 https://kopp-report.de/praesident-des-verfassungsgerichtshofs-warnt-vor-corona-sonderrechtsregime/

their maintenance. The purpose of a constitutional state is first and foremost the protection of freedom. One cannot justify every encroachment on freedom with health protection. [470]

One must "really watch out" that the Basic Law is not undermined by ad hoc emergency regulations, he warned in an interview with the newspaper "Süddeutsche Zeitung", referring to the draft epidemic law in North Rhine-Westphalia as an example. According to this, doctors and nurses should be able to be obliged to do certain work there, but this is not possible according to Article 12 of the Basic Law. Basic rights are not touched even in times of war, and this should apply all the more in this emergency, said Papier. [471]

Hans Michael Heinig, a constitutional law expert from Göttingen, warned that *"our community could turn from a democratic constitutional state into a fascist hysterical hygiene state in a very short period of time"*, and Oliver Lepsius, a constitutional law expert from Münster, said in a WDR TV programme: *"The lockdown in March and April was unconstitutional in any case, at least in large parts, because disproportionate action was taken, numerous measures were taken that cannot be justified. There will be no new lockdown, which would be unlawful in the form we experienced it today!"*[472] But that did not stop the government from committing further violations of the law as we know now.

It is also annoying that many politicians do not even comply with the regulations with which they torment the people. In the parliament, they are supposed to wear masks so that it is not so noticeable, but with the instruction to take a break

470 https://www.tagesspiegel.de/politik/ex-verfassungsrichter-ruegt-regierung-papier-sieht-in-coronavirus-krise-freiheitsrechte-bedroht/25793984.html

471 https://deutsch.rt.com/inland/107990-spahn-will-zeitlich-unbegrenzte-machtbefugnisse/

472 https://www.reitschuster.de/post/corona-ketzerei-jetzt-auch-bei-wdr-und-rbb/

every 30 minutes because of the lack of oxygen. But our children are supposed to suffocate under the mask for one or more school hours. Or the Social Democratic party celebrated the lost election in the state of NRW with a huge party, close together and without masks. There was protest – so what? I haven't heard anything about fines.

"Now the Corona aristocracy has secured another privilege for itself: When politicians travel to so-called risk areas (e.g. to Berlin), they only need to claim that they are doing so 'within the scope of their mandate', and already – what a miracle – they are immune to infections. Which is why there is no need for a 14-day quarantine.

This medical miracle of being immunised against Corona through one's profession also affects associated groups: "According to the Berlin ordinance, all persons whose activities are absolutely necessary for the maintenance of the functioning of the representation of the people, the government and the administration of the Federation, the states and the municipalities are exempt from the quarantine obligation". The employer decides to whom the "compelling necessity" applies.

Where is the outcry from Dr. Christian Drosten? Where the hysterical warning cries of Karl Lauterbach? Nothing to be heard. Doesn't seem to be a problem. But it should be clear: in a real pandemic, with Ebola for example, this regulation would not stand a chance. But we are not talking about such dangerous pathogens."[473]

Actually, we have an institution in Germany that is supposed to protect the constitution: Federal Office for the Protection of the Constitution. But where is it when you need it? It seems to be busy tracking down right-wing and left-wing extremists who would not be in a position to seriously endanger the constitution. The real danger to the Basic Law

---

473 https://www.compact-online.de/die-corona-aristokratie-abgeordnete-muessen-nicht-in-quarantaene/

currently comes from the government itself. But you have to come up with that first.

In Austria, the Constitutional Court overruled the following provisions as unconstitutional at the end of October due to a lack of "documentation of proportionality and necessity": 1) ban on entering restaurants, 2) restrictions concerning the admission of groups of visitors to restaurants, 3) ban on events with more than ten people (discos, etc.) and 4) obligation to wear masks in enclosed public places. This ruling now allows all entrepreneurs in Austria to claim damages from the state. [474]

In complete ignorance of this ruling, the Austrian government imposed a lockdown for the whole of November two days later. Culture, sports, gastronomy (except for delivery services), hotels, and on top of that a nightly curfew from 8 p.m. to 6 a.m. will be closed.

In England, a law firm has come forward to charge every single MP who voted for the Corona Bill with fraud, treason and genocide. These are the first treason charges since World War 2. [475]

In Bavaria, a lawyer wanted the Administrative Court to examine whether the Corona restrictions imposed by the state government were illegal. To do so, she requested the files on the lockdown decision from the Ministry of Health, from which it would be possible to gauge what the decisions were based on. The court should assess whether the government's assessment was constitutional. The ministry replied that there were no files on this. So, the lockdown had been decided "just like that", without a danger and risk assessment, without a plan – non-transparent and undemocratic. [476]

---

474 https://www.youtube.com/watch?v=Pq_q0RedfYg&list=PLnLvsTJGt-6Fdtlnq9ujCsoJQ5AToFXjW&index=1
475 https://www.henrymakow.com/2020/10/mak-devlin-Covid-fraud.html

This procedure of arbitrarily issuing regulations that are not comprehensible, neither in their justification nor in their logic, runs through the entire republic. An atmosphere of arbitrariness by wild-eyed officials and health authorities is spreading. Obviously senseless regulations are issued, high fines are ripped off, then replaced by new standards, tightened up and relaxed again, except for one thing: **abolished**. People are simply tired of it.

At some point, the government's arrogant abuse of power will blow up in its face. One can only hope that it won't be too much longer.

---

476 https://www.br.de/nachrichten/bayern/staatsregierung-keine-akten-zu-corona-beschluessen,SA6NyUL

The legal situation at the 2nd lockdown in November 2020:

A "coup d'état" from above

As early as September, the people were being prepared for a "second wave" by the media. In October, this was brought about by the enormous increase in tests to 1.6 million per week,[477] with additional cross-reactions with other flu viruses.

With autumn and winter, the usual flu mortality rates will also rise again and, as in spring, will be counted among the corona deaths. This will then be used to "justify" even tougher measures. The time limit of the measures until the end of November is only a farce. In order to keep the resistance against them small, the people are left with the hope of an improvement of the situation for the time being. They are still supposed to hope for a Christmas with freedom of travel and assembly, as a carrot that is dangled in front of the donkey's nose so that it will keep running. But the Christmas markets have already been cancelled, and there will probably be no New Year's Eve parties either.

We know from the experience of the first lockdown that it had no effect on the infection figures, and "those up there" know that too. The new restrictions are purely political. Lawyers are horrified and some speak of a *"coup from above"*. Because the rulings of the administrative courts that had overturned curfews or the mask requirement, for example in Heidelberg, as *"unconstitutional"* are simply ignored. After the parliament, the judiciary is now bypassed, too, the executive rules alone, without debates. This is the hallmark of a dictatorship, that it abolishes the separation of powers - once a great good of democracy.

---

477 https://www.rki.de/DE/Content/InfAZ/N/Neuartiges_Coronavirus/ Daten/Testzahlen-gesamt.xlsx?__blob=publicationFile

Something similar last happened in Germany in 1933 with the "Enabling Act".[478] Only one who seemed queasy about this was the prime minister of Thuringia, because he is demanding that the Bundestag declare a "state of health emergency". This would at least formally legalise the restrictions on basic rights, because according to Article 81 of the Basic Law, this can only happen in a state of emergency.[479]

But the government is also overriding other legal principles by allowing *"cooperation between the federal and state governments"* during controls. This means that the Federal Police, the Federal Border Guard and the Federal Armed Forces can now also be involved in the search for violations. In addition, in future controls may be carried out *"without suspicion"*, i.e. without concrete indications of a violation, especially *"near the border"*. Why the virus should be more active near the border than far from it is beyond me. If the darling of the talk shows, spokesman Lauterbach, then gets away with the proposal to abolish the inviolability of the home, then it will not be the Christ Child or Santa Claus who comes on Christmas Eve, but the police, to check whether too many people are celebrating together and – God forbid – perhaps even singing!

Even if the measures are ended at some point, thousands of restaurateurs, hotel employees, artists and event organisers, etc., etc. will be insolvent again. Yet the facts give no reason for the whole thing. The RKI published that most infections happen at home, followed by hospitals and nursing homes.[480] In restaurants, there were only one hundredth as many infections as at home, and of all places, they are being closed down! This is pure harassment. According to the RKI, only 3.5% of infections occur during leisure activities, 0.7% in

478 https://de.wikipedia.org/wiki/Ermächtigungsgesetz
479 https://de.wikipedia.org/wiki/Gesetzgebungsnotstand
480 https://www.rki.de/DE/Content/Infekt/EpidBull/Archiv/2020/Ausgaben/
   38_20.pdf?__blob=publicationFile

day-care centres, schools or universities, 0.5% in restaurants, but 56% in private households. [481]

It is very strange that the state of Saxony-Anhalt has also imposed the lockdown, because, as the prime minister emphasised, it was not even necessary because of the infection figures, but they are going along with it out of *"national solidarity"*.[482] That is the most stupid justification for the destruction of livelihoods that I have ever heard: with solidarity to the abyss.

Apart from the artificial positive figures, there is no significant increase in the number of people who have **actually** fallen ill or died. One only has to look at the RKI reports: the statistics of acute respiratory illnesses "Flu Web"[483] or the already described sentinel of the RKI. The author Michael W. Alberts summarised this in the article "Where is the emergency?" with the result that the numbers of respiratory illnesses in the sentinel doctor's practices, in the patient data in the flu web, as well as in the hospitals are all in the normal range.[484] They are not above those of the previous year, and there was not a single Covid19 case in children under 14.

But *"there could be more"*, and there are enough intensive care beds, but there is a shortage of staff, etc., the agitators tell us on all channels. Conservative party leader Armin Laschet claimed on 28 October that we are not in a state of emergency, but we could end up in one at some point. Yes, war could break out, but we are not prophylactically imposing martial law now. We face a "state of emergency" without emergency.

Even the newspaper "Die Welt" ran the headline on 29.10.20 that the lockdown would only work if Germans gave up

481 https://www.gmx.net/magazine/news/coronavirus/deutschen-coronavirus-infiziert-35027446

482 https://www.mz-web.de/sachsen-anhalt/haerte-mit-bedauern-welche-abweichungen-es-beim-lockdown-in-sachsen-anhalt-gibt-37554678

483 https://grippeweb.rki.de/

484 https://www.achgut.com/artikel/neue_rki_zahlen_wo_ist_der_notstand

logical thinking.[485] But most of them already have, which is why it works so well.

What has been concealed from the German public is the change of mood at the WHO, which is otherwise fond of quoting, in October, at the same time as the scaremongering in the German media:

- The WHO Regional Director for Emergencies, Dorit Nitzan, said on 13 October that there is currently **no second Corona wave**. The types and forms of the virus would prove that. The WHO has noticed that the number of infected people is decreasing.[486]

- One of the WHO's six special envoys, Dr. David Nabarro, said in an interview in the British magazine The Spectator on 8 October: *"We in the World Health Organisation do not advocate lockdowns as a primary means of controlling this virus. And so we really appeal to all world leaders: stop using lockdowns as your primary method of control, develop better systems for it, but remember – **lockdowns have only one consequence, and that is to make poor people many times poorer.**"* [487]

- At the beginning of October, the WHO bulletin by Prof. John Ioannides on the mortality rate of Covid19 sufferers was published. The world's leading epidemiologist evaluated 61 studies in which the actual infection rate of population groups was researched. He compared the data with the official

485 https://www.welt.de/politik/deutschland/plus218861244/Dieser-Lockdown-funktioniert-nur-wenn-man-das-logische-Denken-sein-laesst.html
486 https://ria.ru/20201013/volna-1579544853.html
https://www.wochenblick.at/who-sprecherin-stellt-klar-es-gibt-keine-zweite-corona-welle/
487 Source: https://www.reitschuster.de/post/who-jetzt-gegen-lockdown/

COVID-19 deaths in the respective study areas and corrected the results for the number of antibody types tested. He found that at 51 sites studied, the mortality rate among infected persons averaged only 0.27% (corrected 0.23%), which does not justify lockdowns, masks or spacing rules.[488] **Now official on the part of the WHO that the mortality rate of Corona is in the same order of magnitude as that of influenza.**

All this is ignored by the government and the disinformation media in order to be able to push through the "coup from above". Democracy is endangered, it has already been de facto abolished.

Furthermore, the CDU in Baden-Württemberg demands that police volunteers be used to monitor compliance with the Corona rules. *"Because the police volunteer looks like a normal police officer. Although they are not public servants and have only limited training, they carry a service weapon and uniform. Basic training for police volunteers is 84 hours, and in-service training is 18 hours annually ".*[489]

One wonders how they will handle the weapon during the rapid training. Section 65 of the police law in North Rhine-Westphalia says: *"Firearms may only be used against persons in a crowd if serious acts of violence are being committed by them or from them or are imminent and other measures do not promise any success.* Judging this at a demonstration requires experience and good nerves. And section 64 says: *"Firearms may only be used against persons to prevent the forcible release of a person from official custody."* What happens if someone doesn't want to be quarantined and escapes? Can they be shot then? The step towards a police state is small.

488 https://www.who.int/bulletin/online_first/BLT.20.265892.pdf
489 https://www.reitschuster.de/post/cdu-will-corona-hilfspolizisten/

Meanwhile, the Bavarian police are upgrading, they bought two new armoured "offensive vehicles" with weapon stations and an MG on a rotating ring mount. They look like infantry fighting vehicles and are ideal for domestic operations because instead of "Bundeswehr" (Army), that is forbidden to act in domestic field by constitutional law, it says "Police".[490]

Video blogger Milena Preradovic warned that once freedoms are taken away, they are not quickly given back, then people get used to them and the next generation doesn't even know they once existed. [491]

Another attempt to undermine democracy is a "elaboration" by the Scientific Service of the Bundestag from July 2020, which, however, only became known in October. It is about the possibility of postponing the Bundestag election planned for 2021 "because of Corona" – for up to 48 months! Freelance journalist Boris Reitschuster comments:

"If we didn't live in times when yesterday's "conspiracy theory" is all too often tomorrow's reality, I would have laughed in the spring when insiders told me that there were thoughts of postponing the 2021 federal election. Granting thus Angela Merkel and her team a "term extension". For free, so to speak, without the voters having to agree. I fervently hoped that the information was a "hoax". In other words, a nasty rumour."[492] Let's see, I wouldn't put it past Merkel and her ministers.

Criticism of the new lockdown, which is playfully called "lockdown light", came not only from lawyers, but also from doctors and scientists. The head of the Association of Statutory Health Insurance Physicians (Kassenärztliche Vereinigung), Andreas Gassen, does not consider blanket

---

490 https://de.rt.com/inland/109949-bayerns-polizei-bekommt-gepanzerte-fahrzeuge-mit-waffenstationen/
491 https://t.me/MilenaPreradovic
492 https://www.reitschuster.de/post/bundestagswahl-koennte-wegen-corona-verschoben-werden/

lockdown regulations to be effective, as can be seen in Spain or Italy, where the numbers are rising despite the lockdown. You cannot put whole countries or continents into a kind of coma for months. [493]Yes, you can - unfortunately.

Addendum:

The end of fundamental rights on 18.11.2020

After the chapters above were written, the Infection Protection Act was massively amended: Despite massive protests and a peaceful demonstration in Berlin that was bludgeoned with water cannons and pepper spray, the parliament with a simple majority passed the amendment that allows for a massive restriction of basic rights by the health authorities, without the participation of parliament. The opposition, as well as ten extremely courageous MPs from government parties, voted against.

The most alarming points are:

- Vaccination is compulsory: Anyone returning to Germany from a risk area must either present a vaccination certificate or undergo a compulsory examination. (§36 para. 10 no. 1b)
- All public transport (bus, train, plane, ship) as well as airports, train stations, etc. should immediately report disease and infection "suspects" to the public health department. (§36 para. 10 no. 2 d and f)

---

493 https://deutsch.rt.com/inland/108306-artzeverbande-und-virologen-sprechen-sich/

- Anyone returning from a foreign "risk area" must register in a digital database on their return and state where they have stayed for 10 days before and after crossing the border. (§36 para. 8)

- The Federal Armed Forces are to ensure that the corona protection measures are observed (§54a)

- The RKI is supposed to monitor virology and health of citizens. Although the name is anonymised, it is easy to determine via algorithms on the basis of the other compulsory data. (§13 par. 3-5)

- *The* Ministry of Health is given several new powers: *"The Federal Ministry of Health is empowered to determine by statutory order without the consent of the Federal Council..."*

- The meaningless figure of "50 cases per 100,000" is set here, and a whole series of measures are listed that are to come into force: Closure of restaurants, cultural and leisure facilities and community centres, prohibition of alcohol, prohibition of meetings and events, and, of course, compulsory masks and distance. (§28a para. 1 and 2)

- The law says it permanently restricts fundamental rights: *"Article 1, numbers 16 and 17 restrict the fundamental rights of freedom of the person (Article 2(2), second sentence, GG), freedom of assembly (Article 8 GG), freedom of movement (Article 11(1) GG) and inviolability of the home (Article 13(1) GG)."* *(§7)*" [494]

What is embarrassing is that with this safeguarding of the coercive measures, it is indirectly admitted that, as I already explained above, the ordinances before 18.11. were simply

---

[494] https://t.me/LIONMediaTelegram/2975

not constitutional. The law[495] is valid quasi indefinitely, as long as the parliament does not declare the "epidemic" over. What is dangerous is that it does not only apply to Covid19, which means that the law can be applied at any time in the event of a "threat situation", such as a wave of influenza. Is the dictatorship of permanent pandemics coming now?

The haste with which the law was rushed through is also suspicious: On the same day, the second and third readings were held in parliament and voted on immediately, in the afternoon the Federal Council was called together to give its nod, and in the evening the Federal President signed it. Therefore, it could enter into force the very next day.

An employee of the parliament, who wishes to remain anonymous, told journalist Boris Reitschuster: *"That such an important law with such far-reaching consequences would be pushed through in this way is a novelty and makes a mockery of democratic principles. This is nothing but a spectacle, the procedure is only followed pro forma, the MPs are only called to vote pro forma. In fact, the Bundestag is only needed to play democracy. It is governed from the top down with instructions."* Angela Merkel is familiar with this style of government from the [former socialist] German Democratic Republic, [from where she proceeds], says the staff member pointedly: *"It reminds me of democratic centralism'*, an idea once introduced by Lenin".* [496]

The word *"Enabling Act"* made the rounds, prompting outrage in the media, as so-called "Nazi comparisons" are known to be reserved for leftists and the mainstream. But the comparison is not too far-fetched, as the word *"empower"* or *"authorisation"* appears 24 times in the 38 pages of the law in various contexts. It is also unusual that the English term *"surveillance"* appears several times in a German law. So that it is for Germans not so obvious what is meant. In

---

495 https://dserver.bundestag.de/btd/19/239/1923944.pdf
496 https://www.reitschuster.de/post/corona-gesetz-abstimmung-im-blindflug/

addition, we find the word *"prohibition"* 7 times, *8 times "restriction", 10 times "segregation", 12 times "control", 13 times "distance", 16 times "prohibition", 24 times "restriction", 48 times "contact",* **59 times "vaccination"** *and* **113 times "obligation"**.

Even the UN Commissioner for Human Rights, Michelle Bachelet, warned of a human rights catastrophe because many democratic rights are being restricted worldwide because of Corona. Emergency laws should not be used as a weapon against the opposition, to control the people or even to keep power. The rule of law must be preserved even in the crisis and the measures should be limited in time. [497]

The French philosopher Montesquieu once said:

"There is no crueller tyranny than that which is exercised under the cloak of laws and with the appearance of justice; for that is, as it were, drowning unfortunates on the plank on which they have saved themselves."

However, a law similar to the one in Germany was prevented in Denmark by massive protests. The protesters had loudly voiced their displeasure for nine days with pans and pots in front of the Danish parliament without being attacked with water cannons. On 16 November, the government withdrew the law. The news was suppressed in the mainstream media – Europe-wide, as far as I know. [498]

However, a lawyer of lateral thinkers, Ralf Ludwig, also sees an opportunity in the new law. According to §28a, paragraph 2 of the Infection Protection Act, measures are only permissible if there are infections. Test-positives, however, are not infected. Ludwig says that the health authorities now have the burden of proof for existing infections, i.e. an "agent capable of being bred" must be proven, because only this is

---

497 https://www.nau.ch/news/europa/uno-warnt-angesichts-von-corona-massnahmen-vor-menschenrechtskatastrophe-65699148

498 https://www.compact-online.de/daenemark-nach-dem-nerz-massaker-infektionsschutzgesetz-durch-demonstranten-gekippt/

infectious. Without such an agent, no measures can be taken. Otherwise, every employee would be **liable to prosecution** if the proof was not provided. [499]

The question remains whether the public prosecutors' offices will accept such complaints, since they are "bound by instructions" in Germany.

Ludwig refers to a ruling by the Portuguese Court of Appeal, which one day earlier had declared a decision by the Azores Health Department to be unlawful.[500] Four German tourists were to be quarantined, one was PCR-positive, the others had "contact" with him, as is also regulated in many countries. The court concluded that a PCR test does not prove infection. With a ct of more than 35 cycles, as is common in most laboratories in Europe and the USA, the probability that the result is false-positive is 97%. Since the number of cycles in Portuguese laboratories is unknown, there is no proof of infection. In addition, it is not permissible to make a diagnosis without a licensed doctor. So, it could not be determined whether the person was infected and the others were exposed to a risk. [501]

This was promptly followed by an outcry from the Portuguese mainstream press that the judges had *"exceeded their competences"* and called for disciplinary measures against them. The country's Supreme Judicial Council reviewed the case, upheld the judges and rejected disciplinary measures.[502]

---

499 http://blauerbote.com/2020/11/19/infektionsschutzgesetz-pandemie-vorbei/
500 https://drive.google.com/file/d/1t1b01H0Jd4hsMU7V1vy70yr8s3jlBedr/view
501 https://deutsch.rt.com/europa/109423-portugiesisches-berufungsgericht-haelt-pcr-tests-fuer-nicht-aussagekraeftig/
502 https://de.rt.com/europa/110036-pcr-test-verbreitete-rt-falschbehauptung/

With the scientifically correct argumentation of the judges, the "epidemic situation" can be overturned worldwide, because: *Where no pathogen has been detected, there is no pandemic.*

The criticism from experts

Of course, since the beginning of the Corona crisis, there have been experts who contradict the official propaganda. I will name some of them, but the list is by no means complete, and more are being named every day. All the people mentioned are easy to find on the internet, on video platforms and Telegram.

- Among the first was Dr. Wolfgang Wodarg, to whom the whole thing must have seemed like déjà vu from the swine flu era.

- Prof. Sucharid Bhakti also warned very early and wrote the first book about it together with his wife: "Corona – False Alarm?"

- The ENT doctor Dr. Bodo Schiffmann was a co-founder of the new corona critical party "Resistance 2020", but turned away from the project and has since concentrated on lectures all over Germany. Together with the committed Samuel Eckert, who became very successful as a corona-critical blogger in a short time, he drove around the country with a tour bus to organise information events. In the meantime, he has been fired from his practice and is threatened with a professional ban. [503]

- Dr. Claus Köhnlein, who published vaccine-critical books years ago, gives informative interviews on the internet.

- In the USA, Prof. John Ioannidis is the most renowned corona critic. He is the most cited scientist worldwide.

- Since the parliament ignored the demand for a parliamentary committee of enquiry, the "Corona Investigating Committee" was set up by experienced lawyers, with the support of doctors like Dr. Wodarg. Doctors and other experts have their say in long hearings, the hearings are documented on video and put on the web.[504]

- The Hamburg doctor Dr. Heiko Schöning is co-founder of the "Doctors for Enlightenment Foundation."[505] (Their bank simply closed their account and returned the donations to the donors).

- A group of six health experts around the health scientist Matthias Schrappe prepared a critical "thesis paper on the pandemic". [506]

- The crisis management department KM4 in the Federal Ministry of the Interior prepared the detailed report "Analysis of Crisis Management" together with ten external doctors and medical experts from several German universities. The report attests to serious failures in the government's crisis management,

503 https://www.compact-online.de/praxis-von-querdenker-arzt-bodo-schiffmann-gekuendigt-verliert-er-nun-auch-seine-zulassung/
504 http://www.corona-ausschuss.de/
505 https://www.ärzte-für-aufklärung.de
506 https://www.springerpflege.de/sars-cov-2/thesenpapier-zur-pandemie-durch-sars-cov-2-Covid-19/17868956

deficits in the regulation of pandemics and concludes that the Corona crisis was a false alarm.[507] But the report was neither heeded nor published. The authors of the report then accused the government of ignoring the experts' advice, but the ministry remained silent. Then a BMI employee, Senior Government Councillor Stephan Kohn, leaked the report to critical media, which caused some uproar. Mr. Kohn was suspended from duty and banned from the ministry.[508]

- Doctors and scientists of the "Mediziner und Wissenschaftler für Gesundheit, Freiheit und Demokratie e.V." (Physicians and Scientists for Health, Freedom and Democracy) were refused by the newspaper "Frankfurter Allgemeine Zeitung" to place a paid (and expensive) advertisement calling for a repeal of the Corona measures.[509] Subsequently, the non-profit status was revoked.

- In an open letter, more than 300 Belgian doctors and 1,100 health professionals call on their government to immediately stop the Corona measures. They say they are disproportionate and do more harm than good. There is no medical justification for this policy.[510]

- Dr. Beda M. Stadler, Professor Emeritus of Immunology and former Director of the Institute of Immunology at the University of Bern, criticised the Corona policy in the newspaper "Zürcher Weltwoche" and other media.[511]

507 https://hallo-meinung.de/Innenministerium_Bericht2_geschwaerzt.pdf
508 https://www.tichyseinblick.de/tichys-einblick/brisante-studie-aus-dem-bmi-teil-2-massive-interne-kritik-an-rki-und-bundesregierung/
509 https://www.metropolnews.info/mp463673/aerzte-wissenschaftler-gegen-maskenterror-und-wirtschaftszerstoerung-faz-zensiert-anzeige-journalisten-als-medizinexperten
510 https://docs4opendebate.be/open-brief/
511 https://www.achgut.com/artikel/corona_aufarbeitung_warum_alle_falsch_lagen

- The head of the National Association of Statutory Health Insurance Physicians, Andreas Gassen, warns against excessive political actions. Even 10,000 infections a day would not be a problem as long as only one in 1,000 becomes seriously ill, as is currently the case. According to Gassen, he also does not see a Corona rush in the practices or a shortage of beds in hospitals. [512]

- The head of Frankfurt's public health department, Prof. René Gottschalk, recommended listening not only to virologists but also to pandemic specialists and not to fixate too much on infection figures. There is an urgent need for a broad public discussion on the goals and means of pandemic control. [513]

- The head of the Aichach-Friedberg health department in Bavaria, Dr. Friedrich Pürner, agrees with this criticism and says that the so-called infection figures are not a reliable indicator and doubts the effectiveness of mask-wearing in children. Dr. Pürner was punitively transferred because of his criticism. [514]

- Charité chief epidemiologist Stefan Willich suggested on rbb-Inforadio that the no longer usable limit of 50 new infections should be reconsidered – If only because much more is already being tested and the probability of the value being exceeded is thus higher. [515]

- On 4.10.20 scientists from Oxford, Harvard and Stanford Universities published the "Great Barrington

512 https://de.sputniknews.com/deutschland/20201012328136746-warum-kassenarztchef-ploetzlich-rki-widerspricht/
513 ibid
514 ibid. and https://deutsch.rt.com/inland/108885-wegen-kritik-an-corona-politik/
515 ibid

Declaration".[516] In it, they plead for an end to lock-downs and coercive measures to achieve herd immunity. In just ten days, 7,500 scientists, 17,500 doctors and 270,000 other citizens signed. [517]

- Infectious diseases specialist Prof. Matthias Schrappe, former member of the German Council of Health Experts, and eight other scientists had criticised the government for the sixth time at the end of November and called on it to revise the measures. Schrappe considers the incidence value to be completely unrealistic, that this is not a good policy. To stay permanently below this limit, one would need an infinite lockdown. He considers the federal government to be resistant to consultation."[518] In a TV interview, Prof. Schrappe criticised the RKI's case figures, saying they were not worth the paper they were written on. The RKI is politically controlled because it is subordinate to the Ministry of Health. The Corona Agenda is taking place in the realm of conjecture, fundamental rights are being restricted without having usable figures. As a scientist, he considers it unacceptable to impose such restrictions without a solid basis of figures. [519]

Virologist and top pathologist Dr. Roger Hodkinson from Canada is also CEO of a biotech company that produces COVID tests. He says: *"There is a completely unfounded public hysteria driven by the media and politicians. It is*

516 https://gbdeclaration.org/
517 https://www.naturstoff-medizin.de/artikel/die-great-barrington-declaration-und-die-fulminante-kehrtwende-der-who-in-sachen-lockdown/
518 https://deutsch.rt.com/inland/109618-medizinprofessor-schrappe-regierung-ist-beratungsresistent/
519 https://kenfm.de/der-corona-faschismus-kippt-von-anselm-lenz/

outrageous. This is the biggest hoax ever perpetrated on an unsuspecting public.

There is absolutely nothing that can be done to contain this virus. Except protecting older, more vulnerable people. It should be seen as nothing more than a bad flu season....

Masks are completely useless. There is no evidence whatso-ever for their effectiveness. Paper masks and cloth masks are simply a signal.... of obedience. To see these unhappy, clueless people – I do not say this in a derogatory sense – to see these people running around like lemmings, obeying without any basis of knowledge when you put the mask on their face...

And a word about the tests: I would like to stress that positive test results, underlined in fluorescent colour, do not mean clinical infection. It merely fuels public hysteria, and all test-ing should stop....

You should stay out of the medical business completely. You are being misled by the chief medical officer of the health department of this province. I am absolutely outraged that this is being achieved at this level. Tomorrow all this should stop."[520]

Another competent critic is the former vice-president and chief scientific officer of Pfizer, Dr. Michael Yeadon, a "key witness", so to speak, from the pharmaceutical industry. He said, *"There is no scientific evidence to suggest a second wave,"* pointing out that false positives from the unreliable Covid 19 tests are being used to invent a "second wave" based on "new cases". *"More than half of the positive test results are probably false, possibly all of them. If it weren't for the test data you keep getting from TV, you would rightly conclude that the pandemic is over because nothing much is happening.... It is now recognised that at least 30% of our population had immunological recognition of this new virus*

---

520 https://www.rubikon.news/artikel/nur-heisse-luft-2

before it was even there... Covid-19 is new, but coronaviruses are not.

Epidemiological studies show that with the level of immunity already in place – which we can realistically assume today - only 15 to 20% of the population would need to be infected to halt the spread of the virus. " [521]

Now the question arises why almost none of these high-profile experts were reported on television, which brings us to the next topic:

The role of the media

For years we have been observing a standardisation of reporting in the so-called "mainstream media". This includes the TV channels, public and private, as well as the well-known newspapers and magazines including their online portals.[522] This is partly for economic reasons, at least in the case of the private and print media. As a result of the decline in sales figures, which is entirely self-inflicted by one-sided reporting, jobs have been cut and in-house research has been scaled back. Today, 80% of the reports come from the big press agencies and are only slightly rephrased. That's why you can read pretty much the same thing in all newspapers, only with different words, if at all. Only the local section is still written by the newspapers themselves.

---

521 https://www.rubikon.news/artikel/der-betrug-mit-zahlen
522 As an exception that proves the rule, "Servus-TV" should be praised, the only channel with the courage to criticise Corona (thanks to Messrs Wegscheider and Fleischhacker). Another exception is the following ARTE Corona documentary: https://youtu.be/ebPB5egg4X4 or: https://www.arte.tv/de/videos/098118-000-A/corona-security-contra-freedom/

But this does not affect the "public service" TV stations, since they are financed from compulsory fees and are swimming in money. They can still afford large editorial departments and foreign correspondents and could report independently and critically. But the fact is: they do not. Criticism of government policy, as it used to be, can only be heard on minor issues. The government's overall course is not only spared, but "sold" to the audience in the style of court reporting as if it were paid advertising.

Dr. Wodarg notes that politics controls journalists here, when it should actually be the other way round. The chief posts are filled by the broadcasting councils, and these are politically dominated.[523]

The new ARD[524] TV director Christine Strobl, for example, is the wife of the Baden-Württemberg Minister of the Interior and conservative party CDU Vice-President. But not only that: she is also the daughter of President of the Parliament Wolfgang Schäuble. So, we don't need to be surprised about the reporting.

What was once supposed to guarantee pluralism in reporting has become a uniform mush to the same extent as the parties have developed into one big uniform party, which no longer represent the spectrum of all colours, but only nuances of a single colour. Only the AfD (patriot party) is tolerated as a "grubby child" and fought against according to the motto: *"Look, we're still a democracy after all, because we don't ban them."*

Public media still have the greatest reach as far as the news is concerned. This is where most of the propaganda on Corona is carried out, especially in the news "Tagesthemen", "heute" and the numerous special programmes and talk shows. What has long been clear to the attentive viewer was

523 https://deutsch.rt.com/gesellschaft/107824-corona-ausschuss-imperativ-der-aufmerksamkeit-teil-2/

524 Most-seen public TV station in Germany

confirmed by the study *"The Narrowing of the World. On the Media Construction of Germany under Covid-19".* Two cultural scientists, Dennis Gräf and Martin Hennig, took the trouble to watch more than 90 editions of "ZDF TV Special" and "ARD Extra" between March and May 2020 and to analyse them on the basis of images and words (my condolences).

They concluded that not only the topic "Corona crisis" but the way of reporting itself evoked "danger" and "crisis". The images would correspond to those of Hollywood films such as viral thrillers or apocalyptic visions of the end times, i.e. empty places and abandoned shops. Strategies of staging are used. [525]

This confirms what I said above, namely the deliberate use of fear-producing imagery, often underpinned by an ominous soundtrack as in disaster films. In addition, the researchers mentioned a tendency to approve of government measures and the lack of deeper criticism.

You may regret or criticise this, but you cannot get around the daily news. Because here, what everyone is supposed to think is "reality" and most people do. This is the official framework of "truth" that we have to reckon with. When I wrote in the preface that the media would actually be obliged to correctly substantiate their view with data, then that is just a pious wish. They simply don't do it, they set the framework by force of their power of ratings and focus attention wherever they want.

The sheer mass of Corona programmes and the space given to the subject makes a tremendous impression on the viewer. Crucial is the suggestion: *"If it's reported, it **must be** important."* It is difficult to fight against this "logic". Hence the daily repetition of the alleged "infection figures".

---

525 https://www.mmnews.de/politik/151012-studie-beweist-mediale-manipulation-der-corona-krise

One insight, attributed to Third Reich Minister of Propaganda Josef Goebbels, is that you can instil any lie in the people, you just have to repeat it incessantly. And, I would add, you have to work them into many other areas so that a seemingly coherent overall picture emerges. On TV, that would be documentaries, feature films, series, etc. In everyday life, it's the masks. They are a constant reminder that the whole world has become one big hospital where you have to protect yourself from invisible demons.

What is particularly annoying are the eternal, boring talk shows with the same guests over and over again. Sometimes there is a guest from the "evil" camp, as an alibi, and to be put down. Journalist Klaus Kelle says: *"It's always the same pattern: a do-gooder majority meets a waddling man to publicly flog him or her. And the next morning you can read in the mainstream that good has triumphed once again. It disgusts me."* [526]

But even here there are limits. Competent critics like Prof. Bhakti are banned from the fee-financed *broadcasters*, as the SWR TV director confirmed in writing: *"Offering such controversial theses a platform in public broadcasting is contrary to our mission."*[527]

Aha, the "mission" has changed. In the past, it was definitely a task of the public broadcasters to take up and discuss controversial issues. Today the "mission" is presumably to put down everything that is not 100% compliant.

Unfortunately, the cabaret artists also play the sad game and gleefully pick on those who are a thorn in the government's side. They are the humorous section in the propaganda war and have degraded themselves to hand-me-down court jesters.

---

526 https://www.reitschuster.de/post/wir-muessen-vom-sofa-runter/

527 https://www.reitschuster.de/post/swr-chef-entlarvt-sich-keine-strittigen-thesen-zu-corona/

On 28 September 2020, a petition with over 63,000 signatures was submitted to ARD demanding that a special Corona programme be broadcast on ARD TV, with several experts having their say, including Prof. Bhakdi and Dr. Wodarg.[528] Only on 3 December did a negative reply come. The reasoning is brazen, because it claims a broad spectrum of opinion in ARD, which is clearly refuted by the rejection alone.[529] It would be even nicer to shape the programme according to the wishes of those who finance it with their fees: the public. Then it would be better to do it according to the instructions of those who got you the job.

When state propaganda is so perfectly disseminated to the people over a period of months, it is worth a prize. This was awarded to ARD, ZDF, RTL and SAT1. The laudatory speech for the special prize in the category "Best Information" speaks of an *"outstanding performance in Corona reporting"* and of *"credible journalism"* that can give people orientation.[530] It's nice to be praised by the jury like that. But who is behind the prize? It has been awarded by ARD, RTL, Sat.1 and ZDF themselves for 20 years. The founding committee consists of the managing directors and directors of these broadcasters.[531]

That's what I call chutzpah! The TV stations award themselves a prize, and then for the completely one-sided, annoying and scaremongering Corona propaganda that has caused so much senseless panic. Mr. Drosten has at least had his prizes awarded by others, e.g. by GlaxoSmithKline or straight away by the Federal President.[532] On the other hand – who else would award a prize to one-sided reporting TV stations if they did not do it themselves?

---

528 https://www.openpetition.de/petition/online/ard-sondersendung-wie-gefaehrlich-ist-corona
529 https://de.rt.com/inland/110034-trotz-online-petition-wdr-programmchef-lehnt-corona-kritische-talkshow-ab/
530 https://www.deutscher-fernsehpreis.de/sonderpreis/
531 https://www.deutscher-fernsehpreis.de/preis/
532 https://de.wikipedia.org/wiki/Christian_Drosten#Ehrungen

Internet censorship and "fact checkers"

Censorship does not only exist in the mainstream media. Internet platforms such as Facebook, Youtube and Twitter also make ample use of it. Officially with the justification that they are private companies and are not subject to the obligation of balance like state media (if they would...). This may be formally true, but it does not make it any better because of their quasi-monopoly position.

I have already spoken about censored videos by Prof. Bhakti. Almost all Corona critics are repeatedly affected by deletions and blockings. Oliver Janich's Youtube channel with 160,000 subscribers, over 800 videos and over 40 million clicks was finally closed. Janich is denied the opening of a new channel.[533] Youtube announced that in future it would block any criticism (they call it *"disinformation"*) of the Corona vaccination that contradicts general expert opinion or the WHO.

"Youtube cripples entire channels, nearly two million in the second quarter of 2020 with a total of more than 33 million videos. At the same time, around 2.1 billion were deleted from April to June this year, 99.2% of them automatically."[534]

In September, Facebook eliminated the "Corona Rebels" channel with 80,000 followers. Then, on 13 October, Facebook declared that it would ban all ads on its pages opposing vaccination. [535]

Shortly before the general election in New Zealand, Facebook blocked the account of the new corona-critical

533 https://www.compact-online.de/loesch-orgien-im-netz-jetzt-hat-ein-google-mitarbeiter-offen-zensur-eingeraeumt/

534 https://www.reitschuster.de/post/youtube-bekennt-sich-offen-zur-zensur/

535 https://de.sputniknews.com/panorama/20201015328179544-youtube-kampf-desinformationen-Covid-19-impfungen/

party "Advance New Zealand". It was also banned from TV debates because it was allegedly "right-wing".[536]

This argument is the same worldwide.

It is also known that the "big four", i.e. Google, Facebook, Twitter and YouTube, regularly censored pages, tweets and videos of Trump supporters during the US election campaign (and not only those), but let the material of the other side pass, no matter how dubious. But that's another story – or maybe not.

The crown ("Corona") for cynicism in the media war, however, goes to those who produce rows of fake-news under the pretext of debunking fake-news. That's pretty cheeky. They call themselves "fact checkers", "Corrective" or "Mimikama" and are constantly busy stemming the flood of information from critics of the system and "refuting" it. This usually follows the same pattern: one takes an unwanted report/article/video and tries to refute the thesis. If that doesn't work, then you look for something to cast doubt on, even if it's only incidental. Or one interprets false connections into it, which are then subsequently "refuted". Or one simply confuses "opinion" with "assertion of fact". In the end, you turn it around as if you had refuted the main statement. A lot of independent journalists have already exposed this kind of approach several times.

One of these "fact-checkers" proudly calls himself a "people's snitch" ("Volksverpetzer"). Boris Reitschuster says: *"The portal, which calls itself an "anti-fake news blog", regularly misleads readers. As late as the end of January, "people's snitch" defamed people who warned against Corona – against the 180-degree change of course that was strikingly parallel to that of our government. While in my eyes journalism consists of critically questioning the government, "Volksverpetzer" apparently sees its task in always attacking*

---

536 https://de.sputniknews.com/ausland/20201015328179928-facebook-wahl-neuseeland-partei/

those who do exactly that. In other words, a kind of government internet opinion auxiliary police, reminiscent of authoritarian regimes." [537]

The EU has now put its own "fact-checking" department called "Soma" into service.[538] In Orwell's novel "1984", Soma is the drug that people are regularly given to keep them calm. It prevents aggression and makes people content. So much cynicism is necessary – also in the EU.

I don't mean to say that everything the "fact-checkers" let out is wrong, but most of it is, especially on "politically incorrect" topics. Too much, at any rate, to be allowed to act as objective judges. The author Dirk Maxeiner once questioned this industry. He writes: *"When it comes to describing the somewhat inhibited creation of value in this country, there is a nice saying: "One pushes the wheelbarrow, and two watch over him". Applied to the media, especially those that disrupt the establishment circles, this can be continued: "One writes something, and five watch out for him."*

Now that the journalistic profession is becoming increasingly precarious, more and more members of the profession are shifting to state-subsidised evaluation, monitoring and control. At least you can make a living and, on top of that, you can present yourself as a champion of the true, the beautiful and the good. You don't have to be able to write or be creative, all you need is the right attitude. There are now dozens of such ideological apron organisations that meander through the nets somewhere between truth-check and writing chamber." [539]

In a thesis paper by the University of Bremen, several professors, doctors and lawyers assess, among other things, the role of the media in the Corona crisis. They complained that

---

537 https://www.reitschuster.de/post/wie-corona-faktenchecker-agitation-betreiben/

538 https://norberthaering.de/medienversagen/soma/

539 https://www.achgut.com/artikel/achgut_setzt_correctiv_grenzen

the media took sides themselves and defined what truth was instead of promoting plurality, with fact-checking as self-legitimation. [540]

However, one can defend oneself against the "fact-checkers" in court, they have already lost a few lawsuits. In legal literature, they are considered unlawful because they interfere with freedom of opinion, because opinions may not be arbitrarily graded by others. [541]

540 https://www.socium.uni-bremen.de/uploads/thesenpapier_3.pdf
541 https://meinungsfreiheit.steinhoefel.de/2020/10/29/fall-35-achse-des-guten-triumphiert-ueber-correctiv-oberlandesgericht-karlsruhe-untersagt-rechtswidrigen-faktencheck/

Who is behind the crisis?

The second part of my book deals with the crucial questions about the purpose of Corona's staging. Many readers who have followed me this far are rightly asking: What is the point of frightening and harassing people and ruining the world economy in the process? Surely no one can want that?

But – there are people who want that. They want to change the global structures to their liking, in several areas, in the economy, the financial system, the state structures and the increased control of the population. I can already hear some people retorting, *"Yes, those are all conspiracy theories, they've been around for a while."* That's right. They have been around for longer, much longer than most people realise. But that doesn't mean there aren't conspiracies behind them. *"Then let's see some proof!"* OK, that's your right, and I'll provide it.

To my astonishment, this is not at all difficult, because the actors are not secretive, but put most of their plans quite openly on the Internet, because they are obviously proud of them. There have always been pre-announcements with planning games, films or "warnings" before planned major events, such as 9-11 2001. This seems to be something like a "rule of the game" to at least announce one's intentions, even if almost nobody takes notice of it.

It's like a jigsaw puzzle where the pieces are scattered around. If you put them together correctly, then the whole picture becomes visible. I want to proceed systematically and examine the following points one after the other:

- Who are the most important actors and how are they networked with each other?

- How was the crisis prepared?

- How was it achieved that the same policy was enforced worldwide?

- What are the objectives?

Global upheaval always causes damage. When new actors emerge or expand their influence, others have to step down. Social structures are dissolved and replaced by new ones. Family and cultural ties are broken, whether for ideological or professional reasons. Assets are destroyed in order to create new ones. There are usually more losers than winners in upheavals.

So if someone is planning such upheavals – and I will show that this is the case – it cannot be done democratically. Most voters would be against it because they (rightly) fear they might find themselves more on the losing side. So conspirators cannot openly say what they are planning, except on websites that are only read by a few anyway, and those are usually their own fellow campaigners.

Such planning requires a lot of time and logistics. As in a real war, planning games have to be held, meetings organised where everyone is assigned their tasks, alliances forged, funds made available. All this actually happened.

Networks

In politics, as in business, relationships are enormously important. If you want to rise, you have to find sponsors, and in the "upper spheres" of politics, organisations have been founded for this purpose, which are in turn networked with each other. For outsiders, the interconnections are hard to keep track of, and generations of authors and journalists have been working for decades to shed light on these connections. The Corona Conspiracy is a highly complex operation, as it is carried out worldwide and encompasses several sub-sectors: politics, the economy and – to justify the whole – science.

In order to at least begin to understand the process, we should know the most important people and organisations that are instrumental in its implementation. I will introduce some that can be researched relatively easily. However, I do not venture a guess as to how many actors are working in the dark. At most, we see the tip of the iceberg, and that alone gives an idea of the monstrosity of the Corona project. But enough of the theory, let's look at the practice and start with the most important protagonists.

Bill Gates, his foundation, his connections and his projects

Bill Gates is the best known of the organisers of the Corona Conspiracy. He likes to play the role of a benefactor and says he wants to do good for people, especially through vaccinations and genetic engineering. Such people like to be called "philanthropists", Greek for "friend of human". But the person whose best friend they are is usually themselves.

Since this man apparently plays one of the key roles in the Corona plot, we will take a closer look at him and his activities.

The fame he has acquired is that of a brilliant computer nerd who developed "Windows" in a garage and became unspeakably rich with it. That is not entirely true. In the early years of Silicon Valley, there were many young, enthusiastic programmers who exchanged their programs with each other. Gates, who always had a nose for business, helped himself to the selection and commercialised it. MS-DOS, the basis of Windows, was actually programmer Tim Paterson's Q-DOS.[542]

Bill's mother came from a banking family and gave him his first contact with the IBM board. Bill's father was a lawyer and helped him build Microsoft. You can find some videos about Gates' career at "Corbett Report".[543]

Today, Gates operates through his foundation, the *Bill & Melinda Gates Foundation (B&MGF)*. Founded in 1994, it is the largest private foundation, ahead of the "Wellcome Trust" of the pharmaceutical company of the same name and the "Open Society Foundations" of billionaire George Soros.[544] Incidentally, all three foundations set up branches in Berlin in 2018.

On the board of the B&MGF is also the super-rich hedge fund manager Warren Buffett, who has contributed about half of the approximately $50 billion foundation capital. In return, the B&MGF has a stake of just under $12 billion in Buffett's "Berkshire Hathaway Trust". The trust in turn owns shares in Coca Cola worth $17 billion and Kraft-Heinz worth $29 billion, neither of which is exactly known for "healthy eating".

---

542 https://de.wikipedia.org/wiki/MS-DOS#QDOS_und_86-DOS
543 https://lbry.tv/@corbettreport:0/gates:d
     https://www.corbettreport.com/gates/
544 https://de.wikipedia.org/wiki/Bill_%26_Melinda_Gates_Foundation

But the pharmaceutical industry is always happy to welcome new customers.

One can find hundreds of articles about the B&MGF on the net, most of them praise. This is no wonder, because the foundation is very generous to the media, health authorities and pharmaceutical institutes.

For example, leading German journal "Der Spiegel" received $2.5 million in December 2018, one of leading newspapers "Die Zeit" $300,000 in December 2019, the RKI $250,000, Berlin Hospital "Charité", where Prof. Drosten works, $300,000, the Swiss health authority Swissmedic in Bern received $900,000 in February. "Johns Hopkins University", which in the first few weeks of Corona was setting the infection figures until the RKI was in line, received $870 million for research on "family planning", among other things, $155 million went to the CDC and the vaccine manufacturers Moderna and Novio, $243 million went to the Oxford Vaccine Research Institute, and $143 million went to the University of California.243 million went to Oxford Vaccine Research (Astra Zeneca), $280 million to "Imperial College" in London for a computer programme to model infection and death rates, $9 million to the British "Guardian", $ 18 million to NIA, the main US agency for biomedical research, $ 40 million to the "Chief Medicine Officer", Prof. Chris Witty, and $ 3 billion to GAVI, the "Global Vaccine Alliance", which is funded by countries worldwide at "donor conferences" to implement Gates' vaccination plans. Have I forgotten anyone? Certainly, because these are just the figures you find on the net.

It is no wonder that Gates and his foundation are so popular. Which private person, elected by no one, would otherwise be allowed to advertise his private business for free for nine minutes on the main German TV news, prime time? Including a presenter who dutifully gives the cues?[545]

---

545 https://www.tagesschau.de/multimedia/video/video-687765.html

Gates uses the foundation for his three favourite topics: Vaccinations, genetic engineering, both in medicine and in agriculture, and population control. He takes a commercial approach, which means he does not donate money that does not flow back to him. If Gates wanted to do something good, it would be no problem: the UN estimates that $30 billion could eliminate world hunger. The Gates couple and Warren Buffett together own an estimated $300 billion, they could finance this virtually out of petty cash.

The Gates's are smart when it comes to saving taxes. According to the US Senate, Gates saves about $4.5 billion every year with the help of Caribbean tax havens. That is more than the $3.6 billion he earns annually from his foundation.[546]

The foundation has invested in many large corporations such as BP, ExxonMobil, Shell, Nestlé, Coca-Cola, Procter& Gamble, Wal Mart, McDonald's, Cargill (the world's largest producer of genetically modified soya) and many others. The British NGO "Global Justice Now" critically examined the B&MGF in 2016.[547] The head of the study, Mark Curtis, criticised the foundation's links with large international corporations:

"The investigation into B&MGF's programmes shows that the foundation, whose executives are mostly employed by large US corporations, supports multinational corporate interests – to the detriment of social and economic justice.

The Foundation's strategy is to strengthen the role of multinational companies in global health and especially in agriculture, even though these very companies are largely responsible for the poverty and injustice that already plague

---

546 https://www.heise.de/tp/features/Bill-Gates-zwischen-Schein-und-Sein-3378037.html

547 http://www.globaljustice.org.uk/resources/gated-development-gates-foundation-always-force-good

the Global South. Moreover, the foundation is the world's largest investor in research on genetically modified crops...

In Africa, more than 80% of seeds are still traded on informal markets, i.e. the millions of smallholder farmers breed and exchange the valuable seeds of their crops among themselves." [548]

Because Gates cannot earn anything from it; he is the co-founder of the AGRA initiative[549] in 2006 with $420 million. It is *"the most influential lobby organisation for industrial agriculture on the African continent. It advocates that only certified seeds be traded, which would make the trade in farmers' seeds illegal....*

Interestingly, former UN Secretary General Kofi Annan is a member of AGRA's supervisory board....

Over 1.6 billion people worldwide live in smallholder structures. Their livelihoods are massively threatened by the business practices of B&MGF. " [550]

The philanthropist Gates knows, of course, that food control is an enormous power factor to put pressure on local governments.

AGRA activities brought profits for the agribusinesses, but it only brought problems for Africans. For example, the number of people suffering from extreme hunger in the countries where AGRA is active has risen to 130 million, an increase of 30%. [551]

---

548 https://www.heise.de/tp/features/Bill-Gates-zwischen-Schein-und-Sein-3378037.html
549 "Alliance for a Green Revolution in Africa".
550 https://www.heise.de/tp/features/Bill-Gates-zwischen-Schein-und-Sein-3378037.html?seite=all
551 https://www.rosalux.de/fileadmin/rls_uploads/pdfs/Studien/Falsche_Versprechen_AGRA_de.pdf

Gates' vaccination projects

The foundation's second pillar is vaccinations in the third world. It is a good thing that the B&MGF is invested in the vaccine manufacturers Glaxo Smith Kline, Novartis, Roche, Sanofi, Gilead and Pfizer. Here, too, Gates ensures that money flows into their coffers, with ever more vaccinations at ever higher prices. *"A complete vaccination of a child cost up to 68 times more in 2015 than in 2005 – with the same drugs. The Gates Foundation has demonstrably resisted putting pressure on pharmaceutical companies to lower prices."* [552]

The vaccination campaigns are coordinated by the WHO, together with the local health authorities. As a private association, the WHO depends on donations. Many states pay in, but the USA, formerly the largest donor, pulled out in 2020 because Trump did not agree with the WHO's course.[553] The largest donor is now the B&MGF, which paid more than $200 million in 2018, which is more than the contributions from Germany, France and Sweden combined.

The vaccination alliance GAVI[554] – co-founded and co-financed by Gates' B&MGF - is responsible for the WHO's vaccination activities. GAVI also raises a lot of money from the states at so-called "donor conferences". In 2011, it raised $4.3 billion; by 2020, it had already raised $8.8 billion. [555]

The B&MGF has many offshoots, such as PATH, to develop vaccine technologies. The major vaccine manufacturers Pfizer, Novartis, GlaxoSmithKline and Sanofi Aventis are also

---

552 https://www.heise.de/tp/features/Bill-Gates-zwischen-Schein-und-Sein-3378037.html?seite=all

553 Biden decided to go back to the WHO – who wonders?

554 Global Alliance for Vaccines and Immunisation
https://de.wikipedia.org/wiki/Gavi,_die_Impfallianz

555 https://www.aerzteblatt.de/nachrichten/113511/Geberkonferenz-fuer-Impfallianz-Gavi-sammelt-7-8-Milliarden-Euro-ein

supported by the foundation with money, almost the entire global vaccine industry is controlled by the B&MGF. [556]

Basically, the WHO is just an advertising agency dependent on Gates and the pharmaceutical industry, promoting their products and proclaiming pandemics in their interests.

Gates has the greatest influence of all financiers on the WHO, because his money is only allocated for specific purposes. As a result, the WHO's aid programme has shifted more and more in recent years from preventive health care, hygiene and medical presence in rural areas to vaccination.

In 2017, the newspaper "Zeit" wrote in an article entitled *"The secret WHO boss is called Bill Gates"* that 1,500 people die every day because they do not have access to clean drinking water. This could save more lives than vaccinations. [557]

Vaccination disaster in Kenya

Gates' mania for vaccination has unfortunately already done a lot of damage. In Kenya, a large-scale WHO tetanus vaccination campaign was launched in 2013/14, funded by the B&MGF. But there were some oddities that were different from usual:

- The vaccines were delivered individually and under police protection.
- The planning group did not work in a hospital as usual, but in a hotel in Nairobi.

556 https://multipolar-magazin.de/artikel/der-impfaktivismus-der-gates-stiftung
557 https://www.zeit.de/wissen/gesundheit/2017-03/who-unabhaengigkeit-bill-gates-film

- The vaccine distribution was strictly controlled.

- New ampoules were only available when the used ampoules were returned. These were brought back to Nairobi with police escorts. [558]

But the most astonishing thing was that only women and girls were vaccinated, and only those of childbearing age, although tetanus affects men just as much. This seemed strange to many doctors, and they found help from the Kenyan bishops of the Catholic Church. Together with the doctors, they organised samples of the vaccine and had it tested by independent laboratories.

The results were then published[559] and were highly explosive, because the tetanus vaccine contained the pregnancy hormone ß-hCG.[560] This makes the girls and women infertile. There is no medical or technical reason for the presence of the hormone in the vaccine. [561]

Before the secret vaccine analyses became known, the WHO was *"deeply concerned"* about the *"misinformation"* of the Catholic Church, for which there was no evidence. When the evidence was published, the WHO secretly stopped the campaign. But by then, a million women had already been vaccinated and wondered why they could not have children. The crime was never dealt with in a court of law.

In 2017, a scientific study showed that WHO researchers had been developing the combination of ß-hCG with tetanus vaccine since 1976, which was promoted by the WHO from

558 https://sascha313.wordpress.com/2020/05/14/aerzte-fuer-aufklaerung-die-corona-pandemie-ist-ein-betrueger-trick/

559 http://www.kccb.or.ke/home/news-2/press-statement-by-the-kenya-conference-of-catholic-bishops/

560 ß-hCG, human chorionic gonadotropin, is produced during pregnancy. Vaccination produces antibodies against it.

561 https://sascha313.wordpress.com/2020/05/14/aerzte-fuer-aufklaerung-die-corona-pandemie-ist-ein-betrueger-trick/

1993 onwards as the *"family planning vaccine"*. The combination leads to infertility or, if they are already pregnant, to miscarriages without the women knowing it. Since November 1993, Catholic publications have warned against the *"abortion vaccination"*.

Similar sterilisation operations took place in Mexico in 1993 and in Nicaragua and the Philippines in 1994, where girls and women were unknowingly sterilised. It has been known since the 1970s that the WHO has been running sterilisation programmes on women without their knowledge.[562] Of course, the WHO denies this.

Infertility additives are apparently also added to the tetanus vaccine in the USA, as internist Dr. Carrie Madej found out.[563]

Vaccination disaster in Chad

In the north of Chad/Africa, a vaccination disaster occurred in 2012. The newspaper "La Voix" 500 children had been vaccinated against meningitis with the substance "MenAfriVac". At least 40 between seven and 18 became paralysed, there were also convulsions and hallucinations. After this report, other cases became known. During the protests against the government's negligence, a medical vehicle was set on fire.[564]

There are many more reports of vaccination disasters in India, Africa and the Philippines linked to the B&MGF and the WHO.[565] Of course, such reports are vehemently denied by

---

562 https://multipolar-magazin.de/artikel/der-impfaktivismus-der-gates-stiftung
563 https://www.kla.tv/17550
564https://deutsch.rt.com/meinung/101094-ruecksichtslos-und-unmoralisch-die-machenschaften-der-gates-stiftung/
565 Ibid and:

the defendants. One reads again and again the sentence: *"The vaccine damage was investigated by experts and was not related to the vaccinations."* Well, that reassures us. Which experts? Who commissioned them? Who pays them? Such questions need to be investigated.

Already at the World Economic Forum in Davos in 2010, Gates promised that his foundation would provide $10 billion for even more vaccinations and wanted to make this decade (2010-2020) the decade of vaccines. With Corona, Gates now hopes for the biggest vaccination programme ever, namely for all of humanity.

In Brussels in January 2015, Gates said his organisation was taking genetically modified organisms to inject into the arms of young children, before adding that they would simply be shot directly into the vein.[566] Robert F. Kennedy Jr. commented that Gates considers himself competent to dictate vaccination policy to all mankind, but does not even know that vaccines are not intravenous drugs. Gates also admits to injecting genetically modified organisms. Yet there is not a single study that indicates that this is safe.[567]

Robert Kennedy points to numerous B&MGF misdeeds on his website[568] and that the worst epidemics in Congo, Afghanistan and the Philippines were caused by vaccines. Also 70% of the world's polio cases by 2018 were caused by vaccine strains.

This is plausible, since the CDC is suspected of trying out barely tested new vaccines in large field trials in developing countries together with the pharmaceutical industry anyway.[569] Africa, Asia and Latin America are a field of experi-

https://multipolar-magazin.de/artikel/der-impfaktivismus-der-gates-stiftung
566 https://de.news-front.info/2020/05/14/bill-gates-gibt-zu-kindern-genetisch-veranderte-organismen-in-den-korper-zu-spritzen/
567 ibid
568 https://childrenshealthdefense.org/
569 https://deutsch.rt.com/meinung/101094-ruecksichtslos-und-unmoralisch-die-machenschaften-der-gates-stiftung/

mentation for them because there are hardly any controls, and if there are any, then it can be settled with money. No wonder the African press writes that Africans are the guinea pigs for the pharmaceutical industry." [570]

Birth control

The Gates Foundation is also conspicuously involved in the issue of birth control. For decades, the US company Pfizer has been offering "Depo Provera", a contraceptive injection that women receive every three months, causing menstruation to stop. A practical and inexpensive method, but with high risks: double the risk of AIDS and breast cancer, osteoporosis, prolonged bleeding, depression, lack of drive, possibly infertility after discontinuation. Deaths may also occur.

Pfizer sold specifically to African-American and Latino women, without warning labels. "Planned Parenthood Federation", an organisation that promotes population reduction via birth control and abortion (and whose head was Gates' father), which was the largest distributor of the drug in the USA, also hid the warnings. The drug was banned in Europe, Israel, India and the Middle East. In 1998, the FDA, as the regulatory authority, required the company to identify the side effects as a "black box warning", the most severe type of warning. Pfizer circumvented the obligation and later had Bayer produce it under licence. [571]

The case went to trial and in 2012 Pfizer paid a fine of $2.3 billion, the second highest ever imposed in such a case. But this did not bother Pfizer much, because in the meantime, with the help of B&MGF, PATH (also funded by the B&MGF)

---

570 on 25.7.2013 in the South African newspaper "Times Live".
571 https://www.modernghana.com/news/563556/contraception-depo-provera-african-diaspora-call.html

and the US development aid USAID, they had opened up Africa as a new market, there the drug is called "Sayana Press". At that time, there was a new agreement between the Bill & Melinda Gates Foundation, CIFF and Pfizer to sell Sayana® Press to the women of the 69 poorest countries in the world. [572]

At a "family planning summit" in London in 2012, Melinda Gates touted the drug as the optimal contraceptive and "preferred choice" for African women. Since then, sales there have been going like hot cakes, and by 2014 Pfizer and Gates had already raked in $36 billion – without a "black box warning", but still with strong side effects. [573]

But Gates goes even further: although the foundation announced in 2014 that it would no longer fund abortions in the Third World, it remained the largest funder for "Marie Slopes International", a British abortion organisation that performs over 3 million abortions a year in special clinics worldwide. In many African countries this is illegal, for example in Burkina Faso, where the US organisation "Gynuity" carries out abortion experiments up to the 6th month (!). And who is at the top of their sponsor list? The Gates Foundation.[574] Whether legal or illegal, the population of Africa is apparently to be reduced. An interesting video about this topic was published by an African woman.[575]

In 2010, Gates said at a TED Talk that you could maybe reduce the number of people in the world by 10 or 15% if we do a good job on health care, family planning and new vaccines. [576]

---

572 https://www.bd.com/de-de/about-bd/showcase/expanded-access-to-family-planning-option---link-to-do

573 https://c-fam.org/turtle_bay/nyt-whitewashes-dangerous-contraceptive-poor-women-depo-provera/

574 https://gynuity.org/donors

575 https://youtu.be/3wQx-BjmfJk

576 https://www.ted.com/talks/bill_gates_innovating

Until now, I didn't think health care was about reducing the number of people. So, vaccinations for population reduction?

Why are Bill Gates and his wife so eager to reduce the number, especially among Africans, Asians and Latinos? Bill's father, the lawyer William Henry Gates II, was a board member of the aforementioned "Planned Parenthood Federation of America",[577] the largest commercial abortion organisation in the US. Its founders were close to eugenics and racial hygiene.[578] Bill's father is still co-chairman of the B&MGF.

Bill had learned that as wealth increases, fewer children are born per family because it is no longer necessary to have as many children as possible for old-age provision. This is true, but it is also due to better social security with higher incomes. Bill Gates, however, claims by implication that the reduction in the number of children should lead to more prosperity, which is how he justifies his activities. Is this a fallacy or a protective claim?

The fact is that Gates buys himself attention with a lot of money and has an almost religious relationship to vaccination. On his website he writes that he likes to talk about the *"magic of vaccines"*, just as he used to talk about the *"magic of software"*.[579]

Gates speaks at many congresses, calls for a world government[580] and says strange things, such as that people could be manipulated to be less devout through vaccination. He mentioned it would be a good way to spread genetically ma-

to_zero/transcript?language=en
577 http://www.pbs.org/now/transcript/transcript_gates.html
578 https://www.die-tagespost.de/politik/aktuell/die-abtreibungslobby-woelfe-im-schafspelz;art315,211184
579 https://www.gatesfoundation.org/Who-We-Are/Resources-and-Media/Annual-Letters-List/Annual-Letter-2011
580 https://web.archive.org/web/20160409111411/http://evangelicalfocus.com/lifetech/344/
   Bill_Gates_We_need_Global_Government

nipulating vaccines through the air, just like with influenza or flu.[581] That sounds dangerous to me. Has too much power and money gone to his head? Who would want to be "saved" by someone like that?

Speaking of "spreading through the air": Gates is funding, among other things, a geoengineering project at Harvard University called "ScoPEx", which wants to pump millions of tonnes of dust into the atmosphere to block solar radiation.[582] This is supposed to slow down (or really trigger?) the "climate catastrophe".

Like so many of the "rich and beautiful" in the USA, he also met several times with the notorious paedophile Jeffrey Epstein, as the "New York Times" reported.[583] The article is accompanied by a photo of the two of them together in 2011. The NYT clarifies that Gates' acquaintance with Epstein would have begun *after* Epstein's conviction for his paedophile activities. So, he must have known about it.

According to the NYT, Gates met with Epstein frequently from 2011 onwards, at least three times in the palatial Manhattan townhouse and at least once late into the night, according to documents and several witness statements. B&MGF employees were also said to have been there several times. The foundation and JPMorgan Chase Bank allegedly negotiated with Epstein about a planned billion-dollar charity fund, which would have brought Epstein enormous income.

581 Quote from a lecture at the Pentagon in 2005
    https://lbry.tv/@corbettreport:0/gates:d
582 https://uncut-news.ch/bill-gates-bekommt-gruenes-licht-um-die-sonne-
    zu-blockieren/
583 https://www.nytimes.com/2019/10/12/business/jeffrey-epstein-bill-
    gates.html from 12.10.2019

Gates in the headwind

Gates has not only made friends with his activities. Bill Gates and his company Microsoft have been banned from Russia. Both have been put on a checklist by the Russian Federal Security Service because of doubts about the security and reliability of Microsoft software. Russia has started to remove all Microsoft products. [584]

In Tanzania, the government ended all experiments with genetically modified crops by Monsanto and B&MGF in 2018 and ordered the destruction of the trial fields after it became clear that the ban on unlicensed seeds was impoverishing farmers. South Africa joined in and banned the gene projects.[585]

The Indian government has also moved away from Gates and his vaccination programmes. As early as 2017, the New York Times reported that the government was foregoing further funding for vaccinations from the B&MGF. [586]

This was preceded by a scandal triggered by a large-scale polio (child polio) vaccination programme from 2000 to 2017. Gates, with B&MGF as the main donor, had taken control of the running of the programme from the Indian agency NTAGI.[587] In Gates' plan, children were to receive up to 50 doses of polio vaccine in the first five years. Severe side effects with acute flaccid paralysis like polio, called NPAFP, occurred with these hefty doses.

According to Indian doctors, between the years 2000 and 2017, a total of 490,000 children were paralysed beyond the

584 https://europeansworldwide.wordpress.com/2020/05/15/putin-closes-gates/

585 https://netzfrauen.org/2018/11/28/tanzania/

586 https://www.nytimes.com/2017/04/20/world/asia/india-health-nonprofit-gates-foundation.html

587 National Technical Advisory Group on Immunization

usual rates. In 2017, the government stopped the vaccination programme and asked Gates to leave the country along with its vaccination policy. As a result, NPAFP (paralysis) rates dropped sharply. The WHO had to admit that the worldwide explosion of new polio cases was mainly caused by the polio vaccine strain of the many vaccination programmes. Mutated strains of the virus produced more paralysis than the "wild" natural polio virus ". [588]

The same thing happened recently in Sudan: on 25.8.2020, the WHO declared Sudan and several other African countries polio-free areas, polio had been eradicated. At the beginning of November, the WHO had to admit that a new outbreak had occurred – with the polio virus strain of the vaccinations![589] This is now to be combated, among other things by vaccination. Ingenious vicious circle: we vaccinate for polio in order to be able to vaccinate even more. It would be a pity for business if infectious diseases disappeared.

Problems had already arisen in 2009 with a vaccination study conducted by the B&MGF, its offshoot "PATH" and the WHO. The vaccine Gardasil from Merck was tested against the HP virus. In several schools in the Khammam district of India, 16,000 girls between the ages of 9 and 15 were vaccinated with three doses under government supervision.[590]

Many girls became ill and five died. Two others died in another province. Over 120 girls suffered severe side effects such as epileptic seizures, severe abdominal pain, headaches and mood swings. In Japan, too, there were so many side effects that the authorities no longer recommend the vaccine "Gardasil".[591]

---

588 https://deutsch.rt.com/meinung/101094-ruecksichtslos-und-unmoralisch-die-machenschaften-der-gates-stiftung/
589 https://uncut-news.ch/2020/11/05/suedsudan-bestaetigt-neuen-ausbruch-von-impfstoffbedingter-kinderlaehmung/
590 Human papilloma virus, which is said to cause cervical cancer.
591 https://netzfrauen.org/2017/04/25/gates/

At a meeting of Gates with British Prime Minister Boris Johnson in November 2020, Johnson said that they should have listened to Gates' pandemic warnings and now needed his foundation to be better prepared in the future. Gates called on the government to reduce public scepticism about vaccination in the face of "conspiracy theories" and mentioned in passing that he was working with the Wellcome Trust. However, he said that despite vaccination, the crisis would not end until an efficient "super-vaccine" was administered, which could still take years.[592]

Until then, the "less efficient" mRNA vaccinations keep the cash register ringing.

592 https://summit.news/2020/11/12/uk-pm-meets-with-bill-gates-to-discuss-implementing-global-vaccine-program/

Tedros Adhanom Ghebreyesus

The man with the unpronounceable name[593] is the first WHO director without medical training. He got the post in 2017 through massive support from communist China, which Tedros greatly admires. The WHO's uncritical support of Chinese propaganda has already led to several calls for Tedros' resignation.[594] Previously, he was Minister of Health and later Minister of Foreign Affairs in the Ethiopian government, as well as Chair of the *"Roll Back Malaria Partnership Board"* and Co-Chair of the *"Partnership for Maternal, New born and Child Health Board".*[595] Both organisations are funded by the B&MGF. So, the acquaintance with Gates is older.[596]

Tedros was a top member of the politburo of the Central Committee of the *Tigray People's Liberation Front (*TPLF),[597] a former Marxist-Leninist liberation movement that has been in the Ethiopian government since 1991. The TPLF is still listed as a *"terrorist organisation"* in the Global Terror Database. Under its rule, ethnic cleansing is said to have taken place among the competing Amhara tribe.

Among other things, Tedros is held responsible for the persecution of government opponents and journalists in Ethiopia. The country was until recently known for the worst human rights violations. Tedros was also promoted by the B&MGF,

---

593 In Ethiopia, the name is followed by that of the father and then the grandfather. Surnames are not common.
594 https://de.wikipedia.org/wiki/Tedros_Adhanom_Ghebreyesus#cite_note-2
595 https://www.who.int/dg/biography
596https://en.wikipedia.org/wiki/Partnership_for_Maternal%2C_Newborn_%26_Child_Health
 https://www.who.int/phi/documents/roll_back_malaria.pdf?ua=1
597 "Tigray People's Liberation Front"

which invested in large health programmes in Ethiopia that Tedros had facilitated. [598]

During his time as foreign minister, the Ethiopian government sold large tracts of land to foreign investors at cheap prices. The 15,000 inhabitants were forcibly resettled. The mass protests against this escalated in 2016, the police shot 500 protesters, arrested 70,000 people and forced critical journalists into exile, according to "Human Rights Watch". Foreign Minister Tedros rejected the international protest against the mass shootings and denied the events, which are, however, documented on videos. Demands were then made that Tedros be cited before the International Court of Justice for human rights violations. [599] This did not happen, however, and Tedros became WHO chief instead.

Update: In the meantime, the WHO chief has indeed been indicted at the International Court of Justice. US economist David Steinman accuses him of being one of the three heads of security forces between 2013 and 2015, i.e. during the torture and killings, in addition to his job as foreign minister. [600]

598 https://docplayer.org/191825998-Us-milliardaer-bill-gates-und-who-direktor-tedros-zwei-kriminelle-nichtmediziner-entscheiden-ueber-die-gesundheit-von-8-mrd.html

599 https://www.corvelva.it/de/approfondimenti/sistema-sanita/oms/i-crimini-di-tedros-adhanom-direttore-generale-dell-oms.html
https://www.roughestimate.org/roughestimate/the-crimes-of-tedros-adhanom

600 https://www.thetimes.co.uk/article/who-chief-tedros-adhanom-ghebreyesus-may-face-genocide-charges-2fbfz7sff or:
https://www.dailymail.co.uk/news/article-9052247/WHO-chief-Tedros-Ghebreyseus-accused-aiding-genocide-Ethiopia-nobel-peace-prize-nominee.html

Christian Drosten

We have met another protagonist of vaccinations several times before: Prof. Christian Drosten. Since his rapid invention of the SARS test in 2003, he has received special attention, not only in the media. As you can read on Wikipedia, he has been richly rewarded with prizes, some of them highly endowed.[601] At the hospital Charité in Berlin, which recently received $300,000 from the Gates Foundation, he holds two professorships, although he has not habilitated. That is rare among professors of medicine. The professorships at the Charité are indirectly co-financed by a foundation of the Quandt family,[602] one of the richest families in Germany (BMW, pharmaceutical industry). There seem to be other connections of Drosten to this family.[603] He is apparently exempt from the obligation of most professors to lecture several hours a week.

Drosten is well connected in the medical establishment, and pandemic viruses are his speciality. According to the "Labor-Journal", Corona is a stroke of luck for virology. The virologists who get good media exposure are more likely to receive grants and research funding.[604]

Drosten has attracted attention with his constant scaremongering scenarios. He is not a general practitioner and certainly not an epidemiologist. His forecasts were already completely off the mark with the swine flu, and with Corona he again predicted fantasy numbers of deaths that fortunately did not even come close to happening. In journalistic circles, the derisive saying goes: *"Drosten is a rare genius: always mistaken, but never wrong."* The fact that he never-

601 https://de.wikipedia.org/wiki/Christian_Drosten#cite_ref-46
602 https://www.corodok.de/drosten-prof-charite/
603 https://www.corodok.de/drosten-grimme-preis/
604 https://www.compact-online.de/169498-2/

theless (or because of this?) recently received the Federal Cross of Merit underlines his role as a useful government virologist.

Peter Frey, the editor of "Peds Ansichten" writes: *"What I personally accuse a Christian Drosten of is his permanent, unreflective stoking of fears, his immoderate need to talk in a matter that urgently needed moderation. His repeated, speculative, highly emotional statements about a possible grave danger – solely from the virologist's point of view, – which were never supported by real evidence, can only be classified in the category of irresponsibility. He has not stopped this latent, almost manic fear-mongering to this day."* [605]

Is Drosten a doctor?

Wikipedia says that Drosten received his doctorate from the Goethe University in Frankfurt in 2003. Interested journalists and researchers wanted to read his doctoral thesis, which was supposed to be available for inspection at the university and at the German National Library. But it could not be found there or in 12 other university libraries until June 2020, not even as a pdf file. Dr. Markus Kühbacher, who specialises in academic fraud, researched the case and found out that Drosten's doctoral thesis was missing from the German National Library and the Frankfurt University Library, where it should actually be. Even more: it was not catalogued anywhere. [606]

In the summer of 2020, a copy of the work did turn up in the cellar of the Frankfurt archive, claiming that it had been there

605 https://peds-ansichten.de/2020/05/christian-drosten-verantwortung-schweinegrippe-sanofi-glaxosmithkline-ehrung
606 https://www.new-swiss-journal.com/artikel/Verdacht-erhärtet%3A-Drosten-kein-richtiger-Doktor

for 17 years "due to water damage". According to Dr. Kühbacher's research, however, there are even more remarkable oddities:

- The thesis was written together with other co-authors, including his doctoral supervisor(!), which casts doubt on the required "independence".[607]

- Parts of the work have already been published in three journals before completion – which is unusual, to say the least.

- The work, supposedly written in 2001, contains a *"sworn declaration"* from 2003 by Drosten – but without his signature. The date is: *"in April 2003"*.

- According to the doctoral thesis, the oral examination allegedly took place on 22.3.2003 – a Saturday. Which university exams on Saturdays? I don't know of any.

- The University of Frankfurt had initially claimed that there was a "revision certificate" confirming the existence of the dissertation. This is a submission form where, among other things, the author grants permission for publication. At the end of November, the university had to admit that no such certificate existed.[608]

A doctoral certificate may only be awarded when all requirements have been fulfilled, which also includes the submission of the deposit copies of the dissertation. [609]

607 https://corona-transition.org/dissertation-von-prof-christian-drosten-erst-seit-sommer-2020-im-bestand-der

608 https://corona-transition.org/causa-drosten-wird-gerichtsverfahren-uni-frankfurt-raumt-falschaussage-zur

609 https://www.new-swiss-journal.com/artikel/Verdacht-erhärtet%3A-Drosten-kein-richtiger-Doktor

Dr. Kühbacher now wants to have the case clarified in court. You can find a video interview about the events here.[610] If it turns out to be true that Drosten did not properly complete his doctorate, this would also be an enormous embarrassment for the government, and it would also be the end of the professorships at the Charité.

Apparently, the government has taken precautions and acquired a new expert: Prof. Dr. Michael Meyer-Hermann from the "Helmholtz Centre for Infection Research". He is a physicist and researches mathematical models of the immune system. Incidentally, this centre has also been sponsored by the B&MGF for at least ten years. Just enter both terms into a search engine and you will find quite a lot.

But we should not rejoice too soon to be spared from Mr. Drosten's "research". In the business magazine "Capital" he announced that he would deal with a new topic once the hype was over. He has probably had enough of Covid19 for the time being, because MERS viruses are the next pandemic candidate.[611] So there will be plenty of pandemic supplies.

610 https://dein.tube/watch/zinyzP4l4sI5oEz from minute 17.50
611 https://deutsch.rt.com/inland/109709-neues-thema-aufbauen-drosten-widmet/

Neil Ferguson and Imperial College

Ferguson was for many years the head of the "MRC Centre for Global Analysis of Infectious Diseases" based in "Imperial College" in London. Funded by the B&MGF to the tune of hundreds of millions of dollars since 2002,[612] it works with the UK National Health Service and the CDC, and advises the WHO with analyses of urgent infectious disease problems.

Ferguson created computer programmes for the spread of epidemics. Such programmes are very popular, also in climate research, because they spit out any result if you "set" the parameters accordingly. Ferguson's models were stunning:

- In the 2001 foot-and-mouth disease outbreak, Ferguson warned that 150,000 people would die. The government then had six million animals killed, a loss of billions for agriculture. In the end, 200 people died.

- With the bird flu in 2005, Ferguson predicted 200 million deaths with his mathematical models. It ended up being a few hundred.

- Ferguson was more cautious about swine flu in 2009. He calculated 65,000 deaths for Great Britain. In the end, there were fewer than 500 deaths.[613]

Anyone who can show such "successes" cannot be missed at Corona. Ferguson formed the "Imperial College COVID-19

---

612 https://canucklaw.ca/cv-24-gates-financing-of-imperial-college-london-and-their-modelling/

613 Michael Thrusfield, Professor of Veterinary Epidemiology at the University of Edinburgh: https://telegra.ph/Der-Wissenschaftsbetrug-durch-Prof-Christian-Drosten-07-10

Response Team" with 30 colleagues and, paid by Gates' foundation, delivered the desired result: the "report 9". This formed the "scientific" basis for the WHO's recommendations. The report[614] *"spoke of the greatest health threat from a respiratory virus since the 1918 flu epidemic. If no political countermeasures were taken, the report predicted 550,000 deaths for the UK and 2.2 million deaths for the US, as well as a 30-fold overload of hospital beds."* [615]

According to the report, 85,000 people should have died in Sweden without the lockdown. But 6,000 died from or with Corona, the report predicted 1,200% too high.

The report therefore recommended a hard lockdown, *"possibly 18 months or more", of a combination of case isolation, social distancing for the entire population and either a general household quarantine or school and university closures. This is the only way to avoid overloading the health system and a shortage of hospital beds as long as no vaccine is available.*

Report 9 had a sensational impact. Shortly afterwards, countless countries around the world imposed a hard lockdown with exactly the measures Ferguson and his fellow campaigners had proposed. For example, school closures were implemented in 150 countries, affecting 1.2 billion schoolchildren (about 70% of all schoolchildren worldwide) by the end of May alone.

It was probably the most momentous scientific paper of all time. Neil Ferguson was subsequently dubbed "Professor Lockdown" in the British press. Even today, almost all lockdown measures worldwide, as well as the justifications for them, are based at their core on the argumentation of this paper."

614 https://www.imperial.ac.uk/media/imperial-college/medicine/mrc-gida/
   2020-03-16-COVID19-Report-9.pdf
615 https://kenfm.de/corona-und-gekaufte-wissenschaft-von-christian-kreiss/
   as well as the following quotes

The report was the blueprint for most governments, despite many flaws. *"The model was unreliable, scientists at the University of Edinburgh came to very different conclusions using the same model, and the model had been criticised early on by health experts at Oxford University."*

The Daily Mail headlined on 17 May 2020: "Computer code for Prof Lockdown's (Neil Ferguson) model.... is a mess that data experts say would get you fired in private industry."

A study was published in Canada entitled: "The flawed COVID-19 model that led to the Lockdown of Canada".[616] The author pointed out massive scientific flaws in the Ferguson study. It had not been peer-reviewed[617], many thousands of lines of the model were "undocumented" and thus unverifiable, according to Ferguson himself. A senior software developer at Google looked at the code and found "amateurish errors" in the model."

Why does such a bad report have such an impact? Prof. Dr. Christian Kreiß, whom I quote here, says: *"An interesting constant that runs through the entire Ferguson paper is the mantra-like repeated reference to the necessity of vaccination. No chance of normality without vaccination."* Sure, the whole thing was funded by Gates, and his influence ensured that the WHO took it over.

Ironically, Ferguson then fell into the trap he had set for himself: *"For he was meeting his married mistress at the beginning of May when he lectured the public on the need for strict social distancing. The British tabloid "The Sun" therefore smugly headlined on its front page on 5 May 2020: "Prof. Lockdown broke lockdown to get his trousers down". A day later, the Sun headline read: "Locked Out – Prof. Neil*

---

616 https://www.iedm.org/the-flawed-Covid-19-model-that-locked-down-canada/
617 Reviewed by experts

Ferguson resigns as government coronavirus scientist after 'breaking lockdown rules to meet his married lover'". [618]

That was the red card for Neil Ferguson, the "English drone", he had to go. The measures he demanded, however, remained the basis for the second (third, fourth?) lockdown, despite the false predictions. Researchers can often be bought, and paper is patient.

618 https://www.thesun.co.uk/news/11556697/professor-neil-ferguson-resigns-breaks-uk-coronavirus-lockdown-rules

German Health Minister Jens Spahn

The most powerful politician in Germany at the moment is the Minister of Health, Jens Spahn. He was presumably prepared for an important task many years ago, as indicated by two events: in 2012 he was appointed among the 40 *"Young Leaders"* selected by the *"American Council on Germany"*. The organisation, similar to the *"Atlantic Bridge"*, has been working since 1952 to "improve German-American relations", which is a nice euphemism for: "securing American influence over German leaders".

Moreover, the Council is an offshoot of the CFR[619], a US think tank that has been pulling the strings in the background for decades. Spahn's mindset was evident when he announced in 2018 that Hartz IV (social security program for the poorest) does not mean poverty.[620]

In 2015, the banker was brought into the Ministry of Finance. The next steps were participation in the WEF meeting in Davos, where he was appointed "Young Global Leader", and the "Bilderberg Conference" in Chantilly in 2017. The latter was held for the first time in 1954 at the "Bilderberg Hotel" in the Netherlands. Every year, around 130 of the most influential people from politics, business and the media are invited to deliberate in camera for three days at changing locations. Until a few years ago, these conferences were so secret that only insiders knew about them.

The media remained silent, despite 130 heads of state and corporate leaders sacrificing three days of their busy schedules for a supposedly harmless coffee meeting. As

619 Council on Foreign Relations, et al. in:
https://www.heise.de/tp/features/Der-Klub-der-Weisen-Maenner-3419681.html

620 https://www.zeit.de/politik/deutschland/2018-04/jens-spahn-hartz-vier-empfaengerin-treffen

more and more became known about it on the internet, the conference went public. What exactly is being planned for the world there, however, remains top secret.

On the list of prominent participants, which is by no means complete[621], you can see that not only famous people were there, but also those who nobody knew at the time. But in the same or the next year they got a high office, which is why the conference is sometimes called "kingmaker". The candidates are introduced to "good society" and told where to steer once they are in office.

Back to Jens Spahn. The year after his Bilderberg meeting, he surprisingly became Minister of Health, although his professional competence is limited to his work as a pharmaceutical lobbyist. His lobbying activities are examined in more detail here.[622]

A month later, he received a visit from Bill Gates.[623] How could it be otherwise, they talked about vaccinations, and presumably about pharmaceutical lobbying. The conversation must have made an impression on him, because from 2019 he campaigned intensively for compulsory measles vaccination, despite strong opposition from medical circles.[624] Spahn got his way; from March 2020, school and day-care children must be vaccinated, with heavy penalties for refusal.

Spahn met with Gates in 2018. In September 2019, before Corona, Gates invested $50 million in the Germany-based vaccine manufacturer BioNTech, which is working with Pfizer. In 2020, BioNTech receives subsidies of €375 million from the German government to develop an mRNA Covid19

621 https://de.wikipedia.org/wiki/Liste_von_Teilnehmern_an_Bilderberg-Konferenzen

622 https://www.tichyseinblick.de/tichys-einblick/jens-spahn-seit-2002-im-bundestag-und-im-geschaeft/   or here: https://de.rt.com/inland/110961-alte-bekannte-spitzenjob-und-immobiliengeschaft/

623 https://twitter.com/BMG_Bund/status/986969841977430016

624 https://www.merkur.de/politik/masern-impfpflicht-aerzte-ueben-massive-kritik-an-spahn-zr-12251003.html

vaccine.[625] In November, Spahn demands that the EU Commission buy 300 million vaccines from Biontech *"immediately"*. Two days later, the EU buys the requested amount, even though the vaccine is not yet licensed and six times as expensive as the one from competitor Astra Zeneca.[626] Find out more about BioNTech and the alleged "90% safety" of its vaccine here.[627]

A strange story: Gates acquires shares in the company, German taxpayers' money is given away sevenfold, whereupon the stock market value of the small start-up BioNTech rises to more than 20 billion, and on top of that, Mr. Spahn gets a super order from the EU. And this for a barely tested, unapproved vaccine, developed by a company that has never produced any drug.

The previously unknown BioNTech boss became a billionaire as a result and is now allegedly one of the 500 richest men in the world. Our tax money is in good hands there. The whole thing smells of corruption at the highest level. Presumably that's why the Viagra producer Pfizer got involved in the German mini-company, in order to be able to tap into the federal subsidies. Perhaps he was also convinced by the company's address with the street name *"At the goldmine 12"* (really!). There are suggestions that lobbying is particularly efficient when you are in government yourself.

Together with his husband Daniel Funke, who is well connected as the capital city bureau chief of the powerful "Burda Media", Spahn afforded himself an expensive villa in a posh Berlin district in the summer. One is not allowed to write anything about the price, although it has long been known,

---

625 375 million from the federal government alone https://www.manager-magazin.de/unternehmen/biontech-erhaelt-vom-bund-375-millionen-euro-fuer-impfstoff-gegen-coronavirus-a-2221de21-80c7-4d17-b9a8-ab01c30523cd

626 https://de.sputniknews.com/wirtschaft/20201111328385978-ersten-deutscher-corona-impfstoff-hintergrund/

627 https://www.nachdenkseiten.de/?p=66762

because every journalist who did so was warned off by Spahn's lawyers.[628] But if *"Hartz IV is not poverty"*, a luxury villa is probably not wealth either.

Jens Spahn is also a member of the "Atlantic Bridge", [629]an important network between the USA and German leaders. The board and membership list[630] reads like a "who's who" of top German politicians, industry executives and media bosses. A Swiss study has broken down the connections and presented them in a very good graphic.[631] You can see that *all the* major TV stations and *all the* major print media in Germany are represented.

One can see here the connections to the Bilderbergers, who are connected to the CFR, and to the "Trilateral Commission",[632] which works closely with NATO. The well-known historian and social critic Noam Chomsky assesses their goals as an attempt to push back democracy and educate people to be more passive and obedient so that state power can act more freely. The CFR considers the youth to be "too free" and that they should be better controlled.[633]

Another network, this time in the field of science, is the little-known German National Academy "Leopoldina". Their experts officially advise the German government on Corona[634] and in October recommended lowering the incidence value to 35 per 100,000 inhabitants, as well as uniform and stricter measures for the 2nd lockdown.

---

628 https://wir-treten-zurueck.de/villa-jens-spahn/
   https://www.spaet-nachrichten.de/2020/09/geheimnisvolles-neu-spahnstein-und-die-pressefreiheit/
629 https://de.wikipedia.org/wiki/Atlantik-Brücke#cite_ref-54
630 https://lobbypedia.de/wiki/Atlantik-Brücke
   https://de.wikipedia.org/wiki/Atlantik-Brücke
631 https://swprs.org/netzwerk-medien-deutschland/
632 International "think tank" founded by David Rockefeller
633 https://de.qaz.wiki/wiki/Trilateral_Commission
634 https://www.tagesschau.de/inland/coronavirus-bundesregierung-berater-101.html

In December 2020, the Leopoldina came under fire for issuing recommendations for the lockdown, which the Chancellor used to justify her tough December lockdown. The paper was criticised unusually harshly in the newspaper "Welt". [635]

Boris Reitschuster writes: *"One of these "contributors" is virologist Christian Drosten. According to him, "the paper does not contain any advice, however, but a 'clear and final warning from science'", as the Welt writes in a brilliant article unfortunately hidden behind a paywall: "If politicians do not listen to this warning, then 'they have no longer decided in favour of science'...*

In fact, four and a half pages of text are extremely meagre for a well-founded scientific treatise. The newspaper ["Die Welt"] concludes: "If a scientific document of this brevity is to comment meaningfully at all on a current event, it would have to refer extensively to substantiated studies". The so-called ad hoc statement of the Leopoldina is "anything but a scientific document", indeed it is not even a scientific summary of a state of research." [636]

For more details, see Reitschuster's article mentioned above.

Incidentally, Prof. Dr. Joachim Sauer, Angela Merkel's husband, is also a member of the Leopoldina. He was appointed to the Academy in 2007.[637]

Speaking of networks: At the beginning of November, it came to light that the head of department at the RKI, Heinz Ellerbrok, is also a partner in the company GenExpress. The RKI is in turn a customer of GenExpress, and has been for

635 https://www.welt.de/kultur/plus222264910/Angela-Merkel-und-das-Leopoldina-Desaster.html

636 https://reitschuster.de/post/pseudo-wissenschaft-fuer-den-lockdown/

637 https://www.leopoldina.org/mitgliederverzeichnis/mitglieder/member/Member/show/joachim-sauer/

20 years. There is also a cooperation with TIB Molbiol, which was the first to market Drosten's PCR. [638]

"Ellerbrok is also a co-owner of the company, which not only develops tests, but also works on bioweapons, the research project "Biological Threats: Risk Assessment, Ultrafast Detection and Identification of Bioterrorism-Relevant Agents (BIGRUDI)". GenExpress can call on other honourable project partners:

- Federal Office of Civil Protection and Disaster Assistance (BBK), Bonn

- Federal Criminal Police Office (BKA), Wiesbaden

- Baden-Württemberg State Health Office (LGA)

- Berlin University of Technology, Institute of Biotechnology

- FU Berlin, Institute for Biotechnology and Biochemistry

- Charité, Institute for Pharmacology, Berlin

- Technical University of Applied Sciences Wildau (TFHW), Biosystems Engineering

- Philipps University Marburg, Institute for Virology

Surely the decision-makers at the RKI don't benefit from mass PCR testing at around 1.8 million tests per week?"[639]

It was also embarrassing that RKI head Wieler refused to say anything about the case at a press conference because he allegedly "lacked the information". Later, a spokeswoman for the RKI admitted that Ellerbrok's "secondary employment" had been known to the RKI since 2008.[640]

---

638 https://www.welt.de/wirtschaft/article221257894/Corona-Tests-Hinweis-auf-Interessenkonflikt-bei-leitendem-RKI-Mitarbeiter.html
639 https://www.compact-online.de/corona-sumpf-rki-angestellter-ist-mitinhaber-von-pcr-test-firma/
640 https://de.rt.com/inland/109844-corona-tests-hinweise-auf-interessenkonflikt/

George Soros

A key player in the Corona plot is Hungarian-born Györgi Schwarz, better known as George Soros, also a "philanthropist".

The billionaire made his fortune with financial speculations of his hedge funds and is considered a generous spender. However, he always gives with a specific purpose, like Bill Gates, to whom he gave two billion dollars for his foundation. His own foundation, the "Open Society Foundations" OSF, is known for supporting protest movements in countries whose governments are not to the liking of the financial establishment. For example, in Ukraine for the Maidan upheaval[641] or the protests in Belarus in 2020. [642]

The rebellions of the "Arab Spring"[643] were also promoted by the OSF, as well as several pro-refugee movements, the "Democrats" in the USA, "Black votes matter", "Fridays for Future", "Extinction Rebellion" or the fact-checkers of "Corrective". In 2016, Soros, as a private person, thought he had to ask the EU to stop giving money to EU countries that oppose his refugee plans (e.g. Poland and Hungary).

One of the foundations funded by Soros is the "Tides Foundation". It received more than $32 billion (!) from Soros' "Open Society" and from his "Foundation to promote Open Society".[644] This makes Soros the biggest funder of Tides. The Tides Foundation finances many NGOs that work in the sense of Soros on a transformation of Western societies

---

641 https://www.nachdenkseiten.de/?p=34805
642 https://www.anti-spiegel.ru/2020/maidan-2-0-bisher-erfolglos-die-lage-in-weissrussland/
643 https://de.wikipedia.org/wiki/
Arabischer_Frühling#Ursachen_und_Beteiligte
644 https://www.influencewatch.org/non-profit/tides-foundation/

towards neo-socialism, including the "Black Lives Matter Support Fund".[645]

The Canadian sector of Tides shares a floor in the "Robertson Building" in Toronto with *"Dominion Voting Systems"*, the manufacturer of the voting machines which were massively involved in the US election fraud in favour of the Democrats, also in Soros' sense.[646] Since 2009, the Dominion machines have been working with the software of "Smartmatic", and its director is the British ex-minister Mark Malloch-Brown, a good friend of Soros.[647][648] He was vice-director in several Soros foundations and has now been appointed by Soros as the new head of his "Open Society Foundations."[649] The predecessor, Patrick Gaspard, had resigned to continue in Biden's cabinet, as did three other OSF staffers.

What Soros doesn't like at all is when people criticise him on TV. Major US broadcasters have internal orders not to talk about him, as can be seen in a video.[650]

Soros has made himself very unpopular with his activities in several countries: in 1992 he contributed to the fall of the British pound by speculating in the billions, making a profit of $1,100 million. In Thailand and Indonesia he engaged in similar speculation, in France he was legally convicted of illegal dealings, and the president of the Philippines threatened to *"personally send him to hell"* if he appeared in

645 https://www.tides.org/our-community/partnerships/tides-welcomes-black-lives-matter/
646 https://nationalfile.com/dominion-voting-systems-shares-floor-space-with-soros-group-partnered-with-soros-friend/
647 https://en.wikipedia.org/wiki/Mark_Malloch_Brown,_Baron_Malloch-Brown
648 https://247sports.com/college/ole-miss/board/103602/Contents/-sorosobama-and-dominion-voting-systems-154816942/
649 https://www.breitbart.com/politics/2020/12/06/george-soros-appoints-chair-of-smartmatic-parent-company-to-lead-open-society-foundations/
650 Glenn Beck: You're not allowed to mention George Soros
https://youtu.be/pGrvhC_cz1c

his country. Israel, Russia, Hungary and Poland banned the activities of Soros and his foundations, and the Czech Republic, Romania and Bulgaria have complained about Soros' interference in their countries' politics.[651]

When Soros' foundation in Budapest was closed by the government in 2018, Berlin's mayor Müller promised that he would welcome it to Berlin *"with open arms"*.[652] Soros' speciality is destabilising the economic and political order in the countries he feels he must transform into "open societies".

The US Attorney's Office is investigating Soros, who is accused of "stealing" the identities of Americans together with a private intelligence company. The data was used to open bank and cryptocurrency accounts. He is also being investigated by the FBI for election fraud. [653]

Also involved in the big Corona business are the World Bank, the International Monetary Fund, both responsible for financing, and the World Economic Forum WEF for coordinating the big corporations.

651 https://somatemps.me/2020/07/07/georges-soros-biografia-incomoda/

652 https://www.tagesspiegel.de/wissen/open-society-foundations-gates-und-wellcome-trust-berlin-wird-zur-stadt-der-stiftungen/22866030.html

653 https://www.conservativebeaver.com/2020/11/14/george-soros-accused-of-election-interference-by-the-fbi/

The World Economic Forum

The WEF was founded in 1971 by the son of a Swabian factory director, the economics professor Klaus Schwab, who is still WEF head today. The WEF is known for its annual meetings, which it holds in Davos with a large media presence. According to its own statement, its "mission" is to *"improve the state of the world"*.[654] That sounds good at first. In the 50 years of its existence, it turned out to be true, but one has to add: *"...for the benefit of our members"*, which are multinationals and financial institutions. One must always put words, just like numbers, into perspective. For example, when Obama says: *"Yes, we can"* one has to ask: "Who is meant by *"we"*?".

The WEF did not choose its location near Geneva at all by chance, because many other UN organisations are represented there in addition to the WHO, a "policy of short distances", so to speak. The WEF is financed by membership fees from its approximately one thousand member's companies. These are usually global companies with a turnover of over 5 billion US dollars, i.e. "global players".[655]

If you look at the list of members[656], you will find almost all the big known corporations. There we have the big network of self-crowned "elites", the military-industrial complex, the worldwide one-size-fits-all mainstream media, the pharmaceutical-medical complex, the online internet platforms, the financial and banking empire, the logistics industry including Amazon, UPS, air and shipping etc. This is where the rich and powerful meet to divide the world among themselves, and Klaus Schwab enjoys the role of host.

---

654 https://www.weforum.org/about/world-economic-forum
655 https://de.wikipedia.org/wiki/Weltwirtschaftsforum
656 https://www.weforum.org/partners

Among the leaders on the Board of Trustees are celebrities such as Al Gore, US presidential candidate for the Democrats in 2000 and main initiator of the climate campaign, and Christine Lagarde, currently President of the ECB.[657] At the annual meetings in Davos, all the heads of state of Europe, the USA, Russia and China have been represented among the 2,500 visitors, as well as leading bankers and company bosses, including Gates and Soros. This is where world politics is made.

An interesting clue to involvement in the Corona plot is that WEF apparently sold all its investments (and presumably bought them back at rock-bottom prices) shortly before the 2020 stock market crash.[658]

The WEF also has a ready-made concept for how the world should continue after the Corona crisis: "The Great Reset". More on this later.

---

657 https://www.weforum.org/about/leadership-and-governance
658 https://www.schildverlag.de/2020/10/26/gruender-des-weltwirtschaftsforums-klaus-schwab-sie-werden-in-10-jahren-nichts-besitzen/

How was the crisis made and for what purpose?

Preparations

The people and organisations mentioned play an important role in the overall plan that is gradually becoming visible. But they are far from being the only ones, rather "the tip of the iceberg". Crucial players are also the leading newspapers and television stations worldwide, as well as most "democratic" parties. All this can be seen from the almost smooth interaction of all participants.

The facts I am about to present to you reveal a scenario that leads to the conclusion that the Corona crisis and – above all – the political reaction to it were deliberate and planned long in advance. It sounds outrageous, and that is precisely why hardly anyone dares to think through the full extent of it. It takes courage to face this possibility with an open mind.

It is not easy for me either to spend months researching the abysses that are opening up more and more. But I see it as inevitable to uncover all this. Ignorance will never get us out of the trap that has been set for us. I follow the philosopher Herbert Fritsche, who once said that if you want to follow your star, you have to stand the look into the darkness.

But back to the facts. A planned pandemic, like any strategic operation, must be rehearsed. Did such exercises take place? The answer is given by the author and co-editor of the magazine "Multipolar", Paul Schreyer, in his very well researched book *"Chronicle of an Announced Crisis – How a Virus Could Change the World"*.[659] You can find an interview

---

659 https://www.westendverlag.de/buch/chronik-einer-angekuendigten-krise/

with him here.[660] In it, he describes several actions in which pandemics were played out:

- In 2000, the Centre for Civilian Biodefense Studies at Johns Hopkins University organised a conference on *"a theoretical plague outbreak in the USA. Topics ranged from medical care to isolating whole populations and controlling the public to quelling possible riots – and vaccination as a panacea ".*[661]

- In 2001, the simulation game "Dark Winter" followed at the US Air Force base Andrews near Washington. *"The question of whether "dangerous information" should be banned by law was discussed, too. The consequences of restrictions on freedom were also discussed.*[662]

- *Using examples of other such conferences and exercises such as "Global Mercury" in 2003 and "Atlantic Storm" in 2005, the author shows how pandemic preparations were internationalised. The participants in the "Atlantic Storm" exercise, for example, represented "exactly the fusion of politics, the pharmaceutical industry, research, the military and the media" that was desired – "everything with a transatlantic character, i.e. under American leadership".*[663]

- A 2010 Rockefeller Foundation study examined the political potential of pandemics: "Lock Step". *"According to the scenario,*[664] *detailed in eight pages, an*

660 https://www.youtube.com/watch?v=2HWo0RJ3eYI&feature=youtu.be
661 https://www.rubikon.news/artikel/die-angekundigte-krise
662 ibid
663 ibid
664 http://web.archive.org/web/20100701154450/http://
www.rockefellerfoundation.org/uploads/files/bba493f7-cc97-4da3-add6-
3deb007cc719.pdf

influenza pandemic led to global panic, with China quickly becoming the world's model and governments everywhere adopting mandatory masking and authoritarian measures. According to the paper, "Even after the pandemic subsided, authoritarian control and surveillance of citizens persisted and even intensified." According to the script, citizens willingly gave up their freedom, broad resistance built up only after many years. " [665]

Then there was a long break. But in January 2017, shortly after Donald Trump became US president, Bill Gates travelled to the WEF meeting in Davos and declared that there needed to be *"serious discussion about how to prepare for a possible biological weapons attack."*

The occasion was the launch of the CEPI (Coalition for Epidemic Preparedness Innovations) vaccine research initiative, which he founded together with the pharmaceutical industry and several governments. This aimed to develop vaccines much faster than before – instead of within ten years in under twelve months – and to secure public-private funding for this." [666]

In the same year, Gates spoke at the Munich Security Conference: "The next epidemic could originate on the computer screen of a terrorist who wants to use genetic engineering to create a synthetic version of the smallpox virus or an extremely contagious and deadly flu agent. We need to prepare for epidemics the way the military prepares for war. This includes manoeuvres ('germ games') and other emergency exercises so that we better understand how diseases spread, how people react in a panic, and how we

665 https://kenfm.de/was-steckt-hinter-der-corona-politik-von-paul-schreyer/
666 https://kenfm.de/clade-x-eine-biowaffe-zur-bevoelkerungsreduktion-von-paul-schreyer/

deal with things like congested highways and communications systems. " [667]

Gates' wish was granted, because three months later, preparations for "Clade X" started at the "Johns Hopkins Centre for Health Security", which also enjoys generous donations from the Gates Foundation.

"In 2018, a small circle of government experts in Washington rehearsed a pandemic triggered by a bioweapon, scripted by a group that wanted to use it to reduce the world's population in order to achieve, literally, "the 'reset' or 'paradigm shift' that would be required to fundamentally alter the balance." [668] The exercise was called "Clade X". [669]

Example Germany: On 8 May 2019 (a symbolic date, the day of the surrender of the Wehrmacht in 1945), the conservative party CDU organised a congress in the Reichstag entitled: *"Strengthen Global Health, Implement UN Sustainable Development Goal".* Note the key words *"global"* and *"UN"*. Apart from the usual members of the CDU Merkel, Spahn, two more ministers, Mr. Drosten (yes, he is also a member of CDU), international guests made their way to Berlin: Joe Cerrell, Director for "Global Policy" of the Gates Foundation, Prof. Jeremy Farrar, Director of the "Wellcome Trust" and WHO head Tedros Adhanom Ghebreyesus. The official programme is known, what was discussed at the subsequent "reception with civil society actors" can only be guessed at. Probably similar preparations took place in other countries around the world. [670]

In October 2019, even before the emergence of "Corona", the most important exercise, "Event 201", was held in New York. We'll take a closer look at that in a moment.

---

667 ibid
668 From the aforementioned book by Paul Schreyer
669 https://multipolar-magazin.de/artikel/clade-x
670 https://www.cducsu.de/veranstaltungen/globale-gesundheit-st-rken-un-nachhaltigkeitsziel-umsetzen/referenten

Schreyer writes: *"What was striking was that in all these exercises, not only was a health emergency played out with overburdened hospitals and many epidemic deaths, but strangely enough, in all the scripts, riots always broke out in the country and one had to react to them with a deployment of the military and severe restrictions on freedom. It seemed that the bioterror exercises with their constant smallpox and plague attack scenarios also served as a pretext for thoroughly rehearsing a state of political emergency."* [671]

Even the so called "pandemics", which were insignificant compared to the "usual" epidemics such as malaria, tuberculosis, hepatitis, etc., can be counted as exercises: SARS 2002/03 (820 deaths worldwide), bird flu 2004 (less than 500 deaths), swine flu 2009/10 (under 19,000 deaths, much less than one thousandth of one percent of the world population), MERS 2012 (under 900 deaths).

By the way, the German government had already ordered the 50 million vaccine doses from GSK in 2007, two years before the outbreak of swine flu and the knowledge of the then "new" virus.[672] This is another indication that pandemics are being planned.

"The field of biosecurity and pandemic control, built up with a lot of money and lobbying over the last 20 years, a complex machinery of internationally coordinated instructions for action[673], has been in standby mode for several years and was basically just waiting for an appropriate go-ahead." [674]

671 https://www.rubikon.news/artikel/die-angekundigte-krise
672 https://www.metropolnews.info/mp457208/gefaehrlicher-angriff-auf-die-menschheit-der-millardaer-die-impfindustrie-die-politik-und-die-who
673 https://apps.who.int/iris/handle/10665/254741
674 https://kenfm.de/was-steckt-hinter-der-corona-politik-von-paul-schreyer/

"Event 201" – the dress rehearsal for Corona

On 18 October 2019, at the invitation of the Johns Hopkins Centre for Health Security, a high-profile simulation of a pandemic caused by a coronavirus was held two months before the Covid19 pandemic outbreak. There must have been clairvoyants at work, because everything corresponded to what we later had to experience, except for the location of the outbreak, which had been moved to Brazil. The event was financed and organised by the Gates Foundation and the World Economic Forum. And it's all officially on the internet, you can even watch videos of the exercise.[675]

Fifteen selected people took part, all competent in their field. Most are from the private sector, none are doctors, but microbiologist George Gao, director of China's disease control agency CCDC, *who in January 2020 alerted his US colleague Robert Redfield to the suspected danger of Sars-Cov-2."*[676] Also, the head of risk at US hotel group Marriott International, the world's largest hotel chain, a president of the world's largest manufacturer of medical devices and Corona rapid tests, a representative of Lufthansa, a former director of the World Bank's Department of Health, a director of ANZ (Bank of Australia and New Zealand) and chair of CEPI, the vaccine development association initiated by Gates, the director of "Edelman", the world's largest PR firm, a director of the "UPS Foundation", the vice-president of NBC (TV media), the vice-president of the pharmaceutical giant "Johnson&Johnson", the Governor of the Central Bank of Singapore, etc.

An illustrious company for planning the pandemic. Of course, there was also a leading man from the Gates Foundation, as well as Avril Haines, former deputy CIA director under

---

675 https://www.centerforhealthsecurity.org/event201/
676 https://www.rubikon.news/artikel/die-angekundigte-krise

Obama and an active supporter of the so-called "enhanced interrogation techniques" (waterboarding etc.). She recently resurfaced as the nominee for foreign intelligence under Biden, should he become president.[677]

In the simulation Event 201, participants were assigned different roles and very realistically made fictitious videos were played that resembled the real ones of today, as can be seen in the videos on the official website.[678]

"The essence of the exercise, as of the real situation that followed, was a specific fusion of the themes of fear, mass death, the state of emergency, government overreach, restrictions on liberty, vaccines, pharmaceutical regulation and media strategy." [679]

A big theme was also controlling the flow of information worldwide and undermining "fake news", i.e. critical information. One of the participants said about social media such as Facebook, Twitter, etc.: *"You need to actively engage in spreading correct information and flood the zone of correct information in partnership with the science and health communities. Because putting the genie of misinformation back in the bottle is impossible."* [680]

Another participant stressed that we need to talk about *"the government using more sovereign power to deal with misinformation." "But we also need to think about a techno-logical solution to the problem.* [681]

"Unfortunately, you don't learn what she goes on to say in the clip. There is work being done on algorithms that comb through the information on these social media platforms, and I know the Gates Foundation and others are sponsoring

677 https://kenfm.de/bidens-schattenkabinett-von-thomas-roeper/
678 https://www.centerforhealthsecurity.org/event201/videos.html
679 https://norberthaering.de/medienversagen/event-201-fake-news/
680 ibid
681 ibid

organisations to work on this so that people can have more confidence in the sources of information they use in a crisis.

The Chinese role-player, George Gao, microbiologist and director of the CCDC, stressed that the most important thing is to inform and instruct medical staff so that they can give the right answers to questions and rumours, for example the rumour that the pandemic is man-made." [682]

---

682 ibid

284

The Corona turn in March 2020

But these are not the only indications that the Corona pandemic was planned. It turns out that there was a shift in both media coverage and government attitudes that took place "as if on cue", all over the world. In January and February, Corona was portrayed as a local Chinese problem. US President Trump was criticised for being the first to stop flights to and from China.

At the beginning of March 2020, the epidemic in China was as good as over, the WHO announced that the number of new infections there had fallen from 2,000 to 45 and that more than 70% of those infected had recovered in the meantime.[683] In Europe, the virus was not seen as a major threat. RKI head Wieler said in a TV interview on 22 January that the virus would probably not spread that much. At the end of February, he was still advising that the virus should be viewed soberly, as if it were a flu epidemic. But by the end of March he had completely changed his mind: *"We are in a crisis, the extent of which I could never have imagined."*[684]

The same goes for Christian Drosten – on 2 March, he still said at the Federal Press Conference that it was a mild illness and in principle not a problem. As with a cold, one normally hardly notices it. He wondered what we were actually worried about.

So did Health Minister Jens Spahn at the beginning of March: *"According to current knowledge, an infection with the coronavirus is mild or even symptom-free for 80% of those infected. For people under 50, the risk is comparatively very low. All the symptoms known so far – cold, sneezing, fever,*

---

683 On 9 March on their website
684 https://www.compact-online.de/compact-gruselkabinett-die-lockdown-wissenschaftler/

cough, shortness of breath – are treated many times every day in the German health system.

The disease is severe in rare cases of pneumonia and treatment in intensive care is required. People over the age of 65 and the chronically ill are at greatest risk for these more severe courses ". [685]

As of mid-March, the Ministry of Health warned against the "rumour" that massive restrictions were planned. Bavaria's president Söder also denied the "rumours" that the restaurants would be closed. Three days later, the "rumours" became true.

The Austrian Chancellor Kurz still said on 8.3.2020 that it was absolutely wrong to walk around with masks, and after three weeks he said that they wanted to rely on wearing masks.

Something caused not only German politicians and media to do a U-turn in their views in March. It could not have been the rising number of "cases", because the curve had not changed its upward trajectory; on the contrary, it had passed the peak and started to fall. Between 9 and 17 March, the lockdown was imposed in almost all European countries, although by then the number of cases was already falling. Other countries around the world followed belatedly, but they followed.

Who were they following? The evidence points to the fact that the networks, of which I have presented a few, jointly "activated" "their" people in politics and the media. Apart from the U-turn, the simultaneity in many countries speaks for a concerted action, although the fall curves were quite different. Those who have Telegram can download the worldwide data and illustrative graphics free of charge on the channel "Corona_Fakten".

---

685 https://www.achgut.com/artikel/ein_mann_fuer_alle_faelle

Carrot and stick

There were certainly countries that did not want to jump on the lockdown bandwagon immediately. The best known, Sweden, benefited from its chief epidemiologist Anders Tegnell, who was able to convince the government. What we would have been spared if the German government had listened to Dr. Wolfgang Wodarg instead of Mr. Drosten! Tegnell was able to push through his ideas, with 90% support among the population. The Swedes had not yet forgotten the vaccination disaster of swine flu, and the children and adolescents who were vaccinated at that time still suffer from the vaccination damage of narcolepsy today. Across Europe, more than 900 people are permanently disabled as a result.

Belarus (White Russia)

In Belarus, the case was different. There, Alyaksandr Lukashenkov has had the final say for decades, and he did not want a lockdown because of the foreseeable economic damage. Wearing masks was something everyone could decide for themselves, and many wore them. Sporting events continued, the football league played on and the only measure was to extend the school holidays. It was freer than in Sweden, yet (or rather because of this) there were only 613 deaths from/with Corona by mid-August.

Italian journalist Nicola Bizzi reported[686] that Lukashenkov had received an offer of $92 million from the WHO to order a hard lockdown "like in Italy". Lukashenkov is known to have always refused to take emergency, lockdown or "socially distancing" measures in his country.

---

686 https://www.databaseitalia.it/aboliamo-la-protezione-civile-ricettacolo-di-ogni-corruzione-e-cavallo-di-troia-del-nuovo-ordine-mondiale/

Lukashenkov rejected the WHO's offer, whereupon the IMF[687] increased it to 940 million dollars, ten times as much. In return, everything was to be closed down "as in Italy". According to Bizzi, similar offers had also been made to other countries in Europe and the world, as he had learned from intelligence sources. Many heads of state, such as Serbian President Aleksandar Vucic, had accepted the offers. It was logical to him that Italy, the "pilot model" of the crisis, would not refuse, judging by the mentality of its politicians. This could be the explanation for where the money for the increase in police forces at the beginning of 2020 came from.[688]

The news was confirmed by the Belarusian news agency "BelTA" on 19 June 2020.[689] In it, Lukashenkov speaks of the "fast-track financing" offered by the IMF and the World Bank, and adds: *"We will not dance to anyone's tune. Conditions are already appearing, along the lines of: you should handle the Corona virus as you did in Italy. So listen, I don't want – God forbid – the situation in Italy to repeat itself here in Belarus. We have our country, we have our own situation. The World Bank is already ready to pay us 10 times more for fighting the disease so effectively. And the IMF continues to demand from us isolation, quarantine and curfew. So listen, what is this nonsense?"* [690]

Lukashenkov rejected the carrot and got the stick. After the election in Belarus, the protests against him were supported not only by the Western press but also by several NGOs funded by Soros' foundation.[691] I don't want to take sides with

687 International Monetary Fund
688 https://connectiv.events/weissrussland-haben-who-und-iwf-lukaschenko-geld-geboten-um-in-seinem-land-einen-lockdown-umzusetzen/
689 https://eng.belta.by/president/view/belarus-president-unwilling-to-accept-additional-terms-to-get-foreign-loans-131164-2020/
690 https://www.compact-online.de/schmutzig-iwf-wollte-lukaschenko-mit-900-millionen-dollar-schmieren-wenn-er-lockdown-einfuehrt/
691 https://www.anti-spiegel.ru/2020/maidan-2-0-bisher-erfolglos-die-lage-in-weissrussland/

the government or the protesters, that's another issue. My point is to show the campaign that was unleashed against Lukashenkov, whose presidency had not interested anyone in the West for decades.

Argentina

Another country took the carrot because it was already economically down: Argentina. The Argentine journalist Nicolás Morás describes in a detailed article[692] what happened after Argentina went into the most severe lockdown in South America on 19 March 2020, although there were only a handful of infected people and *no* Corona deaths: the already debilitated economy collapsed, millions of Argentines fell below the poverty line. Entrepreneurs, trade unions and journalists joined forces to put pressure on the government of President Alberto Fernández, and a tax boycott took hold.

On 7 April, Fernández gave in and announced that the lockdown would be largely lifted on 13 April. But things turned out differently: the lockdown was even tightened and was to become one of the longest in the world, lasting seven months.

What happened? Morás reports: Shortly before the lockdown was to be lifted, at 16:48 local time, President Fernández received a phone call – from George Soros. He made him an *"offer you can't refuse"*, as they say in mafia circles. It was called a friendly "rescue plan", which promised, among other things, the deferral of the country's debt to the International Monetary Fund (IMF) for five years, as well as the construction of a pharmaceutical factory of the Catalan company "Grifols", in which Soros had entered in 2019 with a large block of shares. The factory is to produce blood plasma

---

692 https://www.dvox.co/single-post/2020/04/16/Soros-Fernandez-y-el-colapso-de-Argentina

against Corona. In addition, Soros promised $20 billion, payable in 2021, to avert national bankruptcy. In the event of Trump's election victory, the IMF, the World Bank and a consortium of "philanthropists" will pay. In the event of Biden's election victory, the US Federal Reserve will pay.

Why a private citizen can promise such a thing is an interesting question about the real power relations.

In return, Soros demanded the destabilisation of President Bolsonaro in neighbouring Brazil, the introduction of abortion, educational reform overseen by Soros' "Open Network University", the monopoly of electricity in Argentina for the "Breakthrough Energy Coalition" in which Soros, Gates, Zuckerberg and Bezos are involved, and the shutdown of all economic activity in the country through 1.) a total lockdown and 2.) Inflation of the national currency.

What sanctions were threatened if Fernández refused is not reported. According to unconfirmed rumours, Soros threatened to immediately call in all international loans, which would have meant immediate national bankruptcy.

Fernández broke his promise to his people and accepted the offer. It is not known how much he personally got out of it. The consequences were disastrous: crime and poverty spread and the positive PCR results increased despite the lockdown, presumably because more testing was done there as well.[693]

Journalist Gaby Weber told the Corona Committee that you needed a mobile phone app when you went out of the house, it would be checked by the police if you were even authorised to leave the house. You could not use public transport without a data check, there were up to two years in prison for visiting family, it was house arrest for months. However, there were hardly any people suffering from Covid19. Poor neighbourhoods were cordoned off by the military, which

---

693 https://connectiv.events/das-volk-argentiniens-zwingt-die-regierung-in-die-knie-lockdown-wird-aufgehoben/

patrolled everywhere. The government was worried that soon no one would obey the rules. [694]

Half of the small and medium-sized enterprises went bankrupt, the already high unemployment rate rose by four million, an inflationary spiral devalued the last savings. It is the worst crisis in Argentine history, which is truly not lacking in violent crises.

But after seven months of being locked up, more and more Argentines took to the streets despite the ban, the protests became more and more violent until the government had to lift the lockdown. After seven months, the first shopping centres opened, then the borders to neighbouring countries were reopened and the first tourists could come again. [695]

Africa

There were several reports from Africa about the interference of the "philanthropists" with their international organisations in the Corona politics of several countries.

"At the end of April, the President of Madagascar reported that an extract from the herb Artemisia had shown good results in treating corona diseases. Then, just a few days later, he announced that the WHO had offered him a $20 million bribe if he recanted his claim "[696]

According to a later report, President Andry Rajoelina said that for this sum he should have added "toxins" to the medicine that is popular in Africa, i.e. poison it. He warned his compatriots not only against the Corona vaccination planned for Africa, because it was deadly, but also against a

694 https://deutsch.rt.com/gesellschaft/107313-corona-ausschuss-man-braucht-viele-dumme-leute-damit-das-klappt-teil-2/

695 https://www.schildverlag.de/2020/11/04/das-volk-argentiniens-zwingt-die-regierung-in-die-knie-lockdown-wird-aufgehoben/

696 https://www.anderweltonline.com/klartext/klartext-20202/corona-die-gekaufte-pandemie/

"fake by the Europeans" of this medicine, which could be recognised by its green colour. This is poisoned. The original, on the other hand, is yellow and harmless.[697]

"Artemisia annua" (Sweet wormwood) a species of Mugwort, has been recognised as a medicinal plant since ancient times. In Chinese medicine and in Asia and Africa, it is used against malaria and is also known for its immune-strengthening and anti-inflammatory effects. It is said to have been used in 85% of Chinese Covid patients and is also used in modern pharmacology. A biochemist at the Max Planck Institute in Potsdam has begun a study of the drug in corona patients in Mexico. [698]

The Artemisia preparation recommended by the President of Madagascar is produced directly from the plants there and has been successfully sold throughout Africa under the name "Covid-Organics" since April.[699] Due to several enquiries, the WHO has promised a review for a possible approval.[700] Many Africans think that an approval has only been delayed so far to protect the interests of the pharmaceutical companies.

The president of Burundi, Pierre Nkurunziza, also resisted the "order" to impose a lockdown and expelled the WHO from the country. A few weeks later, the 55-year-old, otherwise always in good health and an athlete, died "of a heart attack". His opponents, who run the radio station RPA abroad, started the rumour that he had died of Corona. The successor was known to want to continue the policies of his

---

697 https://aobrempongnana.wordpress.com/2020/05/15/who-offered-me-20million-dollars-to-put-a-little-toxic-in-my-Covid-19-remedy-madagascar-president-exposes-who/

698 https://www.tagesspiegel.de/berlin/klinische-studie-zu-beifuss-kraut-gegen-Covid-19-wird-in-mexiko-getestet/26144790.html and https://www.dw.com/de/artemisia-ein-kraut-gegen-Covid-19/a-53936500

699 https://www.heise.de/tp/features/Afrika-Die-angekuendigte-Corona-Katastrophe-4794829.html

700 https://www.pharmazeutische-zeitung.de/naturarzneien-aus-afrika-sollen-untersucht-werden-117384

predecessor. He did, with one exception: he imposed the lockdown, and shortly afterwards, on 20 July 2020, $7.63 million was transferred to the country.[701]

In Nigeria, a law on compulsory vaccination of the population was to be enacted at the beginning of May. According to a report in the Nigerian newspaper "Daily Post" on 4 May, the "Coalition of United Political Parties" CUPP learned from intelligence reports that the law was to be waved through in an expedited manner, i.e. without the usual legislative procedures. Allegedly, $10 million had been offered to parliamentarians by Bill Gates in return.[702]

"That this is not another conspiracy theory is proven by the fact that an Italian politician called for Gates' arrest in front of parliament because of this. And no, there was no laughter. Let's not forget that Spain, a leader in the Corona madness, has just received a 130 billion loan from the IMF. Italy has also been considered."[703]

The Italian politician was Sara Cunial, who in May 2020 demanded that Bill Gates be indicted by the International Criminal Court for *"crimes against humanity",* asked the Speaker in Parliament to forward the next call from the "philanthropist" Gates directly to the International Criminal Court. [704]

Interference through blackmail and corruption, with carrots and sticks, is common in world politics. There are specialists for this, so-called *"economic hitmen",* who conduct such negotiations on behalf of the corporations with the help of the World Bank and the IMF, just as it is usual in mafia circles. Only that the sums involved are quite different. One of them,

701 https://www.anderweltonline.com/klartext/klartext-20202/corona-die-gekaufte-pandemie/
702 https://dailypost.ng/2020/05/04/bill-gate-offered
703 https://www.anderweltonline.com/klartext/klartext-20202/corona-die-gekaufte-pandemie/
704 https://connectiv.events/weissrussland-haben-who-und-iwf-lukaschenko-geld-geboten-um-in-seinem-land-einen-lockdown-umzusetzen/

John Perkins, has exposed these practices in a book. It is more exciting than a thriller because it reflects reality.[705]

What is special about the Corona Year 2020 are the enormous sums that have been and will be distributed to enforce the coercive measures. Part of it can be read officially on the IMF website *"COVID-19 Financial Assistance and Debt Service Relief"*[706]. But this is only the tip of the iceberg, because the financing by the World Bank, the UN, the WHO and the various foundations of super-rich "philanthropists" cannot be found here. The IMF funds for Europe, North America, etc. are missing, too.

Strange deaths

There are always people who are healthy and die unexpectedly. That is nothing that needs to be reported. But when several people die *"suddenly and unexpectedly"* in a short period of time who had similar goals and were endowed with a certain power, it at least makes one prick up one's ears. The following cases may be coincidence, but there still remains a suspicion that there could be a connection between them:

On 16 October 2020, journal "Der Spiegel" ran the headline: *"Thomas Oppermann criticises federal and state corona policy",* and on 22 October the social-democrat newspaper "Vorwärts" wrote: *"Oppermann: No acceptance for corona rules without debate".* SPD MP Oppermann was, after all, vice-president of the parliament, and his word carried weight. On 26 October, Oppermann's death at the age of 66 was reported. *"Immediately before recording a TV interview with ZDF, during which he was about to explain his position to the*

---

705 "Confessions of an Economic Hitman",
https://www.goodreads.com/book/show/2159.Confessions_of_an_Economic_Hit_Man

706 https://www.imf.org/en/Topics/imf-and-Covid19/COVID-Lending-Tracker#AFR

TV audience, Oppermann "suddenly collapsed" - and died shortly afterwards."[707] Cause of death unknown. Two months later, there is still no information about the cause of death. Der Spiegel" subsequently changed the title of its article of 16 October, Oppermann's name disappeared, presumably to cover up his connection with the Corona criticism. [708]

On 22 October 2020, the newspaper "Münchner Merkur" ran the headline: *"Head of SMEs warns Söder: Second lockdown would be death blow for economy, warns the president of the SME*[709] *association, Mario Ohoven".* Ohoven announced legal action should a second lockdown be imposed, as many businesses would not survive it. On 29 October, he again criticised the government by questioning the proportionality and the conformity with the Basic Law of the planned measures and announced that he would possibly appeal to the Constitutional Court.[710] On 1 November, it became known that Ohoven had been killed in a traffic accident. His Bentley had hit the crash barrier on the motorway in a straight line for no apparent reason and then crashed into a concrete foundation. [711]

It should be noted that since the death of Austrian liberal party chief Jörg Haider it has been known that modern cars, which are fully electronically controlled, can also be remote controlled. Haider also died in a strange car crash.

On 16 October, Franz Klein, the president of the "Hamburg Hotel and Restaurant Association", publicly announced that he would support the innkeepers' complaint against the new curfew. He criticised the Corona measures in the strongest

707 https://kenfm.de/was-steckt-hinter-der-corona-politik-von-paul-schreyer/
708 https://t.me/FaktenFriedenFreiheit/4790
709 Small and Medium-Sized Enterprises
710 https://de.wikipedia.org/wiki/Mario_Ohoven#Kritik_am_Konjunkturpaket_und_an_zweitem_Lockdown
https://www.presseportal.de/pm/51921/4748386
711 https://www.n-tv.de/wirtschaft/Mittelstandspraesident-Ohoven-tot-article22139196.html

terms and suspected that an example was to be made of the hotels and the gastronomy, which are not at all to blame for the increasing PCR numbers.[712]

"Klein knew his way around the political scene, having first been Senate spokesman and then headed Hamburg's state representation in Berlin until 2015." [713]

On 19 November, the German Hotel and Restaurant Association Dehoga announced a complaint to the Constitutional Court, as it considers the new Infection Protection Act to be incompatible with the Basic Law. Franz Klein, just re-elected as head of Dehoga, died *"suddenly and unexpectedly"* two days later.

"In this context, it is also worth remembering the sudden death of the Hessian Finance Minister Thomas Schäfer on 28 March, at the height of the first lockdown. Less than three weeks later, on 16 April, another high-ranking employee of the Hessian Ministry of Finance was "found lifeless in his office".[714] In both cases, the authorities spoke of suicide. It is striking that these deaths of financial politicians both occurred in Hesse, which is Germany's central financial centre with the banking metropolis of Frankfurt and the stock exchange there." [715]

This may all be coincidence, but it still leaves some doubts.

712 https://www.focus.de/regional/hamburg/franz-klein-dehoga-chef-giftet-gegen-beherbergungsverbot-in-hamburg-was-soll-da-passieren_id_12549509.html
713 https://kenfm.de/was-steckt-hinter-der-corona-politik-von-paul-schreyer/
714 https://www.fr.de/hessen/hessen-thomas-schaefer-zweiter-suizid-finanzministerium-zr-13655044.html
715 https://kenfm.de/was-steckt-hinter-der-corona-politik-von-paul-schreyer/

"The Great Reset"
– the revelation of the New World Order

The grand plan behind all these preparations is no secret: Klaus Schwab, founder and head of the WEF for 50 years, has presented it on his website and published it in July 2020 in his third book: "Covid-19: The Great Reset".[716] There is also a video trailer for it.[717] Schwab is so proud of his theory that he trumpets it big. Well, that makes research easier. I will give you my impressions of this "vision" of our future.

Let's start with the trailer. It contains no information, only emotionally charged images in primitive black and white. First, horrific images of epidemics, environmental destruction and unrest, how bad the world is. Then someone presses the "reset" button on a computer, the scenes run backwards and – poof – we have a beautiful new world with nice people, all wearing masks (!), happy children and lots of great nature shots. That's how Mr. Schwab imagines it.

However, the book describes his vision in great detail. Schwab and his co-author Thierry Malleret design a new world with a completely different society that could have come from a dystopian science fiction film. A dystopia is the opposite of a (positive) utopia, for example "Brave New World" by Aldoius Huxley or "1984" by George Orwell. The vision could be compared to a combination of global super - capitalism for the corporations and a kind of socialism with strict surveillance for the population.

Economist Martin Armstrong calls the vision a "Stalinist-communist eco-dictatorship" and fears it could become the

---

716 With co-author Thierry Malleret
717 https://www.weforum.org/videos/the-great-reset-726dedeacb?
collection=the-great-reset-863c8ea2d4

largest impoverishment and oppression programme in history.[718]

"The makers of the Great Reset have decided that "capitalism and socialism must merge". It's not entirely clear what they mean by this, but we can assume that it will amount to the worst of both worlds – think China rather than Sweden."[719]

In a video, the WEF shows Schwab's forecast for 2030 :

- You will no longer own anything, but you will be happy with it.

- Everything you need is rented and delivered by drone

- The USA will no longer be a leading superpower.

- Organ donations are superfluous because organs are produced with 3D printers.

- Meat consumption is now only allowed occasionally.

- A billion people will relocate due to climate change and we will welcome and integrate them. (This fits Soros' policy)

- CO_2 emissions are becoming expensive, fossil fuels are being phased out.

- We can prepare Mars flights, because science will keep you healthy in space. In the process, you could find extra-terrestrial intelligence.

- Western values will be stretched to the breaking point.[720]

---

718 https://www.schildverlag.de/2020/10/26/gruender-des-weltwirtschaftsforums-klaus-schwab-sie-werden-in-10-jahren-nichts-besitzen/

719 https://www.achgut.com/artikel/
eher china als schweden so tickt die corona internationale

720 https://youtu.be/Hx3DhoLFO4s

This shows, on the one hand, that salvation is sought in technology, and on the other, that pseudo-ecological goals are to be enforced. Not for nothing was Climate Greta allowed to speak to the elite circle in Davos. Schwab's entire agenda is very extensive, I will present a few examples in bullet points:

- Cameras, sensors, artificial intelligence monitor everything, thus crime decreases
- New technologies invade our minds, read our thoughts and influence our behaviour
- Police and courts use this to assess guilt and criminal disposition
- Crossing a national border requires a brain scan to ensure that no "dangerous persons" enter the country
- One business model will be to unlock access to the brain to communicate on the internet only through thought
- A world full of drones can save costs for personnel
- Speech algorithms replace telephone employees
- News is 90% written by algorithms instead of journalists and editors
- Learning takes place online with virtual reality
- "Smart" clothes, homes, cities, energy grids are networked by sensors and controlled by data networks and everything is connected to the internet
- In livestock farming, sensors wired into the cattle will communicate via the mobile network
- Citizens' privacy concerns will "require adjustments in thinking"

- Smartphones or virtual reality headsets are implanted in the body so that they are always with you

- Exoskeletons and prostheses improve performance

- New neurotechnology devices improve our cognitive abilities

- Blends of digital and analogue life will redefine human nature (cyborgs)

- Implantable microchips that break through the body's skin barrier, "smart tattoos", "biological computing" and "tailor-made organisms" open up new worlds

- Sensors, memory switches and circuits are "encoded" in human gut bacteria (?)

- "Smart Dust", swarms of computers with antennae, each much smaller than a grain of sand, can organise themselves in the body (?)

- Brains connect to virtual reality through cortical modems, implants or nanobots

- Inside viable embryos, genes are precisely manipulated so that we can create designer babies in the future

- It is not the way of working that is being changed, but *we are* being changed

- Geoengineering allows the installation of huge mirrors in the stratosphere to deflect the sun's rays, chemical inoculation of the atmosphere and the use of large machines to remove carbon dioxide from the air

- Nanoparticles and other advanced materials enable new products

- Genetic engineering is exempted from restrictions

- What is needed is the "reform of governance models to cope with new technologies".

- Global governance is the name of the new, worldwide order of the new "system leadership".

- Their leadership is in the hands of the corporations

- Democratic structures are a hindrance

- Family structures are being "redefined"

- Cultural belonging is "redefined", for example through migration

- The workforce of the companies is monitored with apps, thermal cameras and facial recognition to comply with social distancing.

Reading all this makes you want to dismiss the "Great Reset" as the megalomaniac fantasies of a crazed Dr. Frankenstein or Dr. No from a James Bond film. Unfortunately, Klaus Schwab is backed by the biggest and most elitist business lobby in the world, and that is why I am devoting so much space to this horror vision.

The year 2020 has shown how quickly the world can be turned upside down, how an unleashed pharmaceutical capitalism produces tests and vaccinations at full speed, how states distribute gigantic subsidies out of thin air, how flourishing industries such as tourism, gastronomy, culture are fundamentally ruined – against better judgement – and that is not even the beginning, if one believes the WEF.

The legal foundations of democracies are being shredded in record time, fundamental rights suspended by decree, not only in Germany. This proves that the "Great Reset" has already begun and bodes ill for the future.

The timetable has also been set. Bill Gates announced in an interview on NBC that masking and restrictions will take four years, but the complete transformation of society would take ten years.[721] I probably forgot to mention that Gates is one of the most important protagonists of Schwab's WEF. Is anyone else surprised? Schwab himself keeps talking about the "reset" being completed by 2030.

Schwab does not always write so directly in his book, he tries to gloss over his ideas with all kinds of neologisms. His favourite word is *"stakeholder"*, *which* he claims to have invented, but he did not.[722] In contrast to "shareholder", i.e. all those involved in and benefiting from a company, including employees, customers, etc., are stakeholders. They should also share in the success. In reality, the concept is deeply undemocratic, leaving decision-making power to planners and technocrats, who are appointed by whom? Well, by the corporations, who else?

The "people" are left only with the role of workers and consumers. However, the planned automation, which out-sources not only physical but increasingly also mental work to robots and algorithms, means that far fewer workers will be needed. Where to put the superfluous people? The big reset is silent about that, and that bodes ill. Perhaps Mr. Gates has a few ideas to contribute?

The former head of the Federal Office for the Protection of the Constitution, Dr. Hans-Georg Maaßen, says that dreams of a Great Reset can be understood as a *"declaration of war on the liberal democratic basic order"*.[723]

Allegedly, Schwab wants to end "neoliberalism", which is surprising, since the WEF members only became super-rich through it. Basically, the weird mixture of super-capitalism for the rich and totalitarian socialism for the working people is already the "success model" of a great power: China.

---

721 https://www.zeitpunkt.ch/der-grosse-reset
722 https://www.infosperber.ch/Wirtschaft/WEF-Thema-2020-Stakeholder-Wer-hats-erfunden
723 https://youtu.be/d7uDtE5CnBU?t=145

Apparently, China is the model for the "Great Reset", and this model is to be introduced worldwide.

Then the corporations can do what they want and make profits without being disturbed by democratic demands or national borders. The state will then only be responsible for administration, surveillance, police and military. Everything else, including schools and education, media anyway, will be privatised so that the old and young working people can be correctly programmed. Welcome to Mr. Schwab's brave new world!

Presumably, many Chinese leaders sympathise with the WEF's *"Politburo of Capitalism"* (Paul Schreyer) in order to be able to spread their system worldwide. This is indicated by the participation of the CCDS chief in the "Event 201" organised by the WEF. Wuhan might have been chosen as the initial igniter for the Corona crisis, the blueprint for the lockdowns in the rest of the world was exemplified here. China suffered few casualties, the crisis was over in China by the time it began elsewhere, and in the end China not only quickly got back on its feet economically, but even got ahead of its competitors on the world market.

There are some indications that China deliberately carried out the role as "trigger" of the Corona crisis.[724] It is also interesting that the WEF will not hold its 2021 meeting in Davos for the first time in 50 years, but – in China. "Because of Corona", of course.

Schwab has a few more slogans to adorn his vision: *"Rethink, Redesign, Re-build "* or *"Build back better"*. The latter slogan, by the way, has appeared more frequently in recent weeks, in speeches by Joe Biden, Boris Johnson, Canadian Prime Minister Trudeau, Bavarian president Markus Söder and Austrian Chancellor Kurz. It's interesting how the "silent mail" is doing the rounds. Other buzzwords include: *"Global Governance", "Biosecurity", "New Norma-*

---

724 https://tkp.at/2020/11/29/china-und-der-great-reset/

lity", "New Deal for Nature" and the "Fourth Industrial Revolution", which by the way are identically proclaimed translated into all languages.

The UN is also supposed to serve the WEF plans. It finds its new role in reshaping the world according to the WEF's specifications. The fact that the UN Charter did not plan it this way does not seem to bother anyone.[725] To this end, in June 2019, the WEF concluded a "Memorandum of Understanding" agreement with the United Nations "to deepen cooperation". Details can be found on Norbert Häring's page, where he writes: "It is another step in the UN's disempowerment and another milestone for the club of multinationals on the way to its declared goal – world domination."[726] Another important point is the abolition of cash in favour of digital currencies. I will come back to this.

The "Great Reset" has advocates among the "elites" and those who think they are. Time magazine, for example, devoted its front page to it on 22.10.2020. The British heir to the throne Prince Charles, IMF chief Kristalina Georgieva and the Director General of the United Nations António Guterres also promote the Great Reset.

EU Commission President von der Leyen is on the WEF list, too.[727] She recently stated that we need new rules for the digital economy and the "digital society" (interesting term). The drive of the "Great Reset" is the (claimed) need for global cooperation and acceleration of change, which she sees as an unprecedented opportunity.[728] "Unprecedented" certainly, it has never happened in this form before, "opportunity" yes, for all players at the WEF. But where does

725 https://www.umb.edu/gri/an_overview_of_wefs_perspective/ united_nations_and_the_private_non_state_world
726 https://norberthaering.de/news/wef-un/?lang=de
727 https://www.weforum.org/agenda/2020/11/the-great-reset-building-future-resilience-to-global-risks/
728 https://deutsch.rt.com/gesellschaft/109670-transhumanismus-wef-gruender-schwab-prophezeit/

that leave us, and – do we even want it? One would like to say that we did not elect them for such ingratiation, but the EU leaders are not elected anyway. Otherwise, they wouldn't be elected.

Schwab continues to bask in the glamour of his friends' media and is courted everywhere. He has received many prizes, such as the "Dan David Prize" from Israel, which is worth one million dollars, as well as many decorations from all over the world, including the Order of Merit of the Federal Republic of Germany.[729]

---

729 https://de.wikipedia.org/wiki/Klaus_Schwab#Einzelbelege

Planned crises as fire accelerators

Changing a stable situation is difficult. Throughout history, it has been common to first create a crisis in order to destabilise and then establish the desired system. Usually, revolutions, wars or economic crises were instigated for this purpose. The Corona crisis is a new category, because it allows police-state control without a real state of emergency – the virus is invisible – and distracts from the actual political events through the constant virus discussions.

What is ominous is that Schwab is quite serious about the metaphor of a "reboot". For a reboot, however, the computer, in this case the economy, must first be shut down completely, and that is by all means planned. ***This means that the destruction of the middle class worldwide is not collateral damage, but so deliberate.*** The companies, gastronomy, logistics companies, retail trade etc. ***are to*** go bankrupt in order to be bought up cheaply afterwards by the large corporations and chains and restructured.

Work will then only be available on temporary contracts through subcontractors, which means that labour law, holiday regulations and social security, everything that the trade unions have fought for over the last hundred years, will be nullified. This is how Mr. Schwab and his corporate friends from the WEF Club would like it. They know full well that Corona is only a farce, a means to an end, because they planned it or – If anyone still doubts it – at least used it.

For Schwab and Malleret's book admits that Covid19 is one of the least deadly pandemics of the last 2,000 years, and that it has the mildest health and mortality consequences compared to previous pandemics. In medical terms, Corona is neither a shock nor an existential threat to the world. Nevertheless, the word "shock" is used again and again to refer to the political upheavals. At least Schwab is honest in admitting that it is not the virus but what is made of it that is the shock to the world. [730]

That the world can only be changed with a crisis towards the "New World Order" has been announced several times:

- As early as June 1991, David Rockefeller said at the Bilderberg Conference in Baden-Baden that we were on the verge of a worldwide change and that all we needed was the right, big crisis for people to join the New World Order. At the same time, he thanked the major US newspapers whose editors-in-chief attended the Bilderbergers and did not report on it for almost 40 years. It would have been impossible to make a plan for the world if the public had known about it. The world was now on the way to world government. The international rule of an intellectual elite together with the leading bankers would be better than the national sovereignty of past centuries. [731]

- On 23 September 1994, he repeated to the US Business Council that all we needed was a really big crisis and then the states would accept the New World Order.[732]

- German parliament president Wolfgang Schäuble said in an interview on 20 August 2020 that the Corona crisis was a great opportunity because there was less resistance to change in the crisis. The economic and

---

730 Martin Armstrong in: https://www.schildverlag.de/2020/10/26/gruender-des-weltwirtschaftsforums-klaus-schwab-sie-werden-in-10-jahren-nichts-besitzen/

731 https://de-de.facebook.com/die.infokrieger/posts/zitat-von-david-rockefeller-bilderberg-konferenz-1991-in-baden-baden-deutschland/127461960608213/

732https://www.wallstreet-online.de/nachricht/12360741-teuflische-plan-Covid-19 https://meinanzeiger.de/gera/bilderberger-mit-dem-ziel-einer-neuen-weltordnung/

financial union, which had not come about so far, was now feasible, he said.[733]

- As early as 2011, he said something similar, namely that the bigger the crisis, the easier it is to implement changes.[734]

- Warren Buffet, co-founder of B&MGF and friend of Gates, said in an interview with the New York Times that there is a class war going on and it is his class, the rich class, which is fighting the war and winning it.[735]

- "Der Spiegel" wrote in March 2020 that crises like Corona require some kind of world government, even if it is provisional and imperfect.[736]

- Robert F. Kennedy said at the big demo in Berlin on 29.8.2020 that governments love pandemics for the same reasons they love wars – because they can then establish control mechanisms that the people would otherwise never accept.[737]

This principle is suspiciously reminiscent of the motto of the Freemasons, which is *"Ordo ab Chao"*, i.e. *"order out of chaos"*, which *of* course means their (world) "order". Well then, the chaos is being created.

Should the installation of the WEF world order falter, then further crises are apparently planned. Klaus Schwab warned on 8.6.2020 of the scenario of a major cyber attack that could completely block the power supply, transport, hospitals and society as a whole, whereas Corona would only seem like a

733 http://www.wolfgang-schaeuble.de/die-pandemie-ist-eine-grosse-chance/
734 In a TV interview on "Phoenix" in December 2011
735 http://www.nytimes.com/2006/11/26/business/yourmoney/26every.html?_r=0
736 https://www.spiegel.de/politik/ausland/coronavirus-krise-wir-brauchen-eine-weltregierung-a-058a25cf-646a-466f-a969-7a40a517feb0
737 https://childrenshealthdefense.org/news/robert-f-kennedy-jr-speaks-at-berlin-rally-for-freedom-and-peace/

minor disruption. Indeed, reports have been piling up in the mainstream lately about possible power cuts in Germany. One had better be prepared.[738]

And WEF Executive Director Jeremy Jurgens threatened that there could be a crisis more significant and more rapid than anything known from Corona, with worse repercussions and more far-reaching social and economic consequences.[739]

There are no plans to ever reverse the "Great Reset", the upheaval is to last for generations. Schwab and his co-planners are already talking about a new era, a "pre-Corona" era (BC) and a "post-Corona" era (AC). This will then be the "New Normal". More details can be found in the very readable article in the Off-Guardian.[740]

738 https://www.bitchute.com/video/ZUcaJKg47C7i/
739 https://www.bitchute.com/video/i8m7EP76QBV3/
740 https://off-guardian.org/2020/10/12/klaus-schwab-his-great-fascist-reset/

ID 2020 – the digital identity

Efficient surveillance involves identifying as many people as possible. It would be in line with Bill Gates' ideas to combine vaccination and software. Gates is promoting vaccination certificates and Microsoft is working with Apple to make the tracking apps of the various systems compatible with each other, which is a prerequisite for seamless surveillance. The pandemic comes just in time.[741]

There is another of Gates' projects: the "Digital Identity Alliance", or "ID 2020" for short. It was founded in 2016 at the UN in New York and deals with the "unique identification of people" worldwide (interesting that the name "ID 2020" was already chosen at that time). Founding partners include Gates' "Microsoft", Gates' vaccination alliance GAVI and the Rockefeller Foundation, one of the oldest and richest foundations in the USA.

ID 2020 has been working with the Bangladeshi government since 2019 to introduce digital identities. This is done by combining vaccinations and fingerprints. The minister responsible reported to the WEF that 200 million such identities have already been created. Officially, this is to enable poor people to participate in the modern world.[742]

There are plans to vaccinate new born children and implant a chip, called "infant biometric technologies". This can of course be used for surveillance and the introduction of digital money.[743]

---

741 https://www.metropolnews.info/mp457208/gefaehrlicher-angriff-auf-die-menschheit-der-millardaer-die-impfindustrie-die-politik-und-die-who

742 https://multipolar-magazin.de/artikel/der-impfaktivismus-der-gates-stiftung

743 https://identity-economy.de/id2020-in-der-kritik

No one is being asked whether we need or want digital identities either, but facts are being created, just like with Corona and vaccination.[744]

The data all converge in the USA, in the data storage facilities of the companies and foundations set up by Gates and others. They then become something like the "virtual passport authority" for the whole world, recording and evaluating all our movements via app. It decides whether and where we are allowed to travel and can locate us at any time if we deviate. What's more, it can be used to check who we have met. The contact controls and, if necessary, restrictions on the grounds of "virus infection" are a large-scale test for a gigantic worldwide surveillance system, in a sense the precursors.

One of the sub-projects is called "The Known Traveller Digital Identity". It was presented by – guess what – the WEF in cooperation with US Homeland Security in Davos 2018. All travellers are supposed to collect their movement and other data and disclose it on demand when crossing the border, unless it has already reached the servers via mobile phone. This does not have to be limited to borders; other occasions are also conceivable.

"An important part of the concept is that users basically log in to their smartphone or computer biometrically, i.e. with fingerprint, facial recognition or voice recognition, so that they can be reliably assigned to their device and the activity carried out with it.

And now, Google and Apple have joined forces, under the pretext of pandemic control, to equip mobile phones with the two all-dominant operating systems, Android and iOS, with the ability to record via Bluetooth technology which people have been in close proximity to each other, across both operating systems."[745]

---

744 http://ariejehuda.de/was-hat-es-mit-id2020-auf-sich/

Incidentally, the German federal government wants to quickly introduce a "personal identification number" with which one must identify oneself to all authorities.[746] Although the Federal Commissioner for Data Protection considers such a "tax ID" unconstitutional and the German Lawyers' Association protests, because this would create the "transparent citizen", the first reading was held in the Bundestag on 19 November 2020 – one day after the historic 18 November.[747]

745 https://norberthaering.de/die-regenten-der-welt/id2020-ktdi-apple-google/

746 https://www.journalistenwatch.com/2020/11/21/totalueberwachung-buergers-die/

747 Day of the most massive restriction of fundamental rights in the FRG through the 3rd amendment of the Infection Protection Act

Is a chip implanted during vaccination?

There are now RFID chips that are so small that they can enter the body through a cannula. What can such chips do? According to my research, they are "only" passive chips, similar to those found in pets, price tags or ID cards. They contain digital information that can be read with a special device.

How far does the field reach? There are many rumours, for example of satellites that could do this, but the laws of radio technology do not allow this in any case. With directional antennas, you can read the chips in passports up to a maximum of 100 metres; the smaller the chip, the closer you have to get. It would be conceivable to have a reader integrated into the mobile phone, which would be close enough to the person and could pass on the data via the radio network in the normal way, possibly also that of bystanders. But this is still speculation, I haven't found any more precise sources.

The identification of people with even unknowingly implanted chips, for example during vaccinations, is therefore technically possible. Vaccination sets with RFID chips from the company "Apiject" are already on the market.[748] It is not said whether the chips can be implanted.

There are also rumours that chips could be inserted into the nose with a cotton swab for PCR tests. That would be possible, but they would not stay there for long, but would be excreted when you blow your nose. One wonders anyway why one has to search so deeply in the nose to find viruses, when they are supposed to fly around everywhere during normal exhalation. Or what else are the masks for?

---

748 https://verborgenes-wissen.ch/die-apiject-spritzen-fuer-die-corona-impfung-in-den-usa-werden-mit-einem-optionalen-rfid-chip-modifiziert-uzzlestueck-5-23/

But it is not possible to actively control people or "read minds" via a chip, as some rumours say. Even the best electronics cannot perform magic. Psychological programmes are needed for that, usually with drug support, but that is another topic. Unfortunately, there is a lot of disinformation in this complicated field. This includes the claim that Corona can be triggered by 5G networks. 5G networks are of course helpful for smartphone surveillance, but their wavelength is a few millimetres, worlds away from the size of virus-like particles. An interaction is out of the question. Despite all the speculation, we have to leave things in the village, we have enough problems to solve as it is.

However, DARPA,[749] the research institute of the US Department of War, is working on implantable chips that measure body data, such as certain blood values, and transmit them to receptors on the skin, which are then stored in the cloud via smart phones. The aim is to monitor the condition of soldiers in action.

Digital identities can be stored with a personalised smartphone, with chips or in "invisible tattoos". The process was developed by the renowned MIT[750] in 2019.[751] You have to imagine it as a small, flat stamp with many microneedles attached that are pressed under the skin. When pulled out, the needle tips break off and stay there. They dissolve and release either vaccines or fluorescent dye (or both). The dye pattern, which contains the digital information (similar to a QR code[752]), is invisible to the eye but can be read with infrared-sensitive cameras.

This can also be done with digital cameras or mobile phones where the IR protective film in front of the lens has been removed. The whole thing is called *"quantum dot tattooing"*

---

749 "Defence Advanced Research Projects Agency"
750 Massachusetts Institute of Technology
751 https://news.mit.edu/2019/storing-vaccine-history-skin-1218
752 These are the square black and white patterns that can be read with the smartphone

and was developed with the support of the Gates Foundation (another "coincidence").[753]

Such fluorescent dyes are called "luciferase", from the Latin "lux", light (Lucifer was originally the "light bearer" in the Bible), which of course gave rise to some speculation, in which I do not want to participate. However, if such a tattoo were to be used as a "PIN" for cashless payments, this would be a memorable parallel to the "Revelation of John" in the Bible: there it says that people would be forced to wear the *"mark of the beast on their hand or forehead"*, without which they would not be able to buy or sell.

Whatever technology is used, the digital marking of all people is firmly planned. This reminds me of a conversation that the US film producer Aaron Russo, who died in 2007, had 20 years ago and later was published. At the time, he was friends with Nicholas Rockefeller, from the notorious billionaire family that is a major player in Bilderberg and the Council on Foreign Relations (CFR). After the publication of the following conversation, however, the friendship was over. Among other things, Russo reported the following:

He asked about the ultimate goal of the family's many activities when they already have more money than they can ever spend. Rockefeller replied that the ultimate goal was to chip everyone in the world in order to control them and work towards the elite and the bankers taking over the world.

He added that if Russo were to join the elite, he would be given a special tag that would prevent unwanted checks by the authorities.[754]

753 https://norberthaering.de/die-regenten-der-welt/id2020-ktdi-apple-google/
754 http://deutschlandpolitik.wordpress.com/2009/06/17/rockefeller-ziel-der-elite-ist-mikrochip-fur-weltbevolkerung/
https://www.youtube.com/watch?v=AYxFlQsadJk

The digital health passport

A digital identification, no matter how it is stored, can be combined with other information such as health data, PCR test results, vaccinations or as a wallet for digital money. The information is to be encoded as a "blockchain", as with Bitcoin. The Federal Printers of Germany is already working on this together with Lufthansa and other companies.[755]

One important project is called "The Commons Project". Norbert Häring writes: *"The World Economic Forum has teamed up with a new "non-profit" organisation set up by the Rockefeller Foundation. They want to use Corona to form a private global health passport authority. In doing so, they are resolutely pushing ahead with their techno-authoritarian "Known-Traveller", ID-2020 and "Lock-Step" plans. In July, the small Rockefeller offshoot operating in the background became a globally operating organisation networked at the highest levels. A Board of Trustees was appointed, with 62 high-ranking representatives of companies and organisations from 24 countries and all corners of the world. The Rockefeller Foundation with its president, Blackrock, JP Morgan, various UN organisations and many companies and associations in the health sector are represented...*

On 7 October 2020, the Commons Project and the World Economic Forum announced the launch of a field trial of the newly developed app "CommonPass". This is an app that is supposed to make international travel possible again for everyone who either has antibodies against Corona or has been vaccinated. After all, governments can't do that. The corporations and their foundations have to help."[756]

---

755 https://www.heise.de/newsticker/meldung/Coronavirus-Blockchain-Zertifikat-als-digitaler-Seuchenpass-4703902.html

756 https://kenfm.de/das-commons-project-der-digitale-gesundheitspass-von-norbert-haering/

It boils down to the fact that the "health passport" is supposed to ensure that only vaccinated or negatively tested people will be allowed to travel, go to discos, sports and other events. The organisers will be pushed so far to the edge of their existence (and beyond) by the lockdowns that they will play the evil game in order to survive.

"The International Air Transport Association (IATA), the umbrella organisation of airlines, is considering the introduction of a vaccination passport. The infrastructure for such a system is currently being built, IATA's managing director Alexandre de Juniac confirmed to the US newspaper "The Hill": "The digital health passport would contain a passenger's test and vaccine information and make information manageable and verifiable for governments, airlines, laboratories and travellers," the article says."[757]

China's President Xi proposed at the last G20 summit the introduction of an international QR code to enable travel. Health and test certificates are to be stored.[758] Britain is planning a two-tier system with a "freedom pass": those who have the pass can "live normally", shop without a mask, attend events, to travel freely. In South Africa, this used to be called "apartheid". For this, you have to get tested twice a week for five pounds each time, a permanent tax for the pharmacy es.[759]

Of course, all this is "voluntary". So much for *"there will be no compulsory vaccination"*. No one *"intended to build a wall"* in Berlin either, and yet suddenly there it was. Whenever the government says it wants to avoid a certain measure (so that we play along dutifully) one can assume that exactly this will come next. Such pseudo denials serve as psychological announcements, the image is already planted in people's

---

757 https://www.heise.de/tp/features/Keine-Reisefreiheit-fuer-Impfgegner-4973891.html
758 https://orf.at/stories/3190935/
759 https://www.reitschuster.de/post/normales-leben-pass-fuer-corona-musterbuerger/

minds. Psychologists know that the subconscious knows no negation. It only sees the image. If you say: "*There is no pink elephant*", then the image of a pink elephant is created inside, it's as simple as that.

The fact that one must no longer believe anything the government says is shown by the example of Jens Spahn, who assured on 1 September that *"with the knowledge of today"* (when he said that) one would no longer impose a lockdown.[760] Minister Altmeier promised the same.[761] So much for the credibility of politics.

760 https://philosophia-perennis.com/2020/12/10/wie-versprochen-so-gebrochen/
761 https://www.pnp.de/nachrichten/politik/Altmaier-Es-wird-keinen-zweiten-Lockdown-geben-3780482.html

What happens to our genetic data?

Here is another find from the German corruption swamp: The company "Centogene" sells Covid tests for travellers at several German airports for a hefty price. We don't know how it won the bid for the flourishing business. All we know is: Merkel visited the company in Rostock at the end of May 2019. In November 2019, the company went public and got on its feet because of Corona. In October 2020, Dr. Andrin Oswald became head of the company. He was responsible for the swine flu vaccine at Novartis in 2009 as head of the "Vaccines Division" and was a director at B&MGF for four years. Coincidences exist...

"Centogene" has also built up an extensive gene database, which by the end of August had collected about 3.6 billion data points from about 570,000 patients from over 120 countries. But not only genetic data is archived, also biological samples, i.e. tissues, cells etc. as reference for research. Allegedly, this is the only database worldwide that can evaluate all data on several levels in parallel.[762]

It stands to reason to assume that the genetic data is taken, among other things, from the samples of the Corona tests and fed into such databases. Dr. Wodarg already complained about the large collection of data through the tests by private companies. No one knows what is done with the test samples. There would be an international programme for genome collection, which would be highly interesting for the pharmaceutical industry. This could explain the completely excessive testing, which would otherwise be nonsensical. More panic makes for more tests and thus more genetic data.[763]

---

762 https://www.corodok.de/centogene-big-pharma-gates/
763 https://de.rt.com/gesellschaft/107312-corona-ausschuss-man-braucht-viele-dumme-leute-damit-das-klappt-teil-1/

In 2010, Bill Gates visited the genetic engineering company "BGI Genomics" in China and decided to bring it to the USA with B&MGF money. The company settled in Washington State, where B&MGF is based, too. Recently, it became known that "BGI Genomics" misused mass corona tests to collect and archive the biometric data of US citizens.[764]

In March 2020, the British Parliament passed the "Coronavirus Act 2020", which allows the police to store the gene data of PCR tests, initially for six months, but renewable. This is supposed to serve "national security" (in case terrorists ever get tested, or why?).[765]

Already in January 2020, Germany joined the European genome project, in which more than one million complete genome data are to be stored.[766] In April 2020, the EU then set up a "Covid19 data portal" in which gene and other data are to be stored.[767] Such data collections are not only of interest to researchers, but specifically to the vaccine and pharmaceutical industries. They have enormous value. Who ultimately has access to our genetic data is unclear completely.

764 https://thenationalpulse.com/exclusive/bgi-genomics-gates-foundation-collab

765 https://www.gov.uk/government/news/biometrics-commissioner-statement-on-the-coronavirus-act-and-the-protection-of-freedoms-act

766 https://www.bmbf.de/de/deutschland-tritt-genomprojekt-der-eu-bei-10676.html

767 https://ec.europa.eu/germany/news/20200421-coronavirusforschung_de

Digital money

The programme to abolish cash and replace it with card or app payments has been running for many years. It has progressed furthest in Sweden, where it is no longer possible to pay cash for many things; even beggars in Malmö take their fare digitally on their smartphones. My grandparents used to say *"only cash is real"*, and I think it's a very wise saying. Digital money has a number of disadvantages:

- It is not anonymous. Every purchase can be traced.
- The card/app can be blocked if tracked, for whatever reason.
- People lose their relationship with money and spend more. Studies have shown that consumption is up to 100% higher than with cash.
- Children do not learn to deal with money at all if it is only abstract.

"Thus, the abolition of cash will lead to an unimagined cementing and almost unlimited expansion of the power of the corresponding corporations and institutions. Not only do the possibilities of control over the citizen and surveillance increase immeasurably through the seamless data collection of all digital payments, but a financial dictatorship is emerging – almost unnoticed by the public. This concept seems unreal at first, but unfortunately it is the consequence.

For control over all money is bundled and concentrated by the abolition of cash in a small number of decision-makers and institutions, raising their power and influence to unimagined heights. An unprecedented shift of power is taking place so that elites control the world and the course of world history centrally and beyond the influence of citizens."[768]

It is obvious that a world without cash allows perfect control. With a blocked card, no one can travel, check in or even buy a bread roll. *If cash is being fought, then the suspicion of totalitarian intentions is obvious.* In recent years, the amounts of cash allowed for buying and selling, or that which one is allowed to carry, have been reduced more and more.

Corona reinforced this trend, many shops only allowed card payments, although they are actually obliged to accept the "legal tender". The excuse was that viruses could run rampant on cash. But strangely enough, not on the PIN keypads.

This increases the acceptance of the card, also among the elderly and cash lovers. During Corona, the number of card payments increased by 48%.[769] Those who want to advocate cash should therefore only shop where they can pay cash. Then the loss of sales of those who do not accept cash will eventually cause a rethink, if enough customers join in.

In 2012, with the help of the UN, the "Better Than Cash Alliance" was founded,[770] co-financed by the B&MGF. Its aim is to push for the abolition of cash. But in September 2020, the initiative faced headwinds in the US with a bill to ban shops from refusing cash.[771] Chinese government also supports the continued existence of cash (for the time being) and is planning penalties for refusing to accept cash.[772]

According to many financial experts, including system critics, the global monetary system has been at its end for years, which can be seen in the zero interest rate policy. It is clear

---

768 https://www.rubikon.news/artikel/das-unhygienische-bargeld
769 ibid
770 https://de.wikipedia.org/wiki/Better_Than_Cash_Alliance
771 https://norberthaering.de/bargeld-widerstand/bargeld-gesetz-usa/
772 https://de.rt.com/asien/110703-chinesische-zentralbank-will-bargeldverweigerer-bestrafen/

that for years more and more central bank money has been pumped into the ailing financial system, which, however, does not reach the citizens, but is used for gambling in out-of-the-way financial casinos (stock exchanges, hedge funds, etc.) and inflates the stock markets. This cannot go on for long, especially since Corona increases these funds enormously instead of slowing them down.

Paul Schreyer pointed out in a lecture that relatively unnoticed by the public, a financial crisis took place in September 2019, which almost resulted in the collapse of many banks, but was just barely prevented with hefty financial injections by the central banks. However, the crisis is not over, and a new monetary system is inevitable, which could have been an important reason for triggering the Corona crisis. For, on the one hand, the measures keep the population calm and controllable, and on the other hand, the virus can be blamed for the dire consequences.[773]

Critical financial experts such as Ernst Wolff, Markus Krall or Michael Mross also[774] hold this view.

For various reasons, digital money, called CBDC,[775] is supposed to go directly from central banks to citizens, for example via a basic income. The fact is that not only Facebook wants to introduce its own money "Diem" (formerly "Libra"), also the FED, the US central bank is preparing for it and China has already started with first trials. The ECB is also planning to start a test phase for the "e-euro" from mid-2021.[776]

But we should not rejoice too soon if a basic income from the central bank should come. It will not be "unconditional", quite the contrary. In a report from Canada on 13 October, a committee member of the Liberal Party of Canada allegedly

773 https://youtu.be/SSnJhHOU_28
774 http://mmnews.de/
775 Central Bank Digital Currencies
776 https://de.rt.com/europa/109938-wird-noch-in-jahrzehnt-digitale/

leaked the government's further plans and the planned development of the Corona crisis.[777]

The truth cannot be verified, but the points mentioned have also been mentioned on other sites. Among them, apart from the 2nd lockdown, which is now here, there is an even tougher lockdown in winter 2021/22, a "new", "even more dangerous" virus "Covid-21", collapse of supply chains and shortage of goods until summer 2021, army operations in cities and along motorways.

In a "world debt reset programme", financed by the IMF, all private and corporate debts are to be taken over and a basic income granted. In return, all claims to present and future property must be surrendered (pure communism) and all vaccinations (there will be several) accepted, in return for which there will be the vaccination card. Anyone who resists is declared a "health risk for others" and must accept reprisals. Allegedly, the FEMA camps in the USA are intended for the internment of the opposition.

This is a horror vision, let us hope that if it is indeed planned this way, it can still be prevented. However, Australia and New Zealand (like Canada also British Commonwealth states) are already on their way there, and the agenda of destroying the economy and over-indebtedness, as described in the "Great Reset", is even more visible here.

It is clear that the financial and economic system of the last decades makes the rich richer and the poor poorer worldwide and leads from one crisis to the next. It cannot be reformed. We need another one. But certainly not what Schwab and his "elite" are planning for us.

---

777 https://thecanadianreport.ca/is-this-leaked-memo-really-trudeaus-Covid-plan-for-2021-you-decide/
https://indexexpurgatorius.wordpress.com/2020/10/22/das-muessen-sie-lesen-der-geheime-plan-welcher-hinter-den-lockdowns-lauert/

Psychological warfare

When you read all these plans, you think, this can't be, *"I'm in the wrong movie here".* That is somehow true, because we have only known such extreme, inhuman scenarios from films. Even catastrophes and wars we only know from television, and that can be switched off. But not the Corona reality, it's there again every morning, you can't escape it. As I said before: there is only escape, attack or play dead. Escape is not possible, there is no visible enemy for an attack, so most people play dead, which is no solution either.

We humans are forced by the crisis to rethink. We have to learn. For example, that there are indeed people who are thoroughly evil, who are not burdened by any conscience because they are incapable of empathy. The dimension of evil, quite real for religious people, is ignored, considered outdated, outmoded, and **that is precisely the perfect camouflage**. What you don't think is possible, you simply don't see. Those who do see it are annoying, inconvenient, finally silenced. The awakening is then all the more unpleasant, but inevitable.

In 1957, the US sociologist Albert Biderman published his Chart of Coercion,[778] describing the techniques used to break prisoners of war mentally and force them into submission. The most important methods are:

- Isolation, physical and mental, reduce contacts with others

- Restrict or prevent private freedoms

- Constant threats, demonstrations of the prisoners' powerlessness

---

778 https://translatedby.com/you/biderman-s-chart-of-coercion/original/

- Constantly changing rules and regulations, permanent uncertainty
- the rules are not supposed to be logical or predictable, submission is demanded
- Restriction of sport, relaxation and recreation opportunities
- Small reliefs now and then, "treats" like in dog training
- Giving hope and then destroying it again, thereby "wearing it down".
- Permanent tension due to disregard and belittlement
- Offer the prospect of a reward for cooperation

So, now please read the whole thing again and compare it with our current situation. The parallels are obvious: Isolation (stay at home, avoid contacts, forced quarantine), changing and illogical rules (curfew, where mask, where not, arbitrariness in punishment, etc.), giving and destroying hope (*"you may celebrate Christmas"*), rewarding submission (*"when vaccination comes, then..."*), bans on sports, parties, culture, dancing, singing, eating out, travelling, etc. You can find an interesting video about this here.[779] So it is no coincidence that it is precisely gastronomy, sport, culture and, in short, everything that is fun, that is being restricted. In addition, communication with fellow prisoners is made difficult or prevented.

The chaotic confusion of lockdown and mask rules in Europe, the federal states, the constant change of regulations, the uncertain future are *not* incompetence of the authorities, *not* coincidence, **they are part of exactly this psychological plan**. We are treated like prisoners of war,

---

779 https://www.bitchute.com/video/wAifPvXifuGQ/   or:
    https://www.bitchute.com/video/oOHUx8XOioU9/

and the measures are meant to make submissive people out of us, with the mask as a symbol of submission. Those who make this out to be a "conspiracy theory" are still too gullible to realise that there is a real conspiracy going on here. Unfortunately. Everything is going according to a grand plan.

An important part of this plan is that rule in the New World Order should not be exercised too obviously. The illusion of living in a democracy is to be maintained. We see that this is (still) working despite all the government's breaches of the law. The concept is as old as the first modern democracy, that of the USA. The French political scientist and historian Alexis de Tocqueville visited the USA in the 19th century and was the first to warn of a "tyranny of the majority". His report is almost 200 years old, but it is amazing how aptly it seems to describe our times:

"Thus the sovereign, having taken each individual into his mighty hands and reshaped him at will, prepares his arms over society as a whole; he covers its surface with a web of small, intricate, narrow and uniform rules that not even the most original minds and strongest souls would be able to penetrate if they wanted to leave the multitude behind them; it does not break the will, but weakens, bends, and guides it; it seldom compels action, rather it constantly stands in the way of action; it does not destroy, it hinders the formation; it does not tyrannise, it harasses, oppresses, debilitates, weakens, stultifies, and finally brings every nation to the point where it is nothing but a herd of timid and busy animals, whose shepherd [is] the government."[780]

This is not a pleasant message, but it is not set in stone. We can still turn the tide by supporting the awakening that has already begun. The "lateral thinking movement" ("Querdenker") has made a start, and it is a good movement, because it focuses on knowledge and peaceful change. It is

---

780 Found on a video worth watching by the philosopher Gunnar Kaiser
 https://www.youtube.com/watch?v=Q9fFT_f4qus

the first German movement in over a hundred years to overcome the artificial left-right divide, even if state propaganda would like to banish it to the "right-wing" mud corner.

According to a recent survey, *"in the last federal election, 21% of today's participants in the Querdenker-Demos voted for the Greens, while the LEFT was the second strongest party with 17%. Only in third place came the [patriotic) AfD with 14%."*

Violence would be fatal, because that is precisely where the opponent is vastly superior due to the state's monopoly on the use of force, which we are increasingly experiencing.[781]

Enlightenment is the only weapon we have at the moment, and I would like to make my contribution with this book. I draw the strength for this from the striving for truth and justice that we all carry within us, and the belief in a higher power, in goodness. In a time when truth is declared a lie and lies the "new normality", the only means that helps is to question everything and to go in search of it ourselves.

Once the lies about the false case numbers of the PCR test collapse, then the fear of the virus and the acceptance of the coercive measures will be over. But we should not wait too long, because the new corona dictatorship is about to take root.

---

781 https://www.compact-online.de/echte-querfront-fast-40-prozent-der-querdenker-waehlten-gruene-oder-linke/

What happens next?

I have not spent months researching and writing to plunge my readers into despair – quite the opposite. Even if all this is not pleasant, what I have dragged into the light, realisation is the first step towards change. Facing the facts, where most people prefer to bury their heads in the sand and think that everything will "pass by itself", enduring the view into the abyss – unfortunately, we first have to go through this and it takes courage. And then?

The fact that certain circles are planning something for the world does not mean that they will get away with it. Hitler's "Thousand Year Reich" ended after 12 years. Even the best plan offers no guarantee, certainly not if it is uncovered. One has to assume that 99% of the people would not agree with these plans if they knew them. General ignorance, along with artificially stoked fear of viruses, is one of the most powerful weapons of the megalomaniac "elite".

We, the people, the 99%, would be superior to them without the disunity, the division of society. Seen in this light, every-thing that is currently happening makes sense and reveals the strategy and tactics of the "Great Reset", of which Corona is only the trigger and beginning.

We don't have to submit, we don't have to be vaccinated, we don't have to wear masks when we have seen through the game. There are always possibilities, a certain grey area in which one can act. That requires courage, and many have lost that. Courage grows out of togetherness, so the first step is to make new contacts, activate old ones. What helps us is the opposite of limiting contact, namely communication, solidarity and mutual support. We have to start to stop playing along with the whole thing.

Because the planners of this evil game are not gods, they are old men whose goals are not ours. No one wants a dictatorship, except the dictators and their entourage who want to profit along with them and live out their private lust for power. But that is a minority.

As long as we do not resign ourselves to this fate, nothing is lost. *"We are the people!"* the people of the GDR shouted in 1989 and won their freedom. Now it is time again to win back freedom. However, it will not be easy, and it will take time, because today we are not dealing with a worn-out Politburo that was economically finished and dropped by the protecting power, the USSR. Today we have more powerful enemies: the entire financial industry and the governments that depend on it (in the networks and financially), some of which can be blackmailed, because only a few get into high positions, of which there are no files with embarrassing or criminal data. Or why do you think all Jeffrey Epstein's luxury villas were equipped with hidden cameras?

Inform, discuss, educate

The worst enemy, however, is the media, especially TV and the press, together with the big platforms Google, Youtube, Facebook, Twitter etc. With their permanent brainwashing, they ensure that the majority of the people may sense that something is "wrong", but cannot break out of the framing as long as they consume the toxic syrup on a daily basis. *Only the massive power of the media has so far prevented the spread of objective criticism and open discussion.*

This is where we can start. First of all, we should consistently avoid the constant stream of official news. Secondly, find other information channels, of which there are many on the internet. Well equipped with facts and arguments, one can then seek dialogue everywhere, on the train, at work, among friends. The best place to start is with acquaintances, even if a lot of opposition is to be expected. You can also make leaflet campaigns (in the letterboxes) or inform local politicians, civil servants, doctors, pharmacists or policemen. This is more likely to work in the local environment than with members of the state parliament. As long as we remain calm and persistent and do not expect quick success, it is important to use doubts about the official version, and these are growing.

For people who would like to expose grievances but do not dare because they expect professional or other disadvantages, there is the association "Mutigmacher".[782] Whistleblowers can find legal and financial support here, including help with finding accommodation and a job, if necessary. You can also support this association to encourage whistleblowers.

The peaceful confrontation

It is important that we remain consistently peaceful. As soon as violence breaks out, the state has the advantage, and this scenario is guaranteed to be planned as a "plan B". At EU level, there has long been the possibility of using the military of other countries in the event of unrest, and for years there has been increased practice of deployment in cities.[783] The Romans already did this by always using troops from foreign provinces as garrisons so that they would not fraternise, if only because of the language problems.

A study by the US political scientist Erica Chenoweth of uprisings between 1900 and 2006, in which at least 1,000 people were involved, revealed an interesting result: the peaceful uprisings were twice as often successful as the violent ones.[784] The consistent pacifism of the "Querdenker" demos, but also of the "Corona Info Tour" by Dr. Schiffman,

782 http://mutigmacher.org/
783 https://kenfm.de/demokratie-die-es-nie-gab-schon-gar-nicht-mit-Covid-von-peter-koenig/
784 https://www.youtube.com/watch?v=YJSehRlU34w

Samuel Eckert and friends, has shown, especially in Berlin and Leipzig, that many police officers do understand that their future and that of their children is at stake.

In Berlin, there were insider reports that some police units had refused brutal deployments. Although the Berlin police leadership tried several times to tilt the situation by using particularly brutal units, which do exist,[785] and thus provide the media with the desired images of riots, the people still remained peaceful. In Leipzig, the media therefore foisted the images of violent antifa actions from Connewitz on the "Querdenker". But this does not work in the long run, the truth gets around. The police know very well who is attacking them and who is not, even if they are sometimes forced from above to take actions that many officers cannot reconcile with their conscience. The "Federal Association of Critical Police Officers" does a good job of providing information. [786]

In Hildburghausen, a small town in Thuringia, there was a tightened curfew, but over 400 citizens walked through the town together anyway, most of them without masks, singing *"Oh, how beautiful it is!"* Nobody organised this, it was a spontaneous protest. The police came and wanted to break up the "gathering", but no one wanted to go home. They then used pepper spray against the peaceful walkers. *"The police wrote 30 charges. Those charged will hang them over the lunch table as a certificate of honour: we were there – hereby officially sealed ".*[787]

On 2.12.20, Nuremberg citizens celebrated without masks in front of the town hall despite the curfew and sang provocative songs they had composed themselves.[788]

---

785 https://reitschuster.de/post/das-ist-nicht-mehr-die-polizei-bei-der-ich-anfing/
786 https://www.kritische-polizisten.de/
787 https://www.compact-online.de/hildburghausen-400-menschen-durchbrechen-ausgangssperre-wir-lassen-uns-von-merkel-nicht-weihnachten-verbieten/
788 https://t.me/Patrioten_Nuernberg/654

Only the peaceful path can be successful in the long run, even if one has to endure terrible injustices along the way. Mahatma Gandhi showed the way.

Cohesion and unity

It is also important to remain united, no matter which political corner someone comes from. We should not let ourselves be set against each other (the attempt will come) and continue to pull together. The movement, in its tolerance and unity, is currently a wonderful counter-project to the division in the rest of Corona society, for which the government and the media are responsible. You can feel that clearly on the demos, and that is a very nice feeling, it gives strength and hope. This solidarity must be cultivated. If the Corona regime falls one day, we can still discuss controversially, openly and peacefully how we want to live in the future. Then we can practise real democracy.

Another possibility is "civil disobedience". This means that one does not simply go along with everything just because it is decreed. Creativity is needed here, and perhaps there will be a forum on the net where the best suggestions are collected and encourage people to copy them. What is needed are not clumsy provocations, but intelligent actions, even if one risks a fine. This is, so to speak, the "guerrilla tactic in the information war".

Support from the judiciary

We must take back the rights that have been taken away from us by laws and regulations that are unconstitutional because they are based on false claims. We are not breaking the law. We are demanding it. The constitution remains the basis of our actions, the government is our opponent **because** it violates it. It will have to answer for this. *Fundamental rights are not negotiable.*

One hope therefore lies with the judiciary. Many an administrative court has already stopped excessive government measures as *"disproportionate"* or even *"unconstitutional"*.

The third amendment to the Infection Protection Act of 18 November 2020 encroaches so much on fundamental rights that it must be clarified whether this would not have required a two-thirds majority in the parliament, as is required for constitutional amendments. Here, every citizen can file a complaint with the Federal Constitutional Court free of charge and without a lawyer. You can find a fact sheet on the procedure here.[789]

Some critics invoke Article 20, paragraph 4 of the Basic Law, which reads: *"All Germans have the right of resistance against anyone who undertakes to eliminate this order, if no other remedy is possible."* The revealed plans of the WEF want to eliminate fundamental rights and thus *"this order"*. Is *"other remedy"* possible? One hope, albeit a small one, lies with the Federal Constitutional Court, and this legal path must first be followed. After that, the *"right to resist"* takes effect. How this is meant in detail, however, leaves much room for discretion. In Denmark, the law restricting fundamental rights was overturned, as I mentioned earlier, because citizens persistently demonstrated in front of parliament.

Many freelance lawyers get involved altruistically, such as the "Lawyers for Enlightenment"[790] or the "Lawsuit Sponsors".[791] There you can find information and help, and those who cannot get involved themselves can at least support with donations. I already mentioned the team around Dr. Reiner Fuellmich,[792] who is a co-founder of the Corona Committee. It goes the way of civil law. Since Dr. Fuellmich is

---

789 https://www.bundesverfassungsgericht.de/SharedDocs/Downloads/DE/merkblatt.pdf

790 https://www.afa.zone/

791 https://klagepaten.eu/

792 https://www.fuellmich.com/

admitted to the bar in Germany and in the USA, he has filed lawsuits for damages in both countries on behalf of companies harmed by the Corona measures. It is directed against Mr. Drosten and the head of the RKI, Mr. Wieler, among others.[793] In the USA, a class action lawsuit is being filed, something that does not exist in Germany.[794] You can find a very interesting interview with Dr. Fuellmich on the Ken-FM site.[795]

In Great Britain, lawyers have founded the organisation "PCR Claims". This organisation has sued the government for damages caused by false positive PCR tests. [796]

What few people know: The burden of proof also lies with the authorities in the case of administrative offences. No one has to make a statement, not even in writing, if a fine is demanded. You say your name and that you have a good reason, for example, for being out and about despite the curfew. You don't have to say what that reason is, so you don't have to give any further information. Now the authorities have to prove that there is *no* good reason, and that is almost impossible. [797]

It is important to know your rights.

793 https://www.fuldaerzeitung.de/fulda/corona-luege-reiner-fuellmich-
    klage-christian-drosten-virologe-lothar-wieler-goettingen-90096522.html
794 https://www.corona-schadensersatzklage.de/
795 https://kenfm.de/reiner-fuellmich/
796 https://de.rt.com/meinung/110377-nach-enthullung-von-schwachstellen-
    beim/
797 According to Dr. Justus P. Hoffmann
    https://t.me/AllesAusserMainstream/1680

Outlook

This struggle will be more of a marathon than a sprint, and it is to be feared that the coercive measures will be maintained for longer and even intensified. But this should not discourage us, because the more repression is imposed, the more people start to think. As with all crises, there is not only negativity, there is also an opportunity for change, and it does not have to be that of Schwab, Gates, Soros and consorts. Things can also take a completely different direction. For example, that more and more people wake up and thoroughly question the current system. There is so much to improve, starting with schools, work, the health system, the money system, politics (is it really democracy if the people are constantly ignored?), the media, NATO, globalisation, etc. etc...

Those who planned the crisis and set it in motion should by no means be sure that it will go according to plan. They have overdone it, overplayed their hand. The backlash will come, how strong it comes depends on us.

I have always liked the sentence Mephistopheles utters in Faust:

"I am part of that force that always wants evil, but always creates good".

I fight, like Mephistopheles, for "Corona" to become the catalyst for a new, better world.

Let's get to work!

Epilogue

So, my indictment stands. It had to be written, and it should be as complete as I can with my simple means. I am not a lawyer, so my *"J'accuse"* is that of the writer, the chronicler.

I place the charge in the hands of lawyers and judges of integrity, but also in the hands of the aggrieved, and that is all of us, mentally and materially. My indictment is not a call for vigilante justice, I reject violence, but it is a call for resistance, be it passive or active. It is also called "civil disobedience". We are in the info-war, we fight with arguments, and we have to fight to prevent worse for the future. If not for us, then for our children and grandchildren who cannot defend themselves.

It is now Christmas 2020. Over the past nine months I have sifted through, archived, edited and summarised thousands of documents. When I started, I had no idea how much material was constantly being added. I devoted two to three hours a day just to the new information that came in. During the writing process, I had to update and add to chapters that had already been written, which is why some information reappears in other places. The reader may forgive me for this.

I would like to take this opportunity to thank everyone who has always encouraged me to complete this project. I would especially like to mention my best friend and my old friend and comrade-in-arms, who kept giving me hints for the research, as well as my editor and my "test readers", who supported me with constructive criticism. Together we are stronger, each with our own abilities.

Even though the events are still in flux – the book has to come out at some point. I hope I have made the key points clear enough so that the basis is there to be able to classify the future events on one's own.

I would like to give my readers one more thing to take away with them: Don't believe anybody, not even me, check it out, do your own research. Anyone can do that, with an internet connection and the courage to have their own opinion. I now conclude my self-imposed task of enlightenment and pass on the initiative to inform my readers:

Dare!

Trust your common sense

and your sense of justice.

The essentials once again in key points

- The PCR test is neither able nor approved to detect infections.

- Positive PCR test results are manipulated by incorrect use (e.g. too many cycles).

- The statistics are dubiously misinterpreted and the figures massively manipulated upwards.

- Calling those who test positive "cases" or "infected" is wrong. Only people with symptoms are sick. There are no "symptomless sick" people.

- People without symptoms are not contagious because the viral load is too low.

- Mortality from Covid-19 is in the range of influenza worldwide.

- The virus is not new, just newly discovered. We have been living with it for a long time.

- There was no excess mortality worldwide because seasonal influenza cases were redefined to "Covid19".

- A great many patients died in the hospitals due to incorrect treatment.

- Masks do not prevent infection, as many studies show.

- Many studies have shown that masks are harmful to health, especially for children.

- There is no 2nd or 3rd wave, only a wave of false-positive tests.

- There was no overcrowding in hospitals in Germany in 2020, nor was there ever a danger of a shortage of intensive care beds.

- There was no excess mortality in 2020. Death rates and intensive care bed occupancy were 5% lower than in 2019.

- Corona deceased lived to an average age of 83. The average age of the population is 81 years.

- Lockdown and distance rules do not achieve anything, as the statistics of various countries show in comparison.

- The "pandemic" was planned and prepared long in advance.

- The "pandemic" is a pretext and cover for a political agenda.

- The agenda is well known and has been published several times.

- The most important protagonists are known and profess with their statements.

- The enormous economic and social damage is deliberate.

- The agenda is to lead to a global surveillance state.

- Most governments are involved and act unconstitutionally against their own people.

- The media are part of the agenda and prevent a factual discussion.

- The means of enforcement are fear, defamation and state violence.

- There is still hope, provided the agenda becomes common knowledge.

Short update on Covid19 vaccination:

(as at: 26.12.2020)

Shortly before submitting the manuscript, I received a few important messages, which I will reproduce here shortly:

The CDC reported that in about 112,000 people vaccinated in the UK, 3,150 (2.7%) experienced side effects so severe in just four days that they are unable to carry out their normal daily activities. They need medical or nursing assistance.[798]

Shortly after vaccinations began in the southwest of England, a new variant of the virus was said to have been discovered in this very area. Prof. Hockertz asked whether this might have occurred in the vaccinated people.[799] It is conceivable that precautions are being taken for expected vaccination damage, which can then be blamed on the "new" virus.

A vaccination guide by the RKI "for doctors only" advises not to issue a confirmation for the new vaccination for the time being, although this contradicts § 22 para. 1 of the Vaccination Protection Act.[800]

Some celebrities have been caught faking their public vaccinations, as with US "vaccine pope" Antony Fauci, who supposedly got a shot in his left arm, but the next day said he hardly felt anything and grabbed his right arm while saying so.[801] Many vaccination advocates do not want to be vaccinated ("for now"?), including BioNTech CEO Sahin, the Austrian chancellor, the Austrian president and the German government.[802]

---

798 https://unser-mitteleuropa.com/usa-ueber-3-000-schwere-erkrankungen-nach-corona-impfung/
799 https://twitter.com/phockertz/status/1340989366857052162?s=21
800 https://www.rki.de/DE/Content/Infekt/Impfen/ImpfungenAZ/COVID-19/Leitfaden-Arzt.pdf
801 https://t.me/LIONMediaTelegram/3916
802 https://reitschuster.de/post/chef-impf-entwickler-laesst-sich-nicht-impfen/

BioNTech's quarterly report is full of doubts about the safety and approval of the new vaccine. It is well worth reading.[803]

Jens Spahn and the President of the Pharmacists' Association (ABDA) Schmidt said in a live chat that pharmacists should not express any reservations about corona vaccination in counselling sessions if possible. The mayor of Passau, Dupper, recommended something similar in a letter to the medical profession.[804]

A new study[805] estimates the risks that the Covid19 vaccination could trigger an ADE[806] reaction to be quite high. This means that the reaction of certain antibodies in an infection can extremely disrupt the immune system.[807]

Researchers at the University of Miami/Florida are investigating whether the Covid19 vaccination can lead to infertility in men. They advise men who still want to have children to freeze sperm before vaccination to be on the safe side until more accurate results are available.[808]

The WHO has once again changed a definition for the benefit of the vaccine manufacturers. Whereas herd immunity used to be attainable through many people who have either experienced a disease or have been vaccinated, since 13.11.2020 only vaccination has been considered a criterion for attaining herd immunity. [809]

---

803 https://www.sec.gov/Archives/edgar/data/
    1776985/000156459020053062/bntx-ex991_6.htm
804 https://corona-transition.org/amtliche-anweisung-an-arzte-und-apotheker-
    bitte-sprechen-sie-die-risiken-nicht
805 https://onlinelibrary.wiley.com/doi/10.1111/ijcp.13795
806 Antibody-dependent enhancement
807 https://www.anonymousnews.ru/2020/11/14/Covidimpfung-zerstoert-
    immunsystem/
808 https://www.local10.com/news/local/2020/12/20/study-investigates-
    effects-of-Covid-19-vaccine-on-male-fertility/
809 https://2020news.de/who-aendert-definition-der-herdenimmunitaet/